Evolutionary Biology at the Crossroads

EVOLUTIONARY BIOLOGY AT THE CROSSROADS

A SYMPOSIUM AT QUEENS COLLEGE

Max K. Hecht, Editor

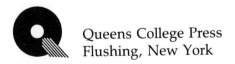

Queens College Press
Flushing, New York

0-930146-21-2

Preface

In celebration of the 50th anniversary of the founding of Queens College, many symposia were held in 1987-88, one of which, *Evolutionary Biology at the Crossroads*, the subject of this volume, marked the concurrent commemoration of the formulation of a general theory of evolutionary biology, frequently referred to as the "Modern Synthesis" or "neo-Darwinism."

The topic of the symposium was selected because of the widespread interest in the issues addressed, and because faculty and their students at Queens College have made significant contributions to evolutionary biology since the early days of the institution. Former and current faculty members and graduates of Queens were a substantial component of the symposium's lead speakers and panelists, joining with outstanding contributors to evolutionary biology and related areas from sister colleges at the City University, neighboring institutions, and universities across the country and abroad.

The symposium was generously supported by the Alfred P. Sloan Foundation, and the organizers of this event, along with the Queens College Division of Mathematics and the Natural Sciences, express their gratitude to the Foundation for making *Evolutionary Biology at the Crossroads* possible.

Norman L. Goldman
Dean, Division of Mathematics and the Natural Sciences
Queens College, CUNY

Contents

Contributors

Walter J. Bock, Department of Biological Sciences, Columbia University, New York, NY 10027

Richard L. Borowsky, Department of Biology, New York University, Washington Square, New York, NY 10003

Arthur J. Boucot, Department of Zoology, Oregon State University, Corvallis, OR 97331

Richard M. Burian, Department of Philosophy, Virginia Polytechnic Institute and State University, Blacksburg, VA 24061

Alberto Cordero, Department of Philosophy, Queens College, CUNY, Flushing, NY 11367

Eric Delson, Department of Anthropology, Lehman College, CUNY, Bedford Park Blvd. West, Bronx, NY 10468

Lee Ehrman, Division of Natural Sciences, State University of New York at Purchase, Purchase, NY 10577

Anthony Hallam, Department of Geological Sciences, University of Birmingham, P.O. Box 363, Birmingham, B15 2TT United Kingdom

Max K. Hecht, Department of Biology, Queens College, CUNY, Flushing, NY 11367

Antoni Hoffman, Zaklad Paleobiologii, Polska Akademia NAUK, Al Zwirki I Wigury 93, 02-089 Warszawa, Poland

Jeffrey S. Levinton, Department of Ecology and Evolution, State University of New York at Stony Brook, Stony Brook, NY 11794-5245

Peter T. Manicas, Department of Philosophy, Queens College, CUNY, Flushing, NY 11367

Malcolm C. McKenna, Department of Vertebrate Paleontology, American Museum of Natural History, New York, NY 10024

John A. Moore, Department of Biology, University of California, Riverside, CA 92521

Stephen J. O'Brien, Laboratory of Genetics, National Cancer Institute, Frederick, MD 21701-1013

David Pilbeam, Department of Anthropology, Peabody Museum, Harvard University, Cambridge, MA 02138

Stanley N. Salthe, Department of Biology, Brooklyn College, CUNY, Brooklyn, NY 11210

Frederick S. Szalay, Department of Anthropology, Hunter College, CUNY, 695 Park Ave., New York, NY 10021

Ian Tattersall, Department of Anthropology, American Museum of Natural History, New York, NY 10024

Bruce Wallace, Department of Biology, Virginia Polytechnic Institute and State University, Blacksburg, VA 24061

Marvin Wasserman, Department of Biology, Queens College, CUNY, Flushing, NY 11367

EVOLUTIONARY BIOLOGY
AT THE CROSSROADS

Introduction

Max K. Hecht

Fifty years ago, concurrent with the founding of Queens College, Theodosius Dobzhansky published his *Genetics and the Origin of Species*. This opus was one of the cornerstones of a new approach to evolutionary theory, which was called by Julian Huxley the "Modern Synthesis." In celebration of these two events we have organized this symposium, *Evolutionary Biology at the Crossroads*, to answer questions raised within the Queens College community generated by articles published in the newspapers and popular science press. Such articles imply to many readers that new data and new fields of research question the now classic view of the Modern Synthesis of evolutionary biology. Is evolutionary biology, therefore, at a crossroads?

To respond to these issues, this symposium was limited to answer only the most frequently raised questions because the spectrum of evolutionary biology is too broad to cover completely in a two-day event. Clearly, a number of relevant areas such as developmental biology, ecology, systematics, and others that are pertinent to the problem as a whole were by necessity omitted. Despite incompleteness of the coverage, many interesting areas were included, not unexpectedly resulting in conflicting points of view. The symposium was outlined in the following manner:

I. The History of Evolutionary Concepts

A historical survey of classical evolutionary theory from the time of Darwin to the present.

II. Populations and Microevolution

A population biologist's view of the mechanics of the evolutionary process, primarily in sexually reproducing organisms.

III. Macroevolutionary Patterns and Evolutionary Mechanisms

A paleontological view of the grander patterns of biological evolution and the questions bearing on their relationship to the population level.

IV. The Contribution of Molecular Biology

The phylogenetic aspects of molecular biology and biochemistry and their relationship to classical morphology.

V. Human Fossil History and Evolutionary Patterns

The major patterns of human evolution as seen from the paleontological, morphological, and biological view.

VI. The Influence of the Evolutionary Paradigm

The impact of evolution from the viewpoint of the historian and philosopher of science.

The symposium was organized by having each of the above areas discussed by a single lecturer covering a specialized area. The lecturers were constrained by time, and, therefore, were required to be most selective in choice of content. For each major lecture a panel of discussants extended the discussion from their own view of the major area. The text presented below is not a verbatim transcript of the proceedings but a revised text and, in some cases, an expanded version.

The History of Evolutionary Concepts and the Nature of the Controversies

John A. Moore
University of California

There is a close relation between the Modern Synthesis in evolutionary biology and the Department of Biology at Queens College, our host for this symposium. Let me recount this fascinating bit of history. I will suggest a phylogeny that some of you may find far-fetched but is considerably more plausible than many phylogenies.

The effective date for the beginning of the Modern Synthesis was the series of Jesup Lectures that Theodosius Dobzhansky gave for Columbia University's Department of Zoology in October 1936. Dobzhansky was 36 years old at the time and was working with the Morgan group at the California Institute of Technology. The lectures were published the following year as Number XI of the Columbia Biological Series, with the title *Genetics and the Origin of Species*. That was an honorable series, which earlier had included fundamental contributions by Henry Fairfield Osborn, Arthur Wiley, Bashford Dean, Edmund Beecher Wilson, William Keith Brooks, Gary Nathan Calkins, Thomas Hunt Morgan, Jacques Loeb, and H. S. Jennings. Dobzhansky's volume was to be followed shortly in the series by the other main contributions to the Modern Synthesis: Ernst Mayr's *Systematics and the Origin of Species* in 1942 and George Gaylord Simpson's *Tempo and Mode in Evolution* in 1944. These three volumes, all by young men (Mayr was 38 and Simpson 42), were the core of the Modern Synthesis. They were followed in 1950 by Stebbins' *Variation and Evolution in Plants*, based on his Jesup Lectures of 1946.

Now back to Dobzhansky. His initial work that attracted so much attention had to do with *Drosophila pseudoobscura* and its relatives, which had first been studied by one of Morgan's students, Donald Lancefield. Dobzhansky and his Cal Tech colleague A. H. Sturtevant discovered that these species had numerous chromosomal arrangements that could be identified easily, and that the overlapping arrangements permitted the establishment of a phylogeny for their origin. Dobzhansky undertook a vigorous study of the geographic distribution and seasonal changes in these chromosomal arrangements. A very large percentage of the initial data for the Modern Synthesis was derived from these studies.

One can argue, correctly I believe, that the rate at which the Modern Synthesis occurred was in large part a consequence of Dobzhansky, Mayr, and Simpson eventually being together in New York—at Columbia University and the American Museum of Natural History. Lancefield had an important though indirect role in Dobzhansky moving to Columbia University.

After receiving his Ph.D. in 1921, Donald Lancefield spent a year in Oregon and returned to Columbia in 1922 as an assistant professor. He remained at Columbia when Morgan, Bridges, Sturtevant, and Dobzhansky, who had recently arrived from Russia, moved to Cal Tech in 1928. Lancefield became an associate professor at Columbia in 1928.

And now for the Queens Connection. In the late 1930s, when Lancefield's research was going slowly and he was still an associate professor, he received an invitation to become the chairman of the new Department of Biology at the recently opened Queens College. He accepted and moved in 1938.

Lancefield's departure left L. C. Dunn as the only geneticist in the Zoology Department at Columbia, and the university administration agreed to allow the department to appoint another geneticist. That opportunity permitted an offer to be made to Dobzhansky, who had made such an impression with his Jesup Lectures of 1936 and his book in 1937. He accepted and arrived at Columbia in 1940. That completed the triumvirate of Mayr, Dobzhansky, and Simpson.

There is no question, therefore, that the Queens Connection with the Modern Synthesis is real. Donald Lancefield, the first chairman of its Biology Department, discovered the biological material that was to be so vigorously exploited by Dobzhansky. His move up from an associate professorship at Columbia to a chair at Queens made it possible for Dobzhansky to move from Cal Tech to Columbia and New York, which became the center of the Modern Synthesis.

The oft-told tale of Charles Darwin's attempt to understand the past history and present diversity of organisms often fails to emphasize the original questions that required an explanation. These questions are not obvious. It is probable, I believe, that had naturalists of former years been familiar with only the species of a restricted locality, and unfamiliar with fossil organisms, they would never have recognized the questions for which the concept of Darwinian Evolution would provide provisional answers.

Those naturalists would not have known, and need not have assumed, that living creatures of today were any different from those living in the past—today's species could be accepted as eternal. Yet inquisitive minds in essentially all cultures would know of the creation myths that formed part of their received traditions. The germ of an idea of descent with modification might have been planted, even though a creation myth implies only a beginning, not a change over time.

6

Throughout recorded history there have been philosophical and scientific attempts to understand the living world. Many of the paradigms, accepted for a moment and then rejected, almost anticipated the notion of evolutionary change and some even suggested it. None was accepted before Darwin because none provided convincing data or analysis.

My task is to consider some of those controversies involved in trying to understand the past history of life. The ones I will choose are:

> The Nature of Fossils
> Natural Theology *vs.* Darwinism
> Was Darwin Right?

These were some of the main controversies in the decades before the Modern Synthesis of the 1930s and 1940s. Not one of them was settled by a neat, elegant, critical experiment. Instead, we will find that the explanatory hypotheses had an evolution of their own, and in the final analysis they became the paradigm of the moment because they accounted for the data somewhat better than the rejected explanatory hypotheses. And acceptance itself always involved adherence to a particular belief system.

In the complexity of the interactions among living populations, their environment, and time, we now realize that no predictable or even single outcome is to be expected. Evolutionary biologists will probably never be able to reach the goal sought by many in the physical sciences, namely that a scientific theory should produce a definite logical model and definite predictions. Or the goal of P. W. Atkins (1981, p. 3):

> I shall take your mind on a journey. It is a journey of comprehension, taking us to the edge of space, time, and understanding. On it I shall argue that there is nothing than cannot be understood, that there is nothing that cannot be explained, and that everything is extraordinarily simple.

Such opinions sound strange coming from the physical sciences where, to this day, that time-honored goal remains unfulfilled: to predict the properties of water knowing only the properties of hydrogen and oxygen.

As organismal biologists I fear we try too hard to emulate the precision of the physical sciences. Our materials and their behaviors are rarely precise or predictable except when we work at the level of molecules that are essential for life but are not alive. It is difficult to imagine a fundamental law of nature that would account satisfactorily for the evolution of mammals from reptiles or the development of an egg into an adult. Neither phenomenon can occur, however, in violation of the laws of nature.

Understanding of the biological and geological phenomena related to evolution comes slowly and inelegantly, as suggested by Preston Cloud (1988, p. 49):

Acceptance of new ideas is usually contingent on three preconditions: (1) the world must be ready for them; (2) they must be convincingly advocated by a persuasive person or group; and (3) they must be perceived as clearly superior to (or, at least, not in serious conflict with) other widely held beliefs.

I should like to add two additional requirements. The first is that a consensus requires adherence by all to the same rules of evidence, and the second is that each generation of scientists requires more rigid proof than did the antecedent generation.

We should remember these principles when surveying some of the main controversies that swirled around attempts to understand the origin of life and its subsequent history.

The Nature of Fossils

A fascinating "What if . . . ?" question is, "What if there were no fossils, would the possibility of organisms changing over time ever have been more than a fringe idea?" A probable answer is suggested by the fact that the various speculations about the possibility of organic change were never more than that: speculations that failed to produce a systematic attempt to study the question. Had the rocks been without their history of life, and if molecular biology had reached the same status as it has today, would the comparisons of molecules in different species have suggested evolution as an explanation for the molecular diversity?

But there are fossils and they have provided the central data for the fact of evolution. It was of critical importance, therefore, that those strange appearances of nature be understood. Slowly they came to be recognized as the remains of long-dead organisms, but the intellectual feats of reaching the conclusion that they had a biogenic origin were monumental.

There were many obstacles. One was the fact that objects that clearly resembled living creatures—fossil mollusks, for example—graded imperceptibly with things that were clearly unrelated to living creatures. Another severe problem was that some objects that resembled living creatures were found in the center of large rocks. How could they possibly have gotten there? And how could they have turned to stone? For some naturalists it was easier to assume that the stony objects that looked like living creatures merely represented some of the remarkable things that rocks could do— such as form crystals. These naturalists accepted the hypothesis that these objects that looked like living creatures were formed by latent "plastick virtue" in the rocks themselves and, so, had nothing to do with long-dead animals or plants.

But slowly, some of the giants of science came to accept the working hypothesis that some fossils are the remains of living creatures. Robert Hooke was one of them (1665, Obser. XVII; 1705). Once that brave step was taken, one necessary deduction was that those fossiliferous rocks high in the mountains must, at one time, have been under water. Another necessary deduction was that at some time in the past or in some other part of the world today, there must have been organisms that produced the fossils of otherwise unknown species.

This was the position vigorously supported by William Martin (1809) at the beginning of the nineteenth century when geology was about to become an established science. His book, *A Knowledge of Extraneous Fossils*, is one of those rare cases when an incisive mind is able to organize the important data and ideas relating to a phenomenon and formulate a conceptual framework that serves to advance a science. He noted that fossils are known from all parts of the world; that they are absent from granite but they abound in limestone; that the parts that fossilize well are those that most resist decay—wood, bones, shells; that the substance of fossils is usually the same as the rock in which they are embedded. His conclusion: "Petrificata own their *form* to organized bodies; their *substance* they derive from *minerals*" (p. 15).

It took generations of naturalists to establish that it is true beyond reasonable doubt that fossils are the remains of creatures that had lived in the past. Moreover, the position of the fossils in sedimentary layers of rock could determine their relative ages. Thus it could be accepted that the sedimentary rocks have preserved some of the history of life on earth.

What came to be the accepted interpretation of fossils was the result of generations of naturalists puzzling about the features of some very dead stones. Gradually those "pertrificata" that represented the remains of organisms were distinguished from somewhat similar objects that represented only phenomena of the nonliving world. The "scientific methods" consisted only of the careful accumulation of observations that supported the hypothesis that "true" fossils represented long-dead organisms.

Once that hypothesis was accepted as true beyond reasonable doubt, two exceedingly puzzling observations had to be explained. One was that fossils thought to be of marine creatures could be found high in the Alps and mountains of Italy—far from the Mediterranean, both horizontally and vertically. Another was that although many fossils resembled living species, others were not similar to any existing species. How could something that did not exist be able to form a fossil? Yet those deductions were necessary, so geologists had to discover how those fossil-containing strata had reached their improbable positions and to explain the seemingly unique fossil species. They were able to do so.

Natural Theology *vs.* Darwinism

The views of William Paley and Charles Darwin are examples of a controversy that remains to this day: the conflict between those who accept supernatural agencies and those who accept only natural agencies as the cause of biological phenomena. This is a type of controversy that cannot be resolved by new observations or new experiments. A resolution, if there can be one, requires that one group make a fundamental change in how it views the world and what it will accept as evidence.

What were the problems that resulted in such different patterns of thought as Natural Theology and Darwinism?

By the beginning of the nineteenth century, these major problems were recognized: Why are there so many species? How old is the earth? What can account for the remarkable adaptations of organisms to their environment? How does it happen that species can be arranged in hierarchical groups? How can it be that species living in the past differ from those living today? What is the basis of geographical variation?

None of these questions required an hypothesis of evolutionary change, and for centuries alternative paradigms had been accepted. The last major one before the Darwinian hypothesis of 1859 was Natural Theology. John Ray and William Paley used the same types of biological data to show the wisdom of God as Charles Darwin would use to show the efficacy of natural selection acting upon inherited variations.

William Paley's *Natural Theology; Or, Evidences of the Existence and Attributes of the Deity Collected from the Appearances of Nature* (1802) went through many editions in the early part of the nineteenth century and was a highly respected work. Both Darwin and Huxley were among its admirers. Those were the decades when the hypothesis of evolution was in poor repute. The arguments of Lamarck and of the then unknown author of *Vestiges of the Natural History of Creation* (1844; the author was later revealed to be Robert Chambers) appeared to be as irritating as they were unconvincing to naturalists, at least to those in England. Although the details of the Genesis account of creation might not be acceptable, a general belief in a Divine Creation was held by better educated persons, including the naturalists.

As information about the living world increased, one of the more impressive discoveries was the incredible adaptation of organisms to their environment. The structure of the smallest creatures, as revealed by the microscope, was almost incomprehensibly complex and subtle. Theologians such as Ray and Paley saw in all this clear evidence of the power of the Deity, as well as his love and concern for even the smallest and most humble of the living organisms he had created.

Paley's *Natural Theology* is really a survey of the available biological information and an explanation of all phenomena as the handiwork of God. This way of looking at nature solved all problems. Things are the way they are because God made them that way. He made lots of species; He made them in groups of similar kinds; He insured that they had a structure that would perfectly adapt them to their environment, and so on. Biology, then, was mainly a description of the handiwork of the Deity; there were no problems of origins and change over time. The creation proved the existence of a Creator and the study of the products of creation gave some hint of the attributes of God.

Things were not so clear and simple for Darwin. He puzzled for decades before he went public with what he knew to be heresy: the hypothesis that the attributes of the creation were to be understood as a consequence of natural selection acting on inheritable variations. Darwin's hypothesis did not exclude a Creator but, beginning with an origin of life—no matter how it had occurred—he did propose that living creatures changed over the vast eons of time and that these changes could be understood solely as a consequence of natural causes. For Darwin's scheme to be possible, the world had to be far older than Bishop Ussher had determined and there was a clear implication that human beings were not the darlings of creation. Copernicus had humbled the earth; now Darwin was humbling all humanity. The earth was just another planet; mankind just another species.

Thus by midcentury there were two totally antagonistic paradigms for the phenomena of life. Natural Theology was based on supernatural assumptions and, so, could answer everything. Darwinism invoked only naturalistic assumptions, yet it was little more than a hunting license for gaining new knowledge.

The structure of the argument in *On the Origin of Species* is bold and fascinating. No one in Darwin's time had any real understanding of inheritance, nor was there any good experimental evidence for the existence of natural selection. Cases were given in the *Origin* that made it highly likely that at least some structures or behaviors are inherited; the main argument for *natural* selection was that *artificial* selection works. Darwin admitted that the *Origin* was basically a long argument. Actually there were two arguments: the first was that organisms had evolved; the second was that natural selection, acting on inheritable variations, was the mechanism of that evolution.

These two aspects of Darwinism had very different histories during the last half of the nineteenth century. Nearly all naturalists, and many educated persons, soon accepted that evolution was a fact. Gradually, however, Darwin's proposed mechanism for evolution was rejected. That was about the state of affairs in the mid-1930s when I was an undergraduate at Columbia: "Evolution is a fact but Mr. Darwin probably did not know how it occurs."

The controversy between the evolutionists and the creationists about whether supernatural or natural explanations are to be employed to explain the phenomena of the origin and change over time of living organisms cannot be resolved unless one group or the other changes its mind. We have had enough experience with this controversy to be sure that neither group is likely to budge. The most that scientists can, and should, do is to give the evidence for their point of view as honestly as possible and to explain the fundamentally different modes of thought being used by those supporting the evolutionary paradigm and those supporting the religious paradigm.

Was Darwin Right?

Variation and natural selection were the key components of Darwin's mechanism for evolutionary change. Both were under severe attack during his lifetime and remain so to this day—though now for different reasons.

It remains astonishing that the Darwin of 1859 could be so correct when the information required for his hypothesis was so inadequate. He was not able to provide useful data on the nature of variation in either the *Origin* or nine years later in *The Variation of Animals and Plants Under Domestication.* His hypothesis demanded the pattern of inheritance discovered by Mendel and Morgan: genes that maintain their integrity generation after generation. Darwin knew of some instances that seemed to fit this pattern but, for the most part, inheritance was poorly understood. If there was any general rule, it was that the offspring seemed to be a blend of the characteristics of their parents.

Darwin believed in 1859, as we do today, that new variations arise spontaneously—that is, the type of variant is not related to the type of stimulation. That probably seemed to be a weak assumption to many naturalists who were so impressed with the obvious adaptive significance of structure and function. Furthermore, the term "spontaneous" can be interpreted as "We haven't the slightest idea what the cause might be."

One of the most powerful arguments against Darwin's assumption that small variations were the building blocks for new species was made by Fleeming Jenkin (1867), who showed clearly that, on the basis of what was then known about inheritance, Darwin's scheme simply could not work. Suppose, Jenkin argued, that an Englishman was wrecked on an island inhabited solely by a large population of dark-skinned natives and, in due time, he began to contribute to the next generation. That generation of mulatto children would be intermediate in skin color. Those children, when mature, would raise families of their own and presumably select mates at random. Each generation would see a gradual dilution of the white skin of the shipwrecked Englishman.

Darwin could not answer that criticism and gradually he was forced to accept that the new variations that were the building blocks of evolutionary change must be caused somehow by the environment. Many other naturalists became more ardent Lamarckians, among them the distinguished American paleontologist Edward Drinkwater Cope (1904, p. 13). Here compare the original Darwinian explanation for the origin of variations (on the right) with that of Lamarckians (on the left).

1. Variations appear in definite directions.	1. Variations are promiscuous or multifarious
2. Variations are caused by interaction of the organic being with its environment.	2. Variations are "congenital" or are caused by mingling of male and female germ-plasmas.

| 3. Acquired variations may be inherited. | 3. Acquired variations cannot be inherited. |

After that, natural selection took over in both columns.

It has been pointed out frequently that when modern genetics was ushered in by a rediscovered Gregor Mendel and the work of Thomas Hunt Morgan, it did not provide the evolutionists' long-sought understanding of the basis of variation. To be sure, the formation of new variants by mutation appeared to be spontaneous and random. Yet the mutants selected for their usefulness in genetic crosses seemed too extreme in their effects to be the materials of evolutionary change. It was also observed that when different types of organisms were crossed, the offspring were almost always found to be intermediate and there was little or no evidence of segregation of independent factors.

Some evolutionists looked upon mutant forms as pathological. In any event, the morphological nature of the mutants turning up in Morgan's laboratory at Columbia bore little resemblance to the morphological differences that seemed to distinguish closely related species.

The other pillar of Darwinism, natural selection, received very little experimental confirmation. It was difficult to see how the spontaneous mutations appearing in *Drosophila* stocks could confer an adaptive advantage on the flies homozygous for them. In fact, when tested in competition with the wild type, the mutants were clearly inferior. One was tempted to conclude, therefore, that mutation was unlikely to provide new genotypes that would permit evolution to a better adapted state.

To be sure, there were a few experimental studies that seemed to indicate that differences existed between individuals that survived and those that did not. English sparrows that died in a snowstorm differed in minute ways from those that survived; an owl in a laboratory experiment caught more mice on soil of a contrasting color than on soil that matched their pelage.

But these experiments did not enter the mainstream. During the period from about 1910 to the mid-1930s, the amazing advances of genetics took center stage. As Mayr (1980, 1982) and many others have described in detail, genetics and evolutionary biology remained estranged until the Modern Synthesis began in the 1930s.

Evolutionary Biology in the 1930s

This is the time I first became aware of the problems of evolutionary biology. I was an undergraduate student (1932-1936) in the Zoology Department at Columbia, the institution that was to play the major role in the Modern Synthesis. As noted before, Morgan and most of his associates had moved to Cal Tech; Donald Lancefield, later to found the Biology Department here at Queens, stayed on at Columbia. He was working at a very slow rate on an unusual situation in *Drosophila* of the obscura group from the western United States. He discovered that two seemingly identical strains hybridized with difficulty or not at all. He called them Race A and Race B, later to be known as *Drosophila pseudoobscura* and *Drosophila persimilis*. They were to be the prime experimental material first for Sturtevant and Dobzhansky and later for Dobzhansky alone.

There was no experimental evolutionary biology in any course at Columbia in those days. The only course of any sort dealing with evolution was "The Evolution of Man," given by James Howard McGregor, who was responsible for a well-known series of reconstructions of early man. In those years the interests of evolutionary biologists were mainly in phylogeny, not in mechanisms of evolutionary change.

It was assumed, of course, that genes did change in evolution. Our picture of the genotype of wild individuals was that of a diagram of a genetic cross: lots of + signs on one chromosome and symbols for a few mutant alleles on the homologous chromosome. We heard little about recombination. In any event it would have been unimportant because it was assumed that there was not much to recombine—most individuals were thought to be essentially homozygous for the vast majority of alleles.

I should add that a graduate student, Donald Charles, had visited the University of Chicago and returned to report that Sewall Wright was working on the mathematics of the evolutionary process. He might even have said something about evolutionary changes occurring without selection, namely by "drift" in small populations. Charles was a gifted mathematician himself but to the rest of us it seemed most unlikely that mathematics would help to understand the phenomena of evolution.

In 1936, the year I graduated from college, Theodosius Dobzhansky gave the Jesup Lectures at Columbia and what was to become the Modern Synthesis started. Speed picked up a few years later when he left the Morgan group at Cal Tech and moved to Columbia. The major message he carried was of the tremendous genetic variation in natural populations. They were far from Johanssen's pure lines or the mental image we had gained from *Drosophila* genetics. Our typological thinking about the genotypes of species in the wild was being replaced.

Evolutionary Biology in the 1940s

Then Ernst Mayr at the American Museum of Natural History became deeply involved. He brought to the Modern Synthesis the tremendous body of information that systematists had gathered about natural populations. Mayr became a close friend of Dobzhansky and many others in Columbia's Zoology Department. From time to time he gave a course at Columbia, and he was a vigorous participant in the departmental colloquia.

The new insight Ernst Mayr brought to our genetics-oriented institution was the rich tradition of naturalists that emphasized the importance of geographic variation and isolation in species formation—a thesis he was to develop in his Jesup Lectures given in 1941. Our view of wild species changed dramatically: far from their being essentially homozygous, they were seen as tremendously diverse and, of greater importance, the variation differed geographically. This seemed to argue for geographic variation being caused by natural selection. The notion that speciation is a product of geographic variation and isolation became the working hypothesis. Ernst Mayr was replacing "typological thinking" with "topographical thinking."

There was renewed interest in natural selection, and the puzzle as to why new mutant forms were uniformly inferior rather than superior was better understood. When time was taken into account a probable explanation emerged. Although mutation was an exceedingly rare event, every locus must have mutated many times in the past. If so, the mutant alleles would have been tested by natural selection in the environment in which they occurred and would have been retained if of adaptive advantage.

If one was to study natural selection, therefore, it would be necessary to start with a poorly adapted strain and then study subsequent events. One bit of evidence showing the results of selection came from laboratory mutants themselves. They were uniformly less viable than wild-type flies and when kept for generations tended to revert slowly toward wild type. The changes were found to result from the selection of modifying genes, not to changes in the mutant allele. Dobzhansky studied the same process by reducing the viability of stocks with radiations and then measuring the recovery to normal viability. And, finally, a large amount of data was accumulating on the not-so-natural selection of microorganisms and insects by antibiotics and pesticides.

George Gaylord Simpson's interactions with the Columbia group came later. His *Tempo and Mode in Evolution* was published in 1944. It was not based on a Jesup Lecture series but it was published by Columbia University Press. Some have maintained that this most important book had finally brought paleontology and genetics into agreement. It is astonishing how anyone could reach such a conclusion. Simpson made no claim that he was demonstrating genetic changes in fossil organisms. He was supporting the opinion that the phenomena of paleontology could be understood in terms of, and were not in conflict with, the explanatory hypotheses of neo-Darwinism. To this day the data of paleontology can be explained equally well by Darwinian and Lamarckian hypotheses. At a time when Lamarckianism was far from dead among paleontologists, Simpson brought his great authority to the Darwinian camp.

Ledyard Stebbins gave his Jesup Lectures at Columbia in 1946 and argued that the evolution of plants could also be interpreted in terms of neo-Darwinism.

Thus by the late 1940s it began to seem that, beyond any reasonable doubt, there was ample genetic variation to serve the evolutionary process, that natural selection was an effective force, and that small populations might experience considerable random genetic changes in addition to those caused by natural selection. Therefore Darwinism—brought up to date by genetics, supported by the observations of field biologists, paleontologists, and systematists, plus a modicum of experimental data—seemed able to provide an acceptable hypothesis for evolution and especially for speciation.

I do not recall that in those early years much notice was taken of macromutation. To be sure, Goldschmidt had championed the hypothesis but he was not listened to, mainly because his views on other matters differed so widely and wildly from those of mainline geneticists. After all, the mainline geneticists were making great progress and there seemed little reason to listen to one who was not. In any event, "Where was the evidence?"

One of the more interesting things about macromutations is that, in theory, there would be little problem in their origin but immense problems in their preservation. Bruce Wallace has mentioned Barbara McClintock's statement that if she could control the time of gene action, she could cause a fertilized snail egg to develop into an elephant. This reflects the point of view of many geneticists that the fertilized egg is little more than a biochemical soup in which the genes do their thing. I suspect she might find it difficult unless she could have that snail's egg formed in an elephant's ovary. At least that might provide an elephant cytoplasm to turn snail genes on and off.

In any event, individuals with their genetically identical cells do even more spectacular things all the time. Consider, for example, the cells of the human body. Cells using the same genes in different ways can produce structures as different as neurons and leucocytes. Comparisons across scale are difficult, but is it unreasonable to maintain that the difference between a neuron and a leucocyte at the cellular level is as great as between a mouse and an elephant at the organismal level? The diversity of cell types in the human body is astonishing, and this diversity is based on the turning on and turning off of different genes at different times during development.

Or consider the case of those species with complex alternations of generations. The hydroids and medusae of coelenterates are vastly different creatures. Typically one is sessile, plantlike, and asexual; the other is a free-swimming jellyfish that reproduces sexually. These differences are attained using the same genome, but using different genes at different times. Consider also a larva, pupa, and adult of *Drosophila*. Surely the larva and adult are as different as mouse and elephant.

Although possible in theory, hopeful monsters are not regularly encountered in the field. If they did occur, there would be serious problems with their survival. The hopeful monster would require a hopeful environment, a hopeful diet, and a hopeful mate. But more than anything else, I suspect, it would require a hopeful homeostasis. We tend to forget the extent to which integration of structure and function is required for an organism to work. In our own case, seemingly slight changes in environmental conditions, blood chemistry, or hormonal and central nervous system control can lead to death.

16

Consider this long-term problem. It is highly improbable that the first amphibian arose as a fishy hopeful monster. The paleontological data suggest that a very long time was required to get an amphibian that worked. Many compromises had to be made. At all times the organism as a whole had to be a success even though its parts might not be as well adapted. The basic pattern of circulation can be an example. The circulatory system of fish is such that blood goes to the gills, where it loses carbon dioxide and picks up oxygen. This blood then passes to all the tissues of the body, where oxygen is supplied and carbon dioxide acquired, before returning to the gills. When the respiratory changes began to occur in the amphibian's lungs rather than gills, the fish's pattern of complete separation of oxygenated and deoxygenated blood ceased. In fact, the evolving vertebrates did not get matters fully straightened out until birds and mammals appeared. Solving the problem of not mixing blood rich in oxygen with blood poor in oxygen required about 200 million years—from the Devonian to the Jurassic. Since it was solved, we can assume that it was selectively advantageous that it was.

One must not assume that the early amphibians were poorer vertebrates than their fishy ancestors because of this seemingly less efficient circulatory system. Selection acts on whole fish and whole amphibians, not solely on their parts. The ability to live partly on land made the early amphibians a much better vertebrate for that environment than the fishes.

The problem of getting a hopeful monster in working order depends of course on the level of its monsterness, but for any large monstrosity, the odds against success seem overwhelming. A little monster, in an isolated and protecting environment, might be fine-tuned over a long period of time and this must happen in some lineages.

Nevertheless, we may suspect that macromutations produce only hopeless monsters.

The Methods of Evolutionary Biology

The conflicts over the interpretation of phenomena related to evolutionary biology are almost always the result of our not being able to make the pertinent observations and collect the critical data. The data of paleontology cannot tell us that, beyond all reasonable doubt, evolution is the result of random mutations being screened by natural selection. Lamarckian evolution or any of a number of other schemes cannot be falsified by what the rocks reveal. We assume we can arrange species in hierarchical groups because they share a common ancestry. It is actually the reverse: we assume different species have a common ancestry because we can arrange them in hierarchical groups. For all we know, most living species could be assumed to have no remote ancestors, since for only a relatively few of the many millions of living species is there a record of recent and closely similar fossil representatives. Nor can the evolutionary biologist supply detailed evidence for evolution in more than a few lineages.

And it does not matter. Conclusions in science are usually based on the analysis of only a few examples of a given phenomenon, for it is often the case that only a few are amenable to observation or experimentation. Furthermore, few scientific problems can be studied directly, historical events never directly. For example, understanding of inheritance comes from checking whether flies have eyes that are white or red. One studies the fine structure of matter by looking for streaks on photographs of cloud chambers. We predict the future of the universe by looking for tiny shifts in the spectral lines of light from distant stars.

We can get a handle on the processes of evolution only in exceptional instances. We must settle for these few opportunities where a critical observation or experiment can be made. We rely greatly on Sumner's mice and Kettlewell's moths in accepting the reality of natural selection. The genetic data used by those making the Modern Synthesis came from a very few species—mainly those of the genus *Drosophila*.

In fact it has been a central feature of evolutionary biology theory, as in all science, that if data can be obtained to explain one phenomenon it is legitimate, as a first approximation, to apply the same explanation throughout what appears to be the same class of phenomena. A chemist does not believe it necessary to analyze all molecules of water before accepting that it is true beyond reasonable doubt that water is composed of two atoms of hydrogen and one of oxygen. In contrast to supernatural patterns of thought, scientists assume that there are regularities in natural phenomena, a given cause will have a given effect, and that understanding, in contrast with belief, is possible.

Therefore we do not assume that the interactions of species, environment, and time are restricted to a few scenarios. We know enough about living organisms to realize that variety, not constancy, is the rule. In most situations we cannot know the details and, as mentioned before, we must base general theory on those rare instances where we can dissect the components of the evolutionary process. Lamarckian evolution was not rigorously excluded by any observations of fossil or living organisms until it became possible to design experiments with microorganisms that could supply the critical data.

Atkins, P. W., 1981, *The Creation*, Freeman, San Francisco.

[Chambers, Robert], 1844, *Vestiges of the Natural History of Creation*, Churchill, London.

Cloud, Preston, 1988, *Oasis in Space: Earth History from the Beginning*, Norton, New York.

Cope, Edward D., 1904, *The Primary Factors of Organic Evolution*, Open House, Chicago.

Darwin, Charles R., 1859, *On the Origin of Species by Means of Natural Selection, or the Preservation of Favoured Races in the Struggle for Life*, John Murray, London.

Darwin, Charles R., 1868, *The Variation of Animals and Plants under Domestication*, John Murray, London.

Dobzhansky, Theodosius, 1937, *Genetics and the Origin of Species*, Columbia University Press, New York.

Hooke, Robert, 1665, *Micrographia or Some Physiological Descriptions of Minute Bodies Made by Magnifying Glasses with Observations and Inquiries Thereupon*, Martin and Allestry, London. Reprinted 1961 by Dover, New York.

Hooke, Robert, 1705, *The Posthumous Works of Robert Hooke*, edited by Richard Waller, Smith and Waller, London. Reprinted 1969 by Johnson Reprint, New York.

Jenkin, F., 1867, The origin of species, *North British Review* **46**: 277-318 (June 1867).

Martin, William, 1809, *Outlines of an Attempt to Establish a Knowledge of Extraneous Fossils, on Scientific Principles*, J. Wilson, Macclesfield. Republished 1972 by the Geological Society of London, Paul P. B. Minet, Chicheley, Buckinghamshire.

Mayr, Ernst, 1942, *Systematics and the Origin of Species*, Columbia University Press, New York.

Mayr, Ernst, 1980, Some thoughts on the history of the evolutionary synthesis, in: *The Evolutionary Synthesis* (Ernst Mayr and William B. Provine, eds.), Harvard University Press, Cambridge.

Mayr, Ernst, 1982, *The Growth of Biological Thought: Diversity, Evolution, and Inheritance*, Harvard University Press, Cambridge.

Paley, William, 1802, *Natural Theology; Or, Evidences of the Existence and Attributes of the Deity, Collected from the Appearances of Nature*, R. Faulder, London.

Simpson, George Gaylord, 1944, *Tempo and Mode in Evolution*, Columbia University Press, New York.

Stebbins, G. Ledyard, Jr., 1950, *Variation and Evolution in Plants*, Columbia University Press, New York.

Populations and Their Place in Evolutionary Biology

Bruce Wallace
Virginia Polytechnic Institute and State University

Although the title of this paper stresses the place of populations in evolutionary theory, I intend to expand its scope so as to deal with the role of mutation in evolution as well. One once learned (Dobzhansky, 1937, p. 13) that mutation is not evolution but, rather, that mutations merely provide the raw material for evolution; natural selection, acting upon this raw material and especially upon the virtually endless gene combinations that differing alleles make possible, guides the path of evolutionary change. The driving force behind natural selection is Darwinian fitness; the outcome of selection is, almost always, greater individual fitness under prevailing environments. Evolution, consequently, can be largely viewed as the sequential accumulation of adaptive changes.

Chance, as the late Sewall Wright stressed for many years, also plays an important role in evolutionary change: capricious events that occur in different local populations prevent these populations from adopting identical, global solutions to environmental challenges. Local environments vary. Local gene pools undergo chance alterations in composition. Consequently, within each local population selective changes occur in gene frequencies—changes that lead to as much adaptive change as is possible given existing conditions.

Migration and the mixing of alleles from different local populations generally prevent any one of these populations from striking out on its own, thereby proceeding down a unique evolutionary path as natural selection—reflected in changing gene frequencies—leads to adaptations that best meet the continuing alterations that occur in a particular local environment.

This paper was prepared while the author's research was supported under grant GM34576, National Institute of General Medical Science, U. S. Public Health Services, and while he was an Alexander von Humboldt U. S. Senior Scientist awardee and guest of Professor D. Sperlich at the University of Tübingen. This paper is dedicated to the memory of Sewall Wright who died on March 3, 1988—the last of the three giants of early population genetics.

The account outlined in the preceding paragraphs contains the essence of neo-Darwinism or the Synthetic Theory of Evolution that emerged during the 1940s from interactions among biologists of many disciplines: genetics (Dobzhansky, 1937), animal systematics (Mayr, 1942), paleontology (Simpson, 1944), and botany (Stebbins, 1950). From the outset, the Modern Synthesis confronted dissent. Goldschmidt (1940), a physiological and developmental geneticist, argued that the genetic gap separating any pair of species must be crossed at a single bound—by a macromutation. Such gaps cannot be crossed, according to Goldschmidt, by the cumulative alteration of allele frequencies at many gene loci. Stated differently, Goldschmidt saw species differences as qualitative, not quantitative ones. Similar views were also held by the German paleontologist Schindewolf (1950; see Simpson, 1953, p. 111). Løvtrup (1987) vigorously presses such views today. Unfortunately, his attempts to define "macromutation" fail: a hereditary variation "which significantly augments or reduces the reproductive survival of the carrier of the mutation in question" (p. 318) could easily be a micromutation; the cited imperceptible effects of Goldschmidt's "systemic mutations" hardly stress the "macro" aspect of these genetic changes.

Recently, a number of persons have expressed dissatisfaction with what they perceive as the Synthetic Theory. Raff and Kaufman (1983) have dedicated their text, *Embryos, Genes, and Evolution,* to Goldschmidt even though they concede that his genetic concepts were frequently wrong. McClintock's views of evolution, by her admission, tend to parallel those of Goldschmidt (see Keller, 1983, p. 100). Eldredge and Gould (1972) and Gould and Eldredge (1977) have expressed reservations concerning the Modern Synthesis and its ability to account for their "punctuated equilibria." To counter the gradualism they ascribe to neo-Darwinism, they frequently cite Mayr's (1954) "founder principle." I (having been close to him at that time) have never placed Mayr's concepts of "founder principle" and "genetic revolution" outside neo-Darwinism; these concepts and subsequent advances in molecular genetics, in my opinion, have led to an evolution of neo-Darwinism, not to a need for its rejection.

The task I have set for myself here is to examine the place of populations in evolutionary theory, to assure as well as I can that vocabulary—the use of words—is not a source of apparent disagreement, and then to consider some of the recent claims that mutation must be assigned a greater role in evolution, either in the guise of "hopeful monsters" (Goldschmidt, 1940) or as the factor that limits the rate at which evolutionary change occurs (Nei, 1987).

Evolution: The Geneticist's Perception

In a personal letter, Mayr has referred to evolution as "a matter of orchids, butterflies, warm bloodedness, mating systems, etc., etc." Elsewhere (Mayr and Provine, 1980, p. 12) he says, "It is simply not true that evolution can

COMMON
PERSPECTIVE

EVOLUTION

GENETICIST'S
PERSPECTIVE

Figure 1. A diagram illustrating the different perspectives of evolution that are characteristic of geneticists and most other biologists: the latter look at and study individuals or collections of organisms, whereas the former speak of "gene pools" that change with time. As long as the only physical link between successive generations are the gametes that parents produce and that unite to give progeny individuals, the two perspectives are equally valid.

be explained as a change in gene frequencies." Perhaps "explained" is the wrong word. In Dobzhansky's opinion (1970, p. 23), the "elementary components of evolutionary changes *are* alterations of the frequencies of gene alleles or chromosomal variants in the gene pool of a population" (my italics). At the basic level, gene frequency changes *are* evolution; they do not *explain* it.

Can we now agree that evolutionary change has a rational, physical explanation? And can we agree that the only physical link between successive generations of Mendelian populations are the gametes that are produced by parents and unite to give rise to progeny? If we can agree to these two points, then the difference Mayr sees distinguishing his views from those of population geneticists largely disappears. The source of the difference is illustrated in Figure 1. Most biologists look at, study, and experiment with organisms. They are familiar with the organism's phenotype in the broadest sense of that term. If organisms evolve, however, as illustrated in Figure 1, and if gametes are the sole physical link between generations, the course of evolution must be reflected within gametes just as surely as it is in the changing phenotypes. That we cannot study evolution by examining genetic material is an accident of history: we are still illiterate. Some stretches of DNA can be interpreted: upstream signals can now be identified, the limits of the structural gene can be defined (and the amino acid sequence of the polypeptide whose synthesis it controls can be deduced), and the presence of nearby enhancers can be detected. In time, geneticists (and I always include population geneticists among geneticists) will be able to read the entire complement of genetic material just as a master musician can read a symphonic score, or a master builder can read a complex set of blueprints. At that time, whether one is familiar with phenotypes or with genotypes will be relatively unimportant because under a given environment the genotype predicts the phenotype. "Noise" exists, of course, but it represents variation that escapes control by either the environment or genotype. The objections Mayr has raised concerning the geneticist's view of evolution as a change in gene frequency will eventually disappear as genetic knowledge increases and as molecular biologists become increasingly fluent in reading genetic programs.

At this point, the consequences of operons and operon-like gene control mechanisms must be stressed. These mechanisms often "read" the environment and, depending upon the signals they perceive, call for differential gene action. Thus, the standard genotype-environment dichotomy is rendered largely obsolete; the environment, through gene control mechanisms, becomes incorporated within the workings of the individual organism. The increasingly adaptive responses of organisms to environmental changes (the "modifications" of Schmalhausen, 1949) have their origins in the realignments of environmental signals and their genetic sensors; ill-adapted morphoses represent responses not yet filtered through the sieve of natural selection.

Figure 1 errs, of course, in showing a single bird at each stage during the evolution of fantail pigeons. Large numbers of birds were (and are) available to pigeon fanciers. Furthermore, these birds have always differed in the degree to which their spines were abnormal. By following an adage of prehistoric origin—like begets like—pigeon breeders of past centuries created not only the fantails illustrated in Figure 1 but also pouters, the Jacobins, the carriers, the tumblers, and many other present-day pigeon varieties. These varieties will continue to change as breeders ply their trade; pigeons are not at evolutionary endpoints, by any means.

Whatever the nature of the genetic basis for the fantail phenotype that is illustrated in Figure 1, it (or its components, if it consists of multiple factors) has a calculable frequency among the gametes produced by the birds of that variety in any one generation, and among those gametes that give rise to the next generation of breeding birds. To separate evolution, especially at its outset, from changing gene frequencies is impossible. The word "frequency" with its well-defined meaning cannot be a source of disagreement; then the word "gene" (whose definition has always been—purposefully and wisely, I think—fuzzy) is the culprit. We shall return to this point again in a few moments.

On the Place of Populations in Evolution

Here is the place to consider the place of populations in evolution, my assigned topic. The organisms being discussed are diploid, cross-fertilizing ones that constitute Mendelian populations. Instant speciation by hybridization and chromosome doubling, for example, is not included here. Furthermore, evolution, not the tracing of lineages, is our main concern; consequently, our interests lie in the bulk of the organism's genetic material (that which Mendelizes) and not in mitochondrial or chloroplast DNA, fascinating and useful as the changes in these bits of circular DNA may be.

Separate sexes, male and female, guarantee that a population or a species persists through time only as a population, not as an asexually reproducing clone of individuals. The closest that events can come to removing the Mendelian population as the unit of evolution is for a parent to produce a cluster of mature germ cells that carry identical dominant or semi-dominant mutations (the result of a spermatogonial or oogonial event) from which sons and daughters exhibiting mutant phenotypes arise. These offspring with their abnormal phenotypes must then either exhibit a strong sexual preference for one another or be the only progeny capable of surviving under the prevailing environmental conditions. If they mate exclusively with one another (because of a strong sexual preference or because there is no alternative), gene frequency with respect to the new mutation within the new "population" will be 50 percent. If homozygous dominants now displace heterozygotes, the mutant gene will reach 100 percent almost immediately.

What has been described in the preceding paragraph, if viewed as an incident occurring in time, is a miracle. It does not represent a series of plausible events because: 1) the population of which the mutant-bearing parent was a member must have been on the verge of immediate extinction; 2) the phenotype resulting from the new mutation must be considerably more "fit" than those exhibited by other population members; 3) the mutation must be accompanied by a strong preference for mating with other mutant-bearing individuals; 4) the early matings would be among brothers and sisters, and the resulting 25 percent homozygosity would expose many previously concealed recessive mutations—the advantage of the new mutation must override the dysgenic effect of incestuous matings.

Much of the miraculous aspect of these postulated events is removed if they are viewed not as isolated happenings in time but, rather, as events occurring in numerous, local, partially isolated populations scattered around the extreme periphery of a species' geographical range. Here, the fitness of the prevailing genotype *is* virtually zero; the organisms are, by definition, unable to adapt to the next adjacent increment of environmental change. The most probable outcome of selection at the species border, however, would not be for the creation and survival of abnormal individuals (hopeful monsters) but for isolating mechanisms that would insert reproductive barriers between the bulk of the species and the individuals constituting a successfully adapting local population. The mechanics of DNA replication, of segregation, and of chromosomal assortment virtually guarantee that any successful isolating mechanism will be genetic—probably chromosomal—in nature (Wallace, 1959a, 1982).

A purist could claim that hopeful monsters, if they arose, still fall within the domain of *population* genetics: gene frequency would increase from 0.0 percent to 50 percent and then, more slowly, to 100 percent. Other less exotic changes in which mutations spread through much of a population, and in which corresponding events progress gradually without intense inbreeding, constitute the normal material of population genetics (see Turner, 1977, for an account of the origin of mimicry in butterflies). Such "less exotic" changes would, in my view, include even those instances of genetic changeover that I have recently described (Wallace, 1986, 1987). Thus, we see that the population virtually by definition *is* the unit of evolution for Mendelizing organisms; there is no alternative. There is, as far as I can see, no escape from this conclusion.

When do Genes Differ? What is a Mutation?

I suggested earlier that most persons agree on the meaning of "frequency" and, therefore, if the expression "gene frequency" causes confusion, the culprit must be the word "gene." And it is true that the term is ambiguous, and has been kept so since at least the 1920s. At one and the same time, the gene has been a unit of physiological action, a unit of recombination, and a unit of mutation. If, to cite a hypothetical example, abnormal wing shape and faulty bristle structure are inherited as a unit (Mendelian ratios and all), we speak of such-and-such gene—using a name that identifies the first noted or most prominent phenotypic effect. Minor effects may be omitted from the gene's name but are not necessarily overlooked on that account. One speaks of the pleiotropic effect of a gene. Dobzhansky (1927; Dobzhansky and Holz, 1943) demonstrated the pleiotropic effects of well-known mutant genes on the shape of the spermathecae in female *Drosophila melanogaster*. These mutant alleles did indeed change the shape of spermathecae, but they are still known as *yellow* (body color), *white* (eye color), *singed* (bristle shape), and by other familiar names.

If, by carrying out an extraordinarily large experiment, someone were to demonstrate that the wing and bristle effects of our hypothetical mutant gene can be separated by recombination, one would (because the gene is a unit of recombination) assign two names to the mutant and cite their genetic distance in centimorgans. A number of gene loci in *D. melanogaster* are known to be occupied by extremely closely linked genes (see Chovnick *et al.*, 1964; Judd, 1964; and Wright *et al.*, 1982); other complex loci of this sort may await discovery.

With the finding (Muller, 1927) that X rays induce gene mutations, the third definition of the gene—a unit of mutation—took on added importance. If, for example, irradiated, wild-type *Drosophila* males are crossed to females homozygous for the hypothetical wing-bristle mutant gene, one expects to find an occasional individual exhibiting abnormal wings and bristles. If, in addition to these expected mutant types, one finds (perhaps more rarely) wing mutants and bristle mutants separately, one speaks of two genes (wings *and* bristle) because the gene is also defined as a unit of mutation. (In this discussion, I have ignored inversions, translocations, and chromosomal duplications that also fall under the term "mutation.")

Small wonder that the term "gene frequency" causes consternation; "gene" is a word of many meanings. Benzer (1955, 1957) attempted to resolve the inherent difficulty by introducing new terms (muton, recon, and cistron), but these words never won the wholehearted support of geneticists—probably because an ambiguous term can be a useful one. An ambiguous term can expand or evolve in accommodating new findings.

What do I regard as a difference between two alleles? When, for example, do I refer to a gene locus as being "heterozygous"? Figure 2 presents my views. The gene under discussion occupies the A locus. It produces a product, P. The gene product emanating from the two A alleles of a diploid individual may differ in 1) structure (in amino acid sequence), 2) time of appearance, or 3) amounts produced. If gene A is autonomous, with its promotors, enhancers, and all forming a tightly linked unit (a Mendelizing gene), the existence of two different products (P_1 and P_2) suggests that the two alleles differ in some way: the locus is said to be heterozygous for A_1 and A_2

If the alleles at the A locus act only in response to signals emitted by a remote (unlinked) regular gene, R, and if the two A alleles produce gene products that differ (perhaps only in amount or time of appearance), it would appear that A_1 and A_2 differ. They react differently to the same

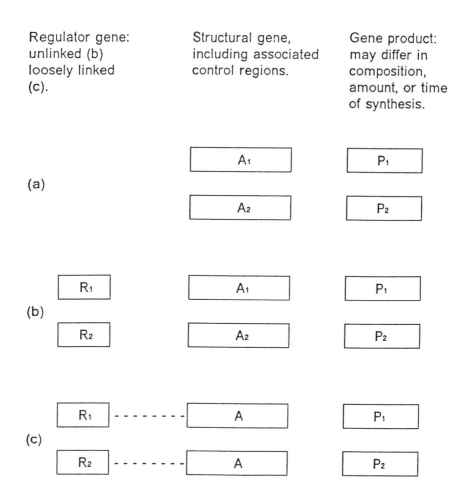

Regulator gene: unlinked (b) loosely linked (c).

Structural gene, including associated control regions.

Gene product: may differ in composition, amount, or time of synthesis.

(a)

A₁

P₁

A₂

P₂

(b)

R₁

A₁

P₁

R₂

A₂

P₂

(c)

R₁

A

P₁

R₂

A

P₂

Figure 2. In my view, the "gene" is the structural gene plus its tightly associated regulator or controlling elements (A); this complex, under most circumstances, represents the Mendelizing unit. It is a unit of physiological action. (a) If there are no remote controlling elements, A_1 and A_2 can be assumed to differ if their products (P_1 and P_2) differ in structure, amount, or time of synthesis. (b) If the remote controlling elements are unlinked to the A-locus, A_1 and A_2 are again assumed to differ if their products differ. (c) If cis-acting, genetically linked controlling elements (even if they are somewhat remote) cause P_1 and P_2 to differ in amount or time of synthesis, I view the structural alleles *(A)* as different even though they may be identical: i.e., if two alleles *behave* as if they differ, I say that they *do* differ.

signal; hence, the difference resides at the A locus. The individual is heterozygous at this locus.

Finally, if R_1 and R_2 are cis-acting, regulator alleles (even though located at some distance from the A locus), and if they cause otherwise identical A alleles to produce gene products at different times, at different rates, or in different amounts, I say that the two alleles at the A locus are *effectively* different. If a gene can act only in response to a controlling element, and if two otherwise identical alleles respond dissimilarly to two different (cis-acting) controlling elements, then, in my opinion, the alleles differ: the individual is heterozygous for alleles (A_1 and A_2) that are effectively different.

Mutations, in a Casual Sense

In explaining the nature of biological species, Wilson (1975, p. 9) cites lions *(Panthera leo)* and tigers *(P. tigris)* as examples of organisms that, although they can be hybridized rather easily in captivity, were reproductively isolated when they coexisted in India prior to the 1880s. Having stated that the lion preferred open country while the tiger was found more frequently in forested regions, Wilson suggests that this difference (among others that characterize the two species) almost certainly has a genetic basis.

Figure 3 presents a schematic view of Wilson's suggestion. Beneath the illustrations of a lion and a tiger (top), each in its normal habitat, are representations of their DNA. I have guessed that some 95 percent of the DNA of lions and tigers is identical; this guess is based on their close relationship (ability to hybridize) tempered by the 1 percent difference they exhibit when their retroviral DNAs are compared to that of the house cat *(Felis domesticus)* (see Benveniste, 1985). The dissimilar 5 percent of the DNA is exaggerated in the lower bars of the upper diagram (lion, black; tiger, white).

The lower figure emphasizes the suggestion that, if the proper bits of dissimilar DNA could be identified, excised, and reinserted into the genomes of the wrong species, tigers would seek open country while the transformed lions would retire to the forests. Such an effort might take place but, before predicting a probable outcome, I would like to see experiments done with foster parents and hybrid offspring. Training ("cultural heredity," in a broad sense) may as easily explain differences in the behavior of higher mammals as genetic differences.

The early genetic analyses carried out by T. H. Morgan and his collaborators utilized morphological mutants almost exclusively. Each mutant gene that was added to their collection had an obvious morphological effect (white eyes, notched wings, missing bristles, forked and singed bristles, and many more). The traits used by Mendel in his study of inheritance in peas were also morphological: tall versus short plants, smooth versus wrinkled peas, terminal versus axial flowers, and others. The emphasis on morphology in early years was necessary, of course, because the external appearance of the organism was what the investigator could see and score.

Figure 3. Diagrams illustrating in a formal way the "almost certain" genetic differences between tigers and lions that have been said to control their choice of habitat. The DNA of the two species is largely homologous, perhaps differing by 5 percent (black and white bars). The insertion of a small black segment into the tiger's genome (and of a corresponding white one into the lion's genome) should, if the behaviors are genetically controlled, make each seek out the habitat that is preferred by the other. This example illustrates what I call a *casual* use of the term "genetic" difference; much research would be required to provide a rigorous proof.

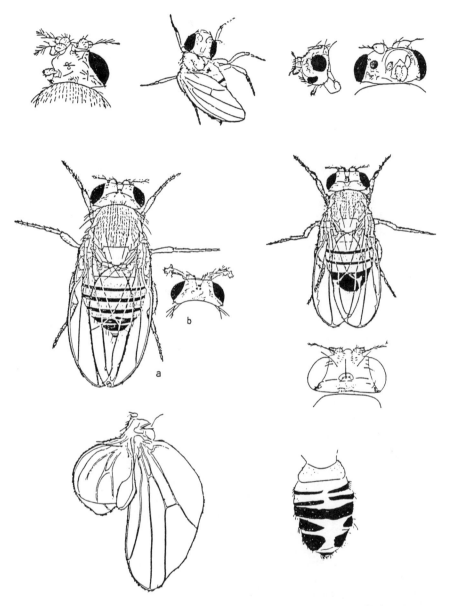

Figure 4. Abnormalities of *Drosophila melanogaster* that are not inherited. According to T. H. Morgan and his colleagues, "there is no certain rule by which such modifications can be distinguished from mutations. Breeding tests are essential to settle this question." The top row of diagrams illustrates asymmetrical abnormalities; these are generally not inherited. The center diagrams illustrate that certain stocks of flies tend to have idiosyncratic abnormalities: (left) *pointed*-winged flies tend to develop wing-like aristae; (right) *delta*-winged flies tend to have abnormal ocelli (inset). The bottom row illustrates an abnormal wing (parts of three wings rather than one) and an abdomen whose segments failed to fuse. Let's assume that these abnormalities arise through the movement of transposons during individual development; it still would remain unlikely that evolution would be speeded up by a mechanism that produces monstrous individuals in profusion. (After Morgan *et al.*, 1925.)

Less well remembered are the morphological disturbances in *Drosophila* that Morgan and his collaborators described as *not* heritable. Not all differences in appearance—even though they may be striking—are genetic (Figure 4). The source of these striking variants is not clear; the terms "environmental accidents" or "developmental accidents" will have to suffice. Morgan (1930) did note that if a wild-type (i.e., red-eyed) female fly were blinded with a hot needle, her offspring and her daughters' offspring possessed darker than normal Malpighian tubules; he even toyed with the notion that this illustrated inheritance of an acquired character. Waddington (1953, 1956) many years later (and also using the phrase "acquired character") showed in effect that a fly's tendency to produce an aberrant phenotype following an environmental insult (heat shock or exposure to ether fumes) has a genetic basis. Consequently, by selecting abnormal flies resulting from an insult, one can often obtain a true-breeding strain of abnormal flies that no longer requires the insult in order to develop abnormally.

The genotype can be viewed as being constructed from smaller units, genes. The phenotype frequently can be viewed (in fact, a great effort is generally made to view it in this way) as being built of small units: toes, fingers, legs, wings, bristles, and the like. Gene mutations are known that alter such phenotypic units. The mutant allele causing polydactyly adds fingers, *bithorax* endows *Drosophila* with an extra pair of wings, while *scute* and *bobbed* reduce the numbers of bristles. Because mutations are known that alter phenotypic units, some persons would assign specific genes for each such unit: finger genes, toe genes, eye-lens genes, cornea genes, and hair genes to name a few possibilities.

From this perspective comes the postulated genetic basis for the paleontological "mutation": a sudden change in morphology which, having occurred, persists for a considerable time. The observed morphological change is ascribed to a correspondingly sudden genetic change—a *gene* mutation.

"Sudden" for a paleontologist may seem like "eternity" for a population geneticist, especially for one who experiments on the effects of artificial selection. A rate of change (measured in *Darwins*) that an animal breeder would probably interpret as no change at all (that is, an ostensible change that is not statistically significant) can, for a paleontologist, represent an exceedingly rapid, saltational change. Ironically, the reverse appears to constitute conventional wisdom: a recent report in the *New York Times* dealing with punctuated equilibria contrasted the snail's pace of artificial selection with the suddenness of paleontological shifts in morphology. Do not be misled by such confusion!

Figure 5 illustrates a morphological "mutation." Three laboratory populations of *D. melanogaster* that were started from a common stock were found one hundred generations (four years) later to be morphologically quite different. When confronted, one fly at a time, with unlabeled specimens from the three populations, I correctly identified more than 90 percent of the females from population 1 (left) and more than 70 percent of the

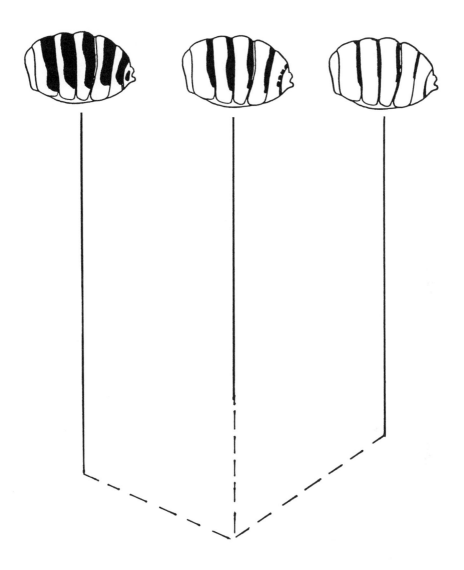

Figure 5. A diagrammatic representation of the morphological divergence of three laboratory populations of *Drosophila melanogaster* over a period of 100 generations. The flies from population 1 (left) could be identified correctly in more than 90 percent of trials using unlabeled specimens; those from population 3 (center) could be identified 70 percent of the time. Flies from population 6 (right) were very lightly pigmented compared to those of the other two populations. The terminal melanic spot that is virtually diagnostic for flies of population 1 exhibited a multifactorial inheritance pattern; it was not caused by a simple allelic mutation. This example illustrates that dissimilar unit phenotypic characteristics do not necessarily reflect unit differences at the genetic level.

females from population 3 (center). Instrumental in achieving this accuracy was the terminal melanic spot exhibited by nearly all of the females of population 1.

Gene mutations that cause spots of melanin in *D. melanogaster* are not unknown; *speck*, the rightmost marker gene on chromosome 2, is an example. Hence, one might claim that population 1 differs from 3 and 6 (on the right in Figure 4) by a "mutation." Test crosses, however, have revealed that this claim would be wrong: the spot in question exhibits typical multifactoral inheritance (Wallace, 1954). Spotted daughters were recovered in F_2 cultures from both spotted and nonspotted F_1 females. The incidence of spotted females in F_2 cultures ranged from 80 percent or more to none. Spotted females had higher proportions of spotted daughters than did nonspotted ones. In brief, a unit phenotypic trait (spot versus nonspot) arose rather suddenly (less than four years) in a population as the result of multiple genetic factors, not as the result of a sudden mutation at one gene locus that then became fixed in that population.

Perhaps it is worth noting here that in all instances known to me of a reversion within a laboratory stock culture of a mutant phenotype to a more normal (wild-type) expression—either of dominant mutations carried by heterozygous individuals or of homozygous recessive mutant stocks— the cause has consisted of genetic modifiers at scattered gene loci. The excellent expression of the *Curly* (wing) mutant in *Curly-Lobe/Plum* balanced lethal stocks stems as much from modifiers on the *Plum* chromosome as from those on the *Curly-Lobe* chromosome itself.

The need to outcross mutant *Drosophila* strains in order to recover the original expression of the recessive alleles has been common knowledge since early *Drosophila* days. Morgan (1919) demonstrated that modifiers of *Notch* were to be found at various other gene loci—including those on other chromosomes. The Morgan group successfully argued against Castle's claim of a continuously varying "hooded" allele in rats. Contrary to Castle's interpretation, the hooded pattern caused by a main (hooded) gene is subject to modification by alleles throughout the rat's genome (see Morgan, 1964, pp. 296ff.).

Waddington (1953, 1956), in his experiments on genetic assimilation (originally referred to by Waddington, unfortunately, as the inheritance of acquired characters), exposed flies to environmental insults (heat shocks to pupae; exposure of fertilized eggs to ether fumes) and then selected as parents the few flies that exhibited abnormal phenotypes, but phenotypes resembling those caused by well-known genes. With one possible exception, the ultimate fixation of the mutant phenotype in Waddington's selected lines resulted from selection of alleles at loci other than the obvious one (either *crossveinless* or *bithorax*)—the one known to produce the abnormal phenotype. The eventual identification of seven crossvein-modifying loci was accomplished by Milkman (1965, and earlier papers).

The Role of Mutation in Evolution

The traditional, neo-Darwinian view of mutation (whether genic or chromosomal in nature) is that it is *not* evolution. Evolution consists of changes in gene pools (i.e., changes in the relative proportions of various alleles at various loci) that are wrought by natural selection. The sources of genetic variation that are available to the population are mutation and recombination. The stress in the past has been, and I believe rightly so for the most part, on new combinations of alleles continuously arising from existing genetic variation; these combinations, rather than mutations of the moment, provide the basis for evolutionary change.

In his recent book, Nei (1987) places considerably more stress on currently arising mutations than I would. He cites as one of his reasons the contrast between artificial and natural selection: "[T]he response to artificial selection is usually large in the early generations but gradually diminishes as generations proceed. Without input of new genetic variability, the mean value of a character under selection usually reaches a plateau within a few dozen generations." Further, "artificial selection does not provide an accurate picture of long-term evolution by natural selection."

First, I would say that, although the artificial selection described by Nei differs considerably from "long-term evolution by natural selection," *it is not a separate model*. It is an extreme variant of what is essentially one model: *selection*. Artificial selection, as described by Nei, is to natural selection what one-issue candidacies are to democracy. There are candidates who run on single issues (for example, anti-abortion, Creationism, or prayer in the schools) and, if feelings are sufficiently strong among the electorate, they may win. A democracy, however, is continuously faced with a multitude of issues and, if these are to be dealt with successfully, an entire network of compromises must be tolerated. Like long-term evolution by natural selection, a democracy must avoid simplistic, one-issue contests.

The artificial selection referred to by Nei is what is carried out in many laboratories. The experimental animals (*Drosophila, Tribolium,* and mice, for the most part) have no intrinsic value; they exist for experimentation. Thus, we read in the "Materials and Methods" sections of countless publications that the bristles were counted on 50 flies of each sex, and the five males and five females with the highest (or lowest) numbers were retained as parents for the next generation. How about the remaining 45 of each sex? They were destroyed.

There is another artificial selection, however. It is, and has been for ages, practiced on plants and animals that possess an intrinsic value—and, for the most part, practiced by persons ignorant of genetics. Individual plants or animals that disappoint their owners or masters are not carried to the ashbin. Table 1 lists the times of domestication of various animal species, and the number of varieties that have arisen since domestication. No plateau is evident in this material; nor was one evident in Figure 1. Even in selecting

Common name	Years domesticated	Number of varieties
Dog	10,000 +	200
Cat	4000	25
Cattle	6000	60
Sheep	7500	50
Goat	7500	20
Pig	6000	35
Horse	5000	60
Rabbit	3000	20
Duck	3000	30
Chicken	5000	125
Canary	500	20
Parakeet	150	5

Table 1. The text mentions that populations that are subjected to artificial selection tend to change rapidly during the early generations and then to plateau after a dozen or more generations have elapsed. This table is a reminder that in many instances of artificial selection, progress has been sustained for centuries. The rapid change followed by a plateau is characteristic, I believe, of experiments on laboratory organisms that possess no intrinsic value; unwanted individuals are merely destroyed. The animals listed above have an intrinsic value and are kept (and used for breeding) even though they may exhibit unwanted traits. The intensity of selection has not been great, and the supply of genetic variation has been maintained by gene mutation.

for milk production in dairy cattle, no plateau has yet been detected.

Haldane (1957) introduced his account of "the cost of natural selection" with a reference to cattle breeding. If, he reasoned, breeders were to insist on retaining only those animals that met certain high standards, the breed would be lost. The "cost" of selection would be too great for such slowly reproducing animals.

I am inclined to invert Haldane's argument to illustrate what I call soft selection (i.e., frequency- and density-dependent selection): the number of animals retained under a program for improved milk production corresponds to the number of stanchions that are available for accommodating cows in dairy barns. Each cow has an intrinsic value. She may not produce as much milk as some others but she produces more than do donkeys or pigs—or than an empty stall. Haldane's account of selection in cattle is paradoxical: if most animals met the breeders' standards (in which case selection would not threaten the breed's existence), their characteristics would not correspond to the breeders' standards for the latter must always lie at the margin of the animals' ability to meet them.

The basis for Nei's argument lies in the apparent selective neutrality of much genetic and phenotypic variation. Lewontin (1978), for example, has cited one versus two nasal horns for rhinoceroses as an example of a chance event arising during evolution; Dobzhansky (1970, p. 261) has cited divergent and convergent anterior scutellar bristles in *Drosophila* species for the same purpose.

Recently, I have attempted to identify two arenas of interest in the evolution of populations: the *population* and *time* arenas. The former is a geometric plane including for any one generation the point denoting that each mother, on an average, leaves one adult, reproducing daughter as her replacement. This is the plane within which are found norms of reaction (Schmalhausen, 1949; Lewontin, 1974) that reflect the relative fitnesses of different genotypes under various environmental conditions. The time arena, in contrast, is a geometric plane that extends through time and consists of the edges of successive population arenas upon each of which the *average* fitnesses of different genotypes are projected.

Population geneticists often forget the extent to which they compute averages; many forget that the fitnesses frequently cited for genotypes AA, Aa, aa (W_{AA}, W_{Aa}, and W_{aa}) are averages and that average fitness of a population ($\bar{W}$) is an average of many averages. Harper (1977, p. 669) cites an analogous example: "Perhaps some of the emphasis on the constancy of seed size comes from the custom of quoting mean weight based on samples of 100 seeds." Taken to its extreme, each genotype-environment combination ("situation") in my population arena could involve a single individual because nearly every individual's genotype is unique. At the individual level, this or that phenotypic property may determine at a given moment whether the individual lives or dies. *Drosophila* flies, for example, differ individually in their preferences for walking, hopping, or flying. Overall, these choices may be unimportant, but at a particular moment in the life of a particular fly the choice of walking, hopping, or flying may be of vital importance.

Neutrality in the population arena may lie solely in the average arrived at by combining and averaging over many genotypes and many situations; that is, it may lie in the projection of all fitnesses onto the edge of the population arena—the projection that is included within the time arena. Remove from the population certain genotypes or certain environmental conditions and seemingly neutral alleles may become non-neutral. Thus, neutrality is a marginal concept precisely analogous to the marginal over-dominance described by Wallace (1959b). One need not imagine (as Nei does) evolution being limited by rare occurrences of advantageous alleles; rather, the acknowledged store of "neutral" genes may really be a store of alleles, many of which are considered to be neutral only because, when averaged over numerous challenging situations, they *appear* to be neutral. Citing Harper once more, seeds may appear to be of the same size when citations refer to average weights of seeds that are obtained from samples of 100; this average, however, can conceal a great deal of variation among individual seeds. Neutrality of genes, of genotypes, and of phenotypes, like uniformity of seeds, is an impression usually gained by averaging over samples of enormous size.

Transposons, and Such

The pioneer work on transposable elements was carried out at Cold Spring Harbor during the 1950s by Barbara McClintock (1951, 1956). The physical processes underlying phenomena such as she observed (see Table 2, for example) were understood only after similar events were observed and interpreted in bacteria. Nevertheless, McClintock had an insight into her material that has never been expressed more succinctly, nor colorfully, than her statement (paraphrased here) at one of the weekly Cold Spring Harbor staff meetings: "If I could control the time of gene action, I could cause a fertilized snail egg to develop into an elephant. Their biochemistries are not all that different; it's simply a matter of timing."

Genes moving from place to place within the genome have caused many persons to doubt that evolutionary concepts predating McClintock's work have any further relevance. Among these persons is a dear friend who is convinced that all conclusions arrived at by population geneticists before the 1950s must be reevaluated—perhaps discarded. He has a standing invitation from me to prepare an account of his views for *Evolutionary Biology*, of which I am an editor. Until his arguments are committed to print where they can be thoroughly studied, understood, and perhaps rebutted, they make interesting conversation but little more.

I hear people say, "But the frequency of gene transposition increases under stress!" For my part, I shall *not* claim that ignorance is bliss but I *do* claim that the ignorance of early geneticists allowed for many eventualities. That stress increases mutation rate has been known since the early work

	Pale color (no Spm)		Colorless (Spm)		Total
	Y	y	Y	y	
43 ears	273	5,002	4,742	204	10,221
1 ear	65	47	48	59	219

Table 2. Genetic evidence for the transposition of a gene-controlling element (*Spm*) from one location to another within the genome of *Zea mays*. The test involved 44 ears obtained from 17 plants. Forty-three ears gave similar results and are combined in the first line; these data reveal that *y* is not associated with *Spm*, whereas *Y* is associated with that element. The remaining ear (one of several produced by a single plant) shows, in contrast, that the inheritance of *Spm* and *Y* is independent. In this ear, *Spm* has physically moved and is no longer genetically linked to *Y*. (After McClintock, 1957.)

of Muller (1928) and Plough and Ives (1935). The question is not one of an increased mutation rate accidentally generating answers to novel environmental challenges but, rather, of mutation providing, upon demand, reasonably precise genetic solutions to these new challenges. Dobzhansky (Dobzhansky and Boesiger, 1983) expressed matters in terms of *equifinality*. The problem, that is, concerns a genetic mutation that supposedly provides the answer to an environmental challenge—thus modernizing Lamarck's notions of the inheritance of "acquired" characteristics: "[T]here is no known method whereby more pigment in the skin can induce nucleotide substitutions in these genes such that new, mutant alleles will be produced which code for enzymes that would induce more pigment in individuals of the following generation." Dobzhansky's argument can be concluded as follows: "the hypothesis that acquired characters are inherited demands not simply that mutations be induced in genes by changes in the body [under stress], but that these mutations be directional ones causing equifinal effects in the progeny."

A further argument can be made against relying upon an increased mutation rate to provide genetic solutions for novel evolutionary challenges: a gambler's odds would not be increased by increasing the rate at which slot machine wheels rotate. The most obvious effect that would follow from the accelerating slot machines would be to shorten the time before the gambler loses his or her money. A striking feature of my early work on irradiated *Drosophila* populations (see Wallace 1955; 1981, Chapter 13) was the *increase* in fitnesses of populations exposed to low levels of radiation; populations exposed to high levels of radiation (1000r/day) would have become extinct had they not been removed from radiation and given a chance to recover (Wallace, unpublished).

Arguments contrary to those given by Dobzhansky tend, I believe, to be largely suppositious: "Isn't it possible that . . . ?" "Yes," I say, "yes, it is possible but not at all probable." There are some who, for whatever reason, believe that DNA of African origin tends to lower some poorly defined, poorly measured quality known as IQ. "Isn't it possible," they say, "that this may be so? After all, we know that no two populations are genetically identical." Again, I say, "Yes—yes, but you have no proof." And so I am obliged to reject on similar grounds *all* arguments that are based on *possibilities*, arguments advanced by those who are enchanted by the new developments in gene control. I insist upon concrete illustrations, not mere possibilities.

In 1963 I gave the invitational lecture at the annual meeting of the Canadian Society of Genetics and Cytology; it was entitled, "Genetic Diversity, Genetic Uniformity, and Heterosis." That lecture included references to the work of McClintock, Jacob and Monod, and Maas; it cites five of McClintock's publications. I doubt if there is an earlier publication that cites McClintock's work so extensively. The controls of the time of gene action (in the sense both of which cells within the individual and which times within given cells) and of the modulation of the extent to which genes act are not alien concepts that cannot be incorporated under the earlier term "gene"— and, therefore, under "gene frequency." Those who argue that we must start anew, that neo-Darwinism is dead, are, in my opinion, attempting to create a niche for their own speculations. That niche, history will show, is already an integral part of the Modern Synthesis.

Summary and Conclusions

The Modern Synthesis or, as it is also known, neo-Darwinism has yet to be overthrown by a radically different view of evolution. I speak, of course, of cross-fertilizing organisms and of their genetic (chromosomal) endowment. As long as the only physical link between successive generations of a population is the collective pool of gametes from which each new generation will arise, the genetic view of evolution (one expressed as changes in gene frequency) is as valid as the phenotypic view (changes in appearance).

Sexual reproduction precludes the origin of a population or of a species from a single individual. Hence, populations must be the vehicle for evolutionary change. Genetic dissimilarities among the individual members of a population lead to *frequencies* of dissimilar alleles. Changes in the population through time are both reflected in and caused by changing gene frequencies. This statement does not preclude that the array of phenotypes is changing with time as well; it merely states that the increments of change can be assessed by examining genetic material as well as by studying the organisms' physical appearances or behaviors.

The Goldschmidtian suggestion that the origin of each species from its ancestral form has to be a saltational change involving a single individual (the hopeful monster) is at best unlikely and at worst an extreme case of gene frequency change. To refer, as Goldschmidt (1940) does, to chromosomal inversions in *Drosophila* populations as subliminal elements leading to his (unsubstantiated) macromutational change is, in my opinion, sophistry. Inversions (chromosomal mutations) arise within populations, their frequencies change, eventually they span species, some are lost, others become fixed in this species or that, and the rest remain polymorphic in one or more species. Eventually, most species come to have strikingly different gene arrangements within chromosomal elements that otherwise remain remarkably intact (see Dobzhansky, 1970, p. 133). To superimpose on this flow of events the notion of an unobserved, undemonstrated, even undemonstrable macromutation is disingenuous.

Mutations, we should remember, come in discrete steps. There is no gradualism in genetics. Even the modulation of gene activity involves discrete mutational changes. Evolution in genetic terms does not correspond to the sweep hand of a clock that (seemingly) moves with a constant speed. On the contrary, it more closely resembles a digital watch where each second, tenth of a second, or even one-hundredth of a second requires a numerical change on the dial. To get from Wichita to Colby in Kansas, one can drive north to Salina, and then drive due west. Alternatively, one can set off in a northwesterly direction on what appears to be a diagonal. The distances for these two routes are the same: there is no hypotenuse for much of Kansas. Roads in this state run north-south and east-west at one-mile intervals. The apparent diagonal is really a series of little one-mile jogs—now north, now west, now north again. There is no diagonal—no hypotenuse—no gradualism—in genetic change. Each change is discrete, and relatively little correlation exists between the magnitude of change at the molecular level and the phenotypic consequences of that change.

Non-geneticists speak easily of genetic differences or, to be more precise, of phenotypic differences that are said to be genetic. There is no harm in asserting that the choices of habitat by tigers and lions are "almost certainly genetic" even though they may be or they may not be. It is only when the same casual use of "genetic" is applied to the effect of DNA of different racial origins on human intelligence that the damage that may arise from such casual claims becomes apparent.

Similarly, the fossil record may reveal a sudden change in phenotype that then persists for many years—millennia, perhaps. Some may refer to the change as a "mutation"—a term now generally equated with "gene mutation" or "genetic mutation." Again, the change may or may not be genetic. If it is, it may or may not represent a single, sudden change at a particular gene locus. On the contrary, simple ("unitary") phenotypic changes, as we have seen, can have multifactorial or polygenic explanations. Certainly, the bulk of all phenotypic modification in laboratory material (microevolutionary changes) has proven to stem from modifiers at multiple loci.

Apparent neutrality of certain phenotypic differences can result from the tendency of population geneticists to average over many individuals. Alternative states, P_1 and P_2, may *on the average* be equally effective in promoting survival and reproduction; that does not resurrect the hapless individual, however, who succumbed because he exhibited P_1 when P_2 was required for survival. Nei's suggestion that populations must await new advantageous mutations because the bulk of existing genetic variation is neutral is probably wrong: as situations demanding adaptive responses arise, the formerly neutral-on-the-average variation will lose its apparent neutrality and will respond to the new challenge by changes in gene frequencies and in the formation of new gene combinations.

Finally, novel genetic mechanisms cannot merely be cited as *possibly* calling for the abandonment of neo-Darwinism and the creation of a new evolutionary paradigm. Such a call must be accompanied by a tightly reasoned argument replete with examples showing neo-Darwinism's failures and illustrating how the newly suggested view is superior. Words alone are not enough; "possibly" is not enough. In experimental biology, one surrenders an original hypothesis with great reluctance and only after new data have been gathered that make surrender reasonable, if not essential. It is not enough to blandly state (as Judge Bork did while aspiring to the Supreme Court), "I think I'll change my mind." If the old data could be interpreted in either of two ways, they were not critical data. To the best of my knowledge, the new data calling unequivocally for the overthrow of neo-Darwinism and of the population geneticist's view of neo-Darwinism do not exist.

Benveniste, R. E., 1985, The contributions of retroviruses to the study of mammalian evolution, in: *Molecular Evolutionary Genetics* (R. J. MacIntyre, ed.), pp. 359-417, Plenum, New York.

Benzer, S., 1955, Fine structure of a genetic region in bacteriophage, *Proc. Natl. Acad. Scis.*, U.S., **41**:344-354.

Benzer, S., 1957, The elementary units of heredity, in: *A Symposium on the Chemical Basis of Heredity* (W. D. McElroy and B. Glass, eds.), pp. 70-93, Johns Hopkins University Press, Baltimore.

Chovnick, A., Shalet, A., Kernaghan, P. P., and Krauss, M., 1964, The *rosy* cistron in *Drosophila melanogaster*: genetic fine structure analysis, *Genetics* **50**:1245-1259.

Dobzhansky, Th., 1927, Studies on manifold effect of certain genes in *Drosophila melanogaster*, *Z.I.A.V.* **43**:330-388.

Dobzhansky, Th., 1937, *Genetics and the Origin of Species*, Columbia University Press, New York (revised, 1941).

Dobzhansky, Th., 1970, *Genetics of the Evolutionary Process*, Columbia University Press, New York.

Dobzhansky, Th. and Boesiger, E., 1983, *Human Culture: A Moment in Evolution*, Columbia University Press, New York.

Dobzhansky, Th. and Holz, A. M., 1943, A re-examination of the problem of manifold effects of genes in *Drosophila melanogaster*, *Genetics* **28**:295-303.

Eldredge, N. and Gould, S. J., 1972, Punctuated equilibria: an alternative to phyletic gradualism, in: *Models in Paleobiology* (T. J. M. Schopf, ed.), pp. 82-115, Freeman, San Francisco.

Goldschmidt, R., 1940, *The Material Basis of Evolution*, Yale University Press, New Haven.

Gould, S. J. and Eldredge, N., 1977, Punctuated equilibria: the tempo and mode of evolution reconsidered, *Paleobiology* **3**:115-151.

Haldane, J. B. S., 1957, The cost of natural selection, *Jour. Genet.* **455**:511-524.

Harper, John, 1977, *Population Biology of Plants*, Academic Press, New York.

Judd, B., 1964, The structure of intralocus duplication and deficiency chromosomes produced by recombination in *Drosophila melanogaster*, with evidence for polarized pairing, *Genetics* **49**:253-265.

Keller, E. F., 1983, *A Feeling for the Organism: The Life and Work of Barbara McClintock*, Freeman, San Francisco.

Lewontin, R. C., 1974, Annotation. The analysis of variance and the analysis of causes, *Amer. J. Human Genet.* **26**:400-411.

Lewontin, R. C., 1978, Adaptation, *Sci. Amer.* **239**:156-169.

Løvtrup, S., 1987, *Darwinism: The Refutation of a Myth*, Croom Helm, London.

Mayr, E., 1942, *Systematics and the Origin of Species*, Columbia University Press, New York.

Mayr, E., 1954, Change of genetic environment and evolution, in: *Evolution as a Process* (J. Hurley, A. C. Hardy, and E. B. Ford, eds.), pp. 157-180, Allen and Unwin, London.

Mayr, E. and Provine, W. B., 1980, *The Evolutionary Synthesis: Perspectives on the Unification of Biology*, Harvard University Press, Cambridge, MA.

McClintock, B., 1951, Chromosome organization and genic expression, *C. S. H. Symp. Quant. Biol.* **16**:13-47.

McClintock, B., 1956, Controlling elements and the gene, *C. S. H. Symp. Quant. Biol.* **21**:197-216.

Milkman, R. D., 1965, The genetic basis of natural variation. VII. The individuality of polygenic combinations in *Drosophila*, *Genetics* **52**:789-799.

Morgan, T. H., 1919, A demonstration of genes modifying the character, "Notch," in: *Contributions to the Genetics of Drosophila melanogaster* (T. H. Morgan, C. B. Bridges, and A. H. Sturtevant, eds.), pp. 343-388, Carnegie Inst. Wash. Publ. 278, Washington, D. C.

Morgan, T. H., 1930, The apparent inheritance of an acquired character and its explanation, *Amer. Nat.* **64**:97-114.

Morgan, T. H., 1964, *The Theory of the Gene* (reprint), Hafner, New York.

Morgan, T. H., Bridges, C. B., and Sturtevant, A. H., 1925, The genetics of *Drosophila*, *Bibliogr. genetica* **2**:1-262.

Muller, H. J., 1927, Artificial transmutation of the gene, *Science* **66**:84-87.

Muller, H. J., 1928, The measurement of gene mutation rate in *Drosophila*, its high variability, and its dependence upon temperature, *Genetics* **13**:279-357.

Nei, M., 1987, *Molecular Evolutionary Genetics*, Columbia University Press, New York.

Plough, H. H. and Ives, P. T., 1935, Induction of mutations by high temperature in *Drosophila*, *Genetics* **20**:42-69.

Raff, R. A. and Kaufman, T. C., 1983, *Embryos, Genes, and Evolution*, Macmillan, New York.

Schindewolf, O. H., 1950, *Grundfragen der Paläontologie*, Schweizerbart, Stuttgart.

Schmalhausen, I. I., 1949, *Factors of Evolution*, Blakiston, Philadelphia.

Simpson, G. G., 1944, *Tempo and Mode in Evolution*, Columbia University Press, New York.

Simpson, G. G., 1953, *The Major Features of Evolution*, Columbia University Press, New York.

Stebbins, G. L., 1950, *Variation and Evolution in Plants*, Columbia University Press, New York.

Turner, J. R. G., 1977, Butterfly mimicry: the genetical evolution of an adaptation, *Evol. Biol.* **10**:163-206.

Waddington, C. H., 1953, Genetic assimilation of an acquired character, *Evolution* **7**:118-126.

Waddington, C. H., 1956, Genetic assimilation of the *bithorax* phenotype, *Evolution* **10**:1-13.

Wallace, B., 1954, Genetic divergence of isolated populations of *Drosophila melanogaster*, *Caryologia* (Supplement) **2**:761-764.

Wallace, B., 1959a, Influence of genetic systems on geographic distribution, *C. S. H. Symp. Quant. Biol.* **24**:193-204.

Wallace, B. 1959b, The role of heterozygosity in *Drosophila* populations, *Proc. 10th Inter. Cong. Genet.* **1**:408-419.

Wallace, B., 1963, The annual invitation lecture. Genetic diversity, genetic uniformity, and heterosis, *Can. J. Genet. and Cytol.* **5**:239-253.

Wallace, B., 1982, A possible explanation for observed differences in the geographical distributions of chromosomal rearrangements of plants and *Drosophila*, *Egypt. J. Genet. Cytol.* **13**:121-136.

Wallace, B., 1986, Genetic change-over in *Drosophila* populations, *Proc. Natl. Acad. Scis., U. S.*, **83**:1374-1378.

Wallace, B. 1987, Analyses of genetic change-over in *Drosophila* populations, *Z. Zool. Syst. Evolut.-Forschg.* **25**:40-50.

Wilson, E. O., 1975, *Sociobiology: The New Synthesis*, Belknap Press, Cambridge, MA.

Wright, T. R. F., Black, B. C., Bishop, C. P., Marsh, J. L., Pentz, E. S., Steward, R., and Wright, E. Y., 1982, The genetics of dopacarboxylase in *Drosophila melanogaster*. V. *Ddc* and 1 (2) *amd* alleles: isolation, characterization, and intragenic complementation, *Mol. Gen. Genetics* **188**:18-26.

Lee Ehrman

Professor Wallace's presentation represents the thoughtful views of an accomplished scientist who, as a population geneticist trained decades ago, is a clearly florid *panselectionist*. I agree with him and represent myself too, hopefully, not as a naive panselectionist! Why? Because I utterly reject the concept of neutral mutations, even of Bruce's "marginal neutrality," formerly known to our ilk as marginal overdominance.

Bruce cautions us that neutrality may (temporarily?) lie in the averages we routinely calculate—averages estimating Darwinian fitness, i.e., aspects of viability, fecundity, fertility, and/or longevity—in precisely this order, with the third entry the most vital.

Consider the glutamic acid to valine point mutation, in its narrowest sense, etiologic of the sickle cell trait, in one dose, and of the more serious sickle cell anemia in two doses in a homozygote:

Glutamic acid is coded for in two ways, and only in two. This is the smallest degree of coding degeneracy: GAA or GAG.

Valine is coded for in four ways, GUA or GUG or GUC or GUU, six being the maximum degree of coding degeneracy. (Why two or four or equivalent differences? This itself violates neutrality.) Note the third base wobble—indeed an enhanced degree of freedom regardless of the tRNA species subsequently employed—and itself, oft cited as supposedly neutral variation.

The glutamic acid to valine shift within the beta chain of our hemoglobin molecules at the sixth residue, from the initiation of this long chain, results in the sickling of our erythrocytes, altering their normal biconcave shape, with pathologic sequelae. It requires greater or lesser ease (caloric energy and/or chance) to proceed from GAA or GAG to GU anything, ending with GUA, GUG, GUC, or GUU. Neither the two possible starts nor the four possible finalities of an alteration from glutamic acid to valine are equivalent; nor is the GAA to GUA shift equivalent to a GAA to GUG or to GUC or to GUU shift equivalent in likelihood and/or cost to a GAG to GUG or to GUA to GUC or to GUU change. So even point mutations are never quite neutral, as is surely the case with more gross populational phenomena hinging upon such raw material, illuminated by Bruce.

Imagine a comment on our ongoing neutralist:selectionist (nonneutralist) or on the gradualism:punctuated equilibrium/saltational polemics (also raised by this gathering) by the historian S. J. Gould, taken wholly out of context from the May 1988 issue of *Natural History*. There Gould argues in his longstanding column, the title of which is itself excerpted from Darwin, "This View of Life":

> I think that each side of this controversy possesses a central insight, and that their marriage provides a workable solution sensitive to the fundamental concept of each camp. . . . We must assume that change in the history of scientific theories often records more adequate knowledge of the external world and may therefore be called progress. . . . On the other hand we must also admit that the history of scientific theories on any subject is no simple tale of good information driving out bad. The new is not simply more and better information heaped upon the explanatory structure of the old. In this sense, the history of theories is a successive replacement of mutually incompatible world views, not a stroll up the pathway of objective knowledge. (16)

Other related phenomena, alluded to by Bruce and surely, in some way, by all the panelists, may be broadly clumped under the mechanisms devolving upon speciation. How indeed could such crucial considerations ever even remotely be neglected by a gathering such as this one? Species of sexually reproducing organisms are genetically closed systems. They are closed systems because they do not exchange genes or do so rarely enough so that the species differences are not swamped. Races are, on the contrary, genetically open systems. They exchange genes by peripheral gene flow unless they are isolated by extrinsic causes such as spatial separation. The biological meaning of the closure of a genetic system is simple but important: it is evolutionary independence. Consider these four species: human beings, chimpanzees, gorillas, and orangutans. No mutation and no gene combination arising in any one of them, no matter how favorable, can benefit any of the others. It cannot do so for the simple reason that no gene can be transferred from the gene pool of one species to that of another. On the contrary, races composing a species are not independent in their evolution; a favorable genetic change arising in one race is, at least potentially, capable of becoming a genetic characteristic of the species as a whole.

Species are genetically closed systems because gene exchange between them is impeded or prevented by reproductive isolating mechanisms. The term *isolating mechanism* was proposed by Dobzhansky in 1937 as a common name for all barriers to gene exchange between sexually reproducing populations. According to Mayr (1963), isolating mechanisms are "perhaps the most important set of attributes a species has." It is a remarkable fact that the isolating mechanisms are physiologically and ecologically a most heterogeneous collection of phenomena. It is another remarkable fact that isolating mechanisms that maintain the genetic separateness of species are quite different not only in different groups of organisms but even between different pairs of species in the same genus. They fall naturally into two primary divisions: geographical or spatial isolation, and reproductive isolation. In the case of geographical isolation, the populations involved are *allopatric*, which means they are found in different territories, so gene exchange is minimal. Indeed, they may

or may not be genetically similar. For a complete discussion of allopatric and *sympatric* (populations living in the same territory) speciation and of ecological factors in speciation, see Mayr (1963).

The classification of reproductive isolating mechanisms outlined below is a composite one. It is based on the classifications published by Mayr (1942), Muller (1942), Patterson (1942), Allee *et al.* (1949), Stebbins (1950), and Dobzhansky (1951).

Barriers to gene flow preventing the meeting of potential mates:

- Habitat or ecological isolation: populations found in the same general territory but occupying different ecological niches
- Seasonal or temporal isolation: sexual maturity or activity may occur at different times

Barriers to gene flow preventing the formation of hybrid zygotes:

- Mechanical isolation: as occurs if the genitalia of the two sexes do not correspond
- Gametic isolation or prevention of fertilization: as occurs if eggs and spermatazoa do not meet or do not fuse normally
- Sexual, psychological, or ethological isolation: greater mutual attraction of conspecific males and females than between males and females of different species

Barriers to gene flow that eliminate or handicap the hybrid zygotes that have been produced:

- Hybrid nonviability or weakness: lower viability of hybrid zygotes compared with either parental species
- Hybrid sterility: hybrids unable to reproduce because of nonproduction of functional gametes

- Selective hybrid elimination or hybrid breakdown: hybrid products eliminated in the F2 or later generations because they are adaptively inferior

These eight items have a common function. They all have but one net effect—either singly or collectively—to prevent the exchange of genes between populations (Patterson, 1942), as follows: If populations have diverged genetically, developing different coadapted complexes as a result of having adapted to different environments, then gene exchange between these populations is likely to produce ill-adapted genotypes. Natural selection acts to build and reinforce the barriers to gene exchange between populations whose hybridization results in reproductive wastage. The appearance of hybrids with inferior fitness is, in this way, minimized or avoided altogether (Fisher, 1930; Dobzhansky, 1940, 1970). Alternately, Muller (1942) assumes that reproductive isolation arises as an accidental by-product of genetic divergence. As populations become adapted to different environments, they become different in progressively more and more genes. Reproductive isolation arises because the action of many genes is pleiotropic. Some gene differences selected for different reasons or resulting from random genetic drift (Wright, 1955; Dobzhansky and Spassky, 1962) may thus have isolating side effects.

Further, for traits important in habitat selection, it is expected under natural conditions that stabilizing selection occurs to restrain them within relatively narrow limits. Animals showing behavior deviant from the norm in a certain population are unlikely to breed with other members. Additionally, animals occupying the most suitable habitat in a heterogeneous environment have less need to utilize the physiological and behavioral adaptations an animal possesses to combat imperfect environments. Another advantage of occupying a suitable habitat is that the chances of interbreeding by individuals with similar genotypes are greatly enhanced, thereby insuring their continuity. Ultimately, such a process could *gradually* lead to reproductive isolation among populations, an outcome that has occurred frequently in evolution.

Finally, for the most recent observations on this important general topic—reproductive isolation and speciation, especially of asymmetrical sorts—see Ehrman and Wasserman, 1987. There, the question we addressed was: Given the presence of asymmetrical sexual isolation, can one determine, with any degree of confidence and accuracy, the direction of evolution? Asymmetric isolation occurs when females from ancestral populations are displeased by the behavior of males representing their descendant populations *or* find these suitors as or even more acceptable than males of their own types.

It is generally accepted that two populations that are geographically isolated from each other will in time diverge (Ehrman and Parsons, 1981). It would therefore truly be remarkable if all allopatric, or even partly allopatric, populations developed their sexual isolation in exactly the same way and at the same rate, if at all. During the period when sexual isolation is not complete, asymmetrical isolation is probably the rule; however, its direction (ancestral $\male\male >>$ descendant $\male\male$ or the reciprocal or neither and ancestral $\male\male =$ descendant $\male\male$) would be dependent upon the many operative factors, including relative time to sexual maturity and discrimination, and relative male sex drive. Thus, generalizations are bound to prove unreliable.

SUNY at Purchase

47

Allee, W., Emerson, A., Park, O., Park, T., and Schmidt, K., 1949, *Principles of Ecology,* Saunders, Philadelphia.

Dobzhansky, T., 1937, *Genetics and the Origin of Species,* Columbia University Press, New York.

Dobzhansky, T., 1940, Speciation as a stage in evolutionary divergence, *American Naturalist* **74**: 312-321.

Dobzhansky, T., 1951, *Genetics and the Origin of Species,* 3d ed., Columbia University Press, New York.

Dobzhansky, T., 1970, *Genetics of the Evolutionary Process,* Columbia University Press, New York.

Dobzhansky, T. and Spassky, B., 1962, Genetic drift and natural selection in experimental populations of *Drosophila pseudoobscura, PNAS* **48**: 148-156.

Ehrman, L. and Parsons, P. A., 1981, *Behavior Genetics and Evolution,* McGraw-Hill, New York.

Ehrman, L. and Wasserman, M., 1987, Asymmetric evolution, *Evolutionary Biology* **21**: 1-20.

Fisher, R. A., 1930, *The Genetical Theory of Natural Selection,* Clarendon, Oxford.

Mayr, E., 1942, *Systematics and the Origin of Species,* Columbia University Press, New York.

Mayr, E., 1963, *Animal Species and Evolution,* Harvard University Press, Cambridge.

Muller, H., 1942, Isolating mechanisms, evolution, and temperature, *Biol. Symp.* **6**: 71-125.

Patterson, J., 1942, Isolating mechanisms in the genus *Drosophila, Biol. Symp.* **6**: 271-287.

Stebbins, G. L., 1950, *Variation and Evolution in Plants,* Columbia University Press, New York.

Wright, S., 1955, Population genetics: the nature and cause of genetic viability in populations, *Cold Spring Harbor Symposium Quant. Biol.* **7**: 16-24.

Marvin Wasserman

Professor Wallace has stated that neo-Darwinism—which describes the changes that take place at the population and species level—is also sufficient to explain all of evolution. I essentially agree with this, but wish to take a somewhat different approach to the subject.

When we look at the fate of a population or species over a period of time, we see that three things may happen to it:

First, you may have phyletic evolution: changes in gene frequencies and, perhaps, changes in morphological and physiological traits. Depending upon the time frame and the circumstances, the rate of evolution may vary from virtually zero to rapid, "punctuated" changes. Parenthetically, what I, as a population geneticist, find most interesting is not the occasional rapid evolution that one sees in the fossil record, but the stasis, the long periods of time when relatively little or no obvious morphological changes take place.

A second possibility is that speciation occurs, wherein the species divides into two or more forms, each undergoing its own phyletic evolution.

Finally, a third possibility is that the species may cease to exist—become extinct.

Neo-Darwinism (or the Modern Synthesis) is the theory that was developed in the late 1920s and 1930s by R. A. Fisher (1930), J. B. S. Haldane (1932), and S. Wright (1932). It differed in a number of ways from the Darwinism and saltation theories it replaced. Darwinism stressed the importance of natural selection operating upon genetic variability. Darwin, who preceded Mendel, included blending inheritance, which he recognized reduced the amount of genetic variability by approximately one-half each generation. To account for the great amount of variability that must be introduced to each generation to counter this loss, Darwin accepted a form of Lamarckian inheritance: the inheritance of acquired characteristics, where the environment directly causes changes in the heredity of the individuals. This fit in well with his pangenesis. We now know that none of these theories is correct. Saltationists accepted Mendelism and felt that evolution occurred by giant mutations, "hopeful monsters" (Gold-schmidt, 1940). Provine (1971) has reviewed the sometimes vitriolic debates between these two schools.

Neo-Darwinism is in some ways a compromise theory. Its central theme relies heavily on Mendelian inheritance and the Hardy-Weinberg equilibrium law. It is within the framework of these two newer laws and the various modifications that biological systems place on these laws that biologists have drawn their pictures of the evolutionary mechanisms. The parameters—mutation, migration, selection, population size, mating choice—were defined by the early mathematicians, and the theory was refined and extended by those who came after them (see, e.g., Wright 1968, 1969, 1977, 1978). It was the job of the biologists, among whom Professor Wallace played a significant role, to flesh out the theory by determining through experimentation and observation the relative importance of the various factors that the mathematicians programmed into their equations (see, e.g., Dobzhansky, 1970; Hartl, 1980).

Let us begin with a species that is well-adapted to its environment—that is, it is at an adaptive peak. Its genes and blocks of genes have historically been selected for that environment in which the species now exists. Mendelism tells us that the genes and blocks of genes do not change, but rather maintain their integrity as they are passed from one generation to another. It is the gene products that interact with each other and with the environment to produce the phenotype in each generation.

Further, the Hardy-Weinberg equilibrium law tells us that the *frequencies* of the genes and blocks of genes do not

change from generation to generation. Curiously, we see that if nothing else is present to disturb this situation, *evolution should not take place* and the population (= species) should be, and remain, at equilibrium with its environment. However, several factors are in operation that do disturb this equilibrium.

First, there is a certain amount of new genetic variability introduced in the population in each generation. These include mutations, in the broad sense of the term. It doesn't matter whether they arise by the "usual" spontaneous way, or whether they are induced to occur by some "unusual" method such as mutator genes, transposons, meiotic drive, etc. These newly arisen mutations are random with respect to the needs of the population and, in fact, are usually deleterious. In this new genetic variability we would also include those unique or rare genes and blocks of genes brought in by migrants or by occasional interspecific hybridization.

A second factor contributing to an increase in genetic variability is recombination. Meiosis and sexual reproduction shuffle the genes and tend to break up the blocks of genes so that each generation is dealt a new hand, a new combinations of genes. Given a population at equilibrium at an adaptive peak, virtually all of this new genetic variability will be detrimental.

To this we can now add chance, genetic drift. If the population is not infinitely large, there is a degree of sampling error present. The smaller the population size, the more importance chance assumes; in fact, under the influence of random mutation and drift, all populations must lose their adaptiveness and become extinct.

This, of course, does not always happen because another factor is also operating: natural selection. Those genes and gene combinations that best allow their carriers to survive and reproduce will be passed on at a higher rate than the carriers of the newer, harmful variability. This differential reproduction is natural selection. Equilibria are established depending upon the rate of mutation and migration, the strength of selection, and the population size. Random processes may be most important in small populations, but relatively unimportant in large populations. But what is a large population and what is a small population? The answer is not strictly determined by the number of individuals in the population, or even by the effective population size (N_e), which is a measurement related to the number of individuals actually reproducing. But it is related to the product of $4N_e$ x the factor in question. For example, suppose we are interested in determining whether drift or selection will dominate in a population whose N_e is 1000. If the strength of selection (s) is such that it tends to eliminate 10 percent of the carriers of one type of allele, the value $4N_es$ = 400, a large population, and selection will be very effective. If the selective coefficient (s) against an allele of another gene is only 1/50,000, $4N_es$ will be 0.08, a small population where selection will not be effective. Selection cannot choose between the two alleles: they are neutral. Thus we see that a single population may be both small and large at the same time, and evolution may be deterministic for some traits and not for others.

Now, let us change the environment. The population is no longer at the adaptive peak—and may in fact be poorly adapted to its environment. It must change or become extinct. It is clear that mutation pressure, migration pressure, and genetic drift are not sufficient, per se, to bring about rapid adaptive change. For example, with a unidirectional mutation rate of 1/100,000, it would take approximately 110,000 generations to change the frequency of an allele from 0.4 to 0.8. The only mechanism known that can yield increased adaptation is natural selection operating on the available genetic variability. Ford (1940) classified genetic variability into four categories: mutation-selection equilibrium, neutral alleles, transient polymorphism (genes that are in the process of changing), and balanced polymorphism. The latter is a wastepaper basket of phenomena in which Hartl (1980) lists 13 representative examples. Then the question becomes whether there is enough, qualitatively and quantitatively, of this genetic variability in the population to allow for the change. It has been found that there is a tremendous amount of genetic variability for the "structural" genes that code for proteins in most species (Selander, 1976). It has been estimated that individuals are heterozygous for perhaps 10 percent of their "structural" genes and that populations may be polymorphic for up to 30 percent of these genes. What is not clear is how variable populations are for regulator genes and how important these are for evolutionary changes. Thus, although genetic variability for structural genes appears not to be a limiting factor, this may not be sufficient if regulator genes are all-important for significant change. If there is sufficient genetic variability and if it is of the correct type, the best genotypes will increase in frequency. If, on the other hand, the species does not have the genetic variability to cope with the new environment, it will fail to reproduce itself and become extinct. It really doesn't matter whether this extinction is due to competition with another species, the elimination of a major food source, or even an environmental catastrophe that alters whole ecosystems and leads to the extinction of many species.

Haldane (1957) has shown that the cost in genetic deaths of changing—what he termed the "cost of natural selection"—was very high. Brues (1964) pointed out that these genetic deaths were really the "cost of evolution." She agreed with Haldane that the cost in genetic deaths was high, but showed that the "cost of not evolving" was even greater since the population continues to be ill-adapted to its environment. This could lead to extinction, the highest cost of all. But if the species manages to change, we then have phyletic evolution.

Bush (1975) and Futuyma and Mayer (1980) have discussed the events leading to speciation in obligatory sexually reproducing organisms (see also Lee Ehrman's contribution to this volume). Usually, the first necessary step is a geographical separation of the species into two or more physically isolated populations, allopatric speciation. These populations, being in separate regions, independently undergo phyletic evolution, diverge, and eventually develop other isolating barriers. These may be ethological, leading to sexual isolation, or they may be developmental, morphological, or physiological differences leading to the death or sterility of any hybrids that may form if and when the two forms again become sympatric. If incomplete, ethological isolation may be reinforced in the region of overlap. Sympatric speciation may be relatively common in organisms with one or more of the following traits: parthenogenesis, interspecific hybridization, polyploidy, and asexual reproduction. It is rare, occurring only in certain unique circumstances, in obligatory outcrossing species (Bush, 1982).

Thus we see that neo-Darwinism can explain and describe evolution, and I echo Professor Wallace's statement by saying that there is nothing known that cannot be explained within the framework of neo-Darwinism.

Queens College, CUNY

Brues, A., 1964, The cost of evolution vs. the cost of not evolving, *Evolution* **18**:379-383.

Bush, G. L., 1975, Modes of animal speciation, *Ann. Rev. Ecol. Syst.* **6**:339-364.

Bush, G. L., 1982, What do we really know about speciation? in: *Perspectives in Evolution* (R. Milkman, ed.), Sinauer Assoc., Sunderland, MA.

Dobzhansky, Th., 1970, *Genetics of the Evolutionary Process*, Columbia University Press, New York.

Fisher, R. A., 1930, *The Genetic Theory of Natural Selection*, Clarendon, Oxford.

Ford, E. B., 1940.

Futuyma, D. J., and Mayer, G. C., 1980, Non-allopatric speciation in animals, *Syst. Zoology* **29**:254-271.

Goldschmidt, R., 1940, *The Material Basis of Evolution*, Yale University Press, New Haven.

Haldane, J. B. S., 1932, *The Causes of Evolution*, Longmans, Green, London.

Haldane, J. B. S., 1957, The cost of natural selection. *J. Genet.* **55**:511-524.

Hartl, D. L., 1980, *Principles of Population Genetics*, Sinauer Assoc., Sunderland, MA.

Provine, W. B., 1971, *The Origins of Theoretical Population Genetics*, University of Chicago Press, Chicago.

Selander, R. K., 1976, Genetic variation in natural populations, in: *Molecular Evolution* (F. J. Ayala, ed.), Sinauer Assoc., Sunderland, MA.

Wright, S., 1932, The roles of mutation, inbreeding, crossbreeding and selection in evolution, *Proc. 6th Int. Congr. Genet.* **1**:356-366.

Wright, S., 1968, 1969, 1977, 1978, *Evolution and the Genetics of Populations*, vols. 1, 2, 3, and 4, University of Chicago Press, Chicago.

Richard Borowsky

Although I do differ on certain details, I have no major argument with the contents of Wallace's paper, and will confine my comments to related issues.

To my mind, there are three important questions for which a population perspective, in particular a population genetics perspective, helps illuminate evolutionary questions. Since Wallace chose to emphasize only one of these, my first point is to observe the importance of the others.

The question Wallace emphasized was the role of population genetic phenomena in the origin of species. This is a classic topic of perennial interest. But population genetic principles are also critical in understanding the processes of local adaptation and the phylogenetic pattern of evolution. While this pattern is certainly generated by the mechanisms of speciation, it can be studied as a separate question.

My second point is that, of these three questions, the one emphasized by Wallace is the least amenable to direct observation. Clearly, this limitation has something to do with why the question of speciation is still so controversial. In other areas, where it is easier to observe or experiment, well-structured and presented arguments frequently fall before facts. I am in general agreement with the Modern Synthesis and used to think these questions were laid to rest many years ago. Plainly, I was wrong. I now expect this area to be controversial well beyond the one-hundredth anniversary of the College's founding.

My third point is that I don't really think that the neutralist/selectionist controversy is particularly relevant to the question of speciation. I can easily accept that there is a subset of loci, alleles which are subject to strong selection, and another subset, alleles which are effectively neutral. Even if the first subset comprises only a small proportion of all loci, it would still constitute an existing reserve of variation more than sufficient for adaptive evolution in any generation.

Few would argue that mutations are the ultimate source of variation for adaptive evolution. The question seems to be how quickly (measured in generations from the mutational event) they are called upon to stand and serve. We may never know the answer to this.

As to questions of local adaptation and phylogeny, here the dichotomy between neutral and selected loci becomes useful. Let me illustrate with some examples drawn from the work of my colleagues and myself on genetic variation in the fish genus *Xiphophorus*.

These fish have a small number of loci with alleles that have strong, measurable effects on coloration, size, growth rates, metabolic rates, and the storage of reserves (Borowsky, 1984; Kallman, 1975). These are the gene loci we study in trying to understand the mechanisms by which local populations adapt because they are the face of the population that selection sees.

These fishes also have a much more extensive series of enzyme loci that have been studied electrophoretically (Morizot and Siciliano, 1984). These loci range in variability from monomorphic or species diagnostic through polytypic to polymorphic. For reasons not to be dwelled on here—and I wouldn't invest much time in arguing about them anywhere—I believe that most of this variation is effectively neutral. My point is that this variation has proven useful for understanding the patterns of phylogeny in the genus (Borowsky, 1984).

Thus, these two other areas of evolutionary biology—the question of local adaptation and the question of phylogeny—are also illuminated by a population genetic perspective.

New York University

Borowsky, R., 1984, The evolutionary genetics of *Xiphophorus*, in: *The Evolutionary Genetics of Fishes* (B.J. Turner, ed.), Plenum Press, New York.

Kallman, K.D., 1975, The Platyfish, *Xiphophorus maculatus*, in: *Handbook of Genetics*, vol. 4 (R.C. King, ed.), Plenum Press, New York.

Morizot, D.C. and Siciliano, M.J., 1984, Gene mapping in fishes and other vertebrates, in: *The Evolutionary Genetics of Fishes* (B.J. Turner, ed.), Plenum Press, New York.

Walter J. Bock

Professor Wallace was asked to speak about evolution on the population level —microevolutionary change—which he has done most elegantly. For my commentary, I have been asked especially to stress a point that was not covered in full detail in his talk, namely, some aspects of the species concept and speciation. I will be concerned with the species concept as a theoretical definition within the realm of evolutionary biology—the only proper basis for a species definition, contrary to the ideas of many systematists who still believe that there are theoretical taxonomic species concepts, and who continue to argue for a universal species concept applicable to all organisms, an approach that leads only to confusion.

Definition of Evolution

Before discussing the species concept and speciation, a few comments should be offered on the definition of evolution advocated by Professor Wallace. He presents the usual definition of evolution given in most biology and evolutionary texts, having its foundation in the work of genetics beginning in 1900. This definition includes the stipulation that a change must be genetic or heritable to be evolutionary, a stipulation that is too restrictive. I prefer a simpler definition of evolution—Evolution is change in organisms with respect to time—and specify the minimum time period for an evolutionary change to be one generation, the gap between parents and offspring. The reasons for my preference are far too complex to discuss in detail here. Let me say only that I would regard a valid evolutionary change to be the modification from one adaptive state to another. This step can be achieved as a nongenetic change if a feature modifies from a preadapted condition to an adaptive one with the appearance of a particular selective demand acting on the organism.

53

Evolutionary change is divided into two separate processes, phyletic evolution and speciation. Phyletic evolution is change in time along a single phyletic lineage. Speciation is multiplication of species or the division of a single phyletic lineage into two or more separate lineages. Phyletic evolution can occur without speciation, but speciation requires phyletic evolution. Unfortunately, evolutionists have frequently confused these two separate processes of evolution, discussing both as different types of speciation.

A similar problem arises in considering units of evolution, one of the oldest chestnuts in evolutionary theory, and one that is best dropped. Basically, when considering evolutionary causes, the proper units of evolution are individual organisms. But for evolutionary processes, the units of evolution are populations (for sexually reproducing organisms only). I do not subscribe to the idea of a single unit of evolution existing for all types of evolutionary explanations.

Species Versus Phyletic Lineages

A) *Species definition*: The theoretical definition of species deals with the species as a category, not as a taxon as still believed by many biologists, including taxonomists. The species definition lies within the realm of basic biological theory, that is, evolutionary theory, if it is to be used for further theory development. Taxonomic species definitions are, of course, possible, but they would then be limited to strictly practical taxonomic work and would have no part in general theory development or in any other area of biological research.

The single most important point to emphasize is that the species concept applies only to *sexually reproducing organisms*—that is, those in which two different individual organisms must contribute genetic material (vertical genetic transfer) in the production of new organisms.

In spite of continuing protests by a number of taxonomists and philosophers, the species concept does not apply to asexually reproducing organisms except in an artificial practical way as a species *notion* in systematics for describing the existing diversity of organisms. These taxonomic species have no role in evolutionary theory. Aside from a completely artificial one, no general species definition exists that covers *all* organisms. In this commentary, I will deal with the species concept strictly in the sense of evolutionary theory.

A number of species definitions have been offered in recent years. I accept the biological species definition as put forth by Mayr (1942, 1963) and modified very slightly by myself (Bock, 1986, p. 33): "A species is a group of actually or potentially interbreeding populations of organisms which are *genetically* [not only *reproductively*, as in the usual biological species definition] isolated in nature from other such groups." This species definition does not include all aspects of species, and indeed not even all important aspects; it excludes the properties of reproductive isolation and of ecological distinctiveness possessed by fully evolved species (Bock, 1986). But it does include a central characteristic of species, namely, genetic isolation, without which all other species properties break down. The separation and isolation of the genetic complexes (configurations) of diverse species permits members of different species to maintain separate evolutionary histories, including separate adaptive relationships to different sets of environmental demands, etc. The existence of species of biological organisms is a direct consequence of sexual reproduction and its associated mechanisms: reduction-division (meiosis) and zygote formation by fusion of two different gametes. These mechanisms act to break up adaptive complexes of genes present in individual organisms during the production of their offspring. Because of the genetic isolation between them, species protect diverse complexes of adaptive features by insuring reproduction only between members of the same species that share quite similar genetic material (Mayr, 1989).

Many paleontologists and more recently cladists have accepted a species definition designated as an evolutionary or phylogenetic species concept: "An evolutionary species is a lineage (an ancestral-descendant sequence of populations) evolving separately from others and with its own unitary evolutionary role and tendencies" (Simpson, 1961, p. 153), or "An evolutionary species is a single lineage of ancestral-descendant populations which maintains its identity from other such lineages and which has its own evolutionary tendencies and historical fate" (Wiley, 1981, p. 25), or "A species is the smallest diagnosable cluster of individual organisms within which there is a parental pattern of ancestry and descent" (Cracraft, 1983, p. 170; a similar definition is provided by Eldredge and Cracraft, 1980, p. 92). I reject these evolutionary or phylogenetic species definitions because they fail to distinguish between the species and the phyletic lineage, as will be discussed later. Indeed, the "species" definitions of Simpson and of Wiley are actually definitions of the phyletic lineage.

Some recent definitions of the species are no more than restatements of a very old and outdated idea that a species is what a taxonomist recognizes as such. This may sound rather silly, but such definitions have been offered in all seriousness. These definitions include one proposed by Cracraft (1983, p. 170) that "A species is the smallest diagnosable cluster of individual organisms within which there is a parental pattern of ancestry and descent," and the complex definition offered by Mishler and Brandon (1987, p. 406) that

A species is the least inclusive taxon recognized in a classification, into which organisms are grouped because of evidence of monophyly (usually, but not restricted to, the presence of synapomorphies), that is ranked as a species because it is the smallest "important" lineage deemed worthy of formal recognition, where "important" refers to the action of those processes that are dominant in producing and maintaining lineages in a particular case.

These taxonomic species definitions are most unsatisfactory at best and need not be discussed further.

Species are maintained—that is, kept separate from other species—by the possession of intrinsic isolating mechanisms (IIM) that must be clearly distinguished from external isolating barriers, such as geographical-ecological barriers. All IIM are not identical, especially with respect to their reproductive cost. Not all IIM prevent reproduction between members of different species, but they do keep the species isolated genetically.

B) *Comparisons in biology and the species concept*: A point that is rarely discussed is the relationship between the species concept and comparisons in biology. A large part of this problem is that less-than-sufficient attention has been given to aspects of comparison within biology (Bock, 1967). Most workers have assumed that all comparisons in biology are the same. This is not true. At the minimum there are two basic types of comparisons: horizontal and vertical. Horizontal comparisons are between different phyletic lineages, be they comparisons at the same or different points in time. Vertical comparisons are within the same phyletic lineage.

The species concept is restricted to horizontal comparisons. It has no meaning for vertical comparisons, for which the basic unit is the phyletic lineage.

C) *The phyletic lineage*: A phyletic lineage is the temporal continuum—the time line—formed by a species as its members reproduce themselves generation after generation through time (Bock, 1979). A cross-section of a phyletic lineage at any point in time is a species (theoretical, nondimensional). However, different time slices through the same phyletic lineage are not different species, nor are they the same species. They are simply different cross-sections of the same phyletic lineage at different times, with the earlier one being ancestral to the later one. Each time slice is a species, but it makes absolutely no sense to ask whether they are the same or different species; this question lies outside of the theoretical, nondimensional species concept and hence is a nonquestion. This has many important consequences for the development of evolutionary theory, but a discussion of these aspects would take us too far away from the main point of this talk. I wish only to emphasize that because the biological species concept is a nondimensional one, it is not possible to speak of the birth or the origin of a species, of the life history of a species, or of the age of a species.

An examination of the evolutionary and the phylogenetic species concepts demonstrates that these species concepts confuse the quite different notions of the species and the phyletic lineage. These species definitions are actually ones of the phyletic lineages, not species; discussions of the nature of the species based on such species definitions are doomed to failure. Phyletic and/or evolutionary species definitions result from the failure to distinguish between theoretical definitions and their practical application to actual objects in nature. Just as neontologists attempt, to the best of their ability and judgment, to apply the biological species concept to the geographic spread of individual organisms at a given time period, paleontologists attempt to apply the biological species concept to individuals found through time in the fossil record. In practical terms, it makes no sense to label human remains found in Egyptian tombs

or in iron-age peat bogs in Denmark as different species from present-day humans. But at some point in the human fossil record, the characteristics are sufficiently different from modern humans that analysis and discussion of these earlier fossils is easier in a practical sense if they are placed in different species. Problems arise only when workers attempt to develop theory on the basis of these practical considerations. Analysis should proceed only from theory to practical considerations, never the reverse.

Speciation Versus Phyletic Evolution

The two processes of evolutionary change are phyletic evolution and speciation.

Phyletic evolution results from two major causes or mechanisms of evolution: genetic variation formed by diverse mechanisms in populations generation after generation; and phenotypically varying individuals interacting with selective demands arising from the external environment, followed by reproduction of those individuals surviving the action of the selective demands.

Speciation or splitting of phyletic lineages results from the causes of phyletic evolution plus the special boundary condition of an external isolating barrier. In the case of geographic or allopatric speciation, the external isolating barrier is a geographic-ecological one, regardless of the nature of the isolated populations. There are no special causes of speciation distinct from those of phyletic evolution.

Speciation involves the evolution of the separate properties of genetic isolation, reproductive isolation, and ecological separation. These properties do not necessarily evolve at the same time or under the action of the same evolutionary causes.

The intrinsic isolating mechanisms associated with genetic isolation must evolve during the initial allopatric phase of speciation. These IIM evolve as the

56

by-product (pleiotropic) of other evolutionary changes; selective demands *never* favor the evolution of IIM as such during the allopatric phase of speciation or thereafter. These IIM must be fully evolved (100 percent effective) when the external isolating barrier disappears if the speciation process is to continue. If the IIM are not 100 percent effective at this time, speciation will not continue and the two populations will interbreed and once again merge into a single species.

Evolution of reproductive isolation and of ecological isolation may occur during any phase of the speciation process. Generally, the onset of the evolution of these properties begins during the allopatric phase, but their perfection almost always takes place during the neosympatric phase of speciation. These changes lead to the major divergence between offspring species.

Unfortunately, evolutionists have restricted their analysis of speciation to the allopatric phase and to the evolution of IIM. This is correct as far as it goes, but is woefully incomplete as the equally important evolution of reproductive and ecological properties is ignored.

The process of speciation continues during the neosympatric stage with the evolution of the properties of reproductive isolation and of ecological separation. These attributes continue their evolution under the action of selective demands arising from interactions between members of the two species. It is possible that these evolutionary changes will result in the evolution of different IIM, but these IIM continue to evolve as by-products of other evolutionary changes. In no case do the IIM improve. At the start of the neosympatric phase, the IIM are 100 percent effective, and cannot become better.

When the two new species are fully genetically isolated, fully reproductively isolated, and fully ecologically separated, then the speciation process comes to a close. This complete process of speciation is of a longer duration than considered by most evolutionists. These three properties of species must evolve regardless of whether speciation is by allopatric isolation or by hybridization and polyploidy.

Considering the entire process of speciation, much doubt exists on arguments that speciation takes place only or mainly in small populations or involving genetic revolutions. It simply does not seem reasonable that the three separate properties of species can evolve simultaneously in small, isolated populations. Moreover, proponents of speciation occurring only in small populations and involving a genetic revolution have not considered all aspects of speciation; they restricted their analysis to the evolution of genetic isolation. These considerations also argue strongly against ideas of punctuated equilibrium.

Species are composed of units (= individual organisms) that are similar to one another in that they share the same characteristics (family-resemblance properties or essences). Species may be composed of several different types of morphs—such as males and females, or different castes in social insects, or color morphs, etc.—which differ in some of their features, but these several morphs still agree in sharing the basic aspects of the species' properties or essences. The members of a species simply do not show the type of differences characteristic of the diverse parts of individual biological organisms and of many other clear types of individuals such as atoms.

In addition to their lacking these attributes of individuals, species taxa simply do not possess most of the other attributes —such as tight organization, cohesiveness of parts, spatial and temporal connections—which are attributed to individuals.

A strong argument can be made that species taxa should be regarded as family-resemblance classes (Bock, 1986; Caplan and Bock, 1989). The essences or properties possessed by the member organisms of a species taxon are many and can easily be cited as those characteristics that permit the members of the species to interbreed with each other and produce offspring and preclude their exchanging genetic material with members of other species by interbreeding.

Conclusion

Understanding the species concept and the process of speciation is of central importance to evolutionary biology, but they are not the whole of evolutionary theory. One must comprehend clearly the relationships between species and phyletic lineages and between speciation and phyletic evolution. Not all living organisms are arranged into species taxa, and species are not the only unit of evolutionary change. Species taxa are not individuals, but are clearly groups characterized by family-group resemblances.

Columbia University

Bock, Walter J., 1967, The use of adaptive characters in avian classification, *Proc. XIV Internat. Ornith. Cong.*, pp. 61-74.

Bock, Walter J., 1979, The synthetic explanation of macroevolutionary change—a reductionistic approach, *Bull. Carnegie Museum* no. 13: 20-69.

Bock, Walter J., 1986, Species concepts, speciation, and macroevolution, in: *Modern Aspects of Species* (K. Iwatsuki, P. H. Raven and W. J. Bock, eds.), pp. 31-57, University of Tokyo Press, Tokyo.

Caplan, A. L. and Bock, W. J., 1989, Haunt me no longer, *Biology and Philosophy* **3**: 433-454, 472-474.

Cracraft, Joel, 1983, Species concepts and speciation analysis, *Current. Ornith.* **1**: 159-187.

Eldredge, Niles and Cracraft, Joel, 1980, *Phylogenetic Patterns and the Evolutionary Process*, Columbia University Press, New York.

Mayr, Ernst, 1942, *Systematics and the Origin of Species, from the Viewpoint of a Zoologist*, Columbia University Press, New York.

Mayr, Ernst, 1963, *Animal Species and Evolution*, Harvard University Press, Cambridge.

Mayr, Ernst, 1976, *Evolution and the Diversity of Life: Selected Essays*, Harvard University Press, Cambridge.

Mayr, Ernst, 1987, The ontological status of species, *Biology and Philosophy* **2**: 145-166.

Mayr, Ernst, 1989, The why and how of species, *Biology and Philosophy* **3**: 431-441

Mishler, Brent D. and Brandon, Robert N., 1987, Individuality, pluralism, and the phylogenetic species concept, *Biology and Philosophy* **2**: 397-414.

Simpson, George G., 1961, *Principles of Animal Taxonomy*, Columbia University Press, New York.

Wiley, Edward O., 1981, *Phylogenetics: The Theory and Practice of Phylogenetic Systematics*, Wiley, New York.

What Can the Fossil Record Tell Us about Macroevolution?

Anthony Hallam
University of Birmingham

It is not often that one can trace a new development in scientific thought to a single article, but a strong case can be made for the claim that the modern paleobiological challenge to conventional neo-Darwinism began with Eldredge and Gould (1972). With the advent of punctuated equilibrium theory—arising from the fact that the fossil record appears to indicate that long periods of stasis among species have been interrupted at relatively brief intervals to generate new morphotypes—it has been argued that microevolutionary processes as studied by ecologists and geneticists cannot simply be extrapolated to larger-scale, longer-term phenomena. Macroevolution, which is to be understood as evolution at and above the species level, must accordingly be decoupled from microevolution, and patterns of change discernible in the fossil record interpreted in terms of species selection acting in conjunction with punctuated equilibrium (Stanley, 1979). While not denying the basic truth of natural selection theory, a number of paleobiologists have claimed that it is insufficient to account for the history of life over extended time periods beyond the access of biologists, without recourse to hierarchical models involving other factors (Gould 1982, 1985; Vrba and Eldredge, 1984; Vrba and Gould, 1986). Purely adaptationist explanations of evolutionary phenomena have been downgraded at the expense of explanations emphasizing the importance of developmental constraints in ontogeny, the control exerted by regulatory as opposed to structural genes, and stochastic effects such as genetic drift and mass extinctions promoted by drastic changes in the physical environment.

Not surprisingly, this paleobiological challenge has provoked a spirited reaction on the part of defenders of neo-Darwinian orthodoxy (see especially Dawkins, 1986; Levinton, 1983, 1988; and Hecht and Hoffman, 1986). Indeed, some biologists have gone so far as to object to the validity of using fossils in evolutionary studies. Before I can proceed further, it is necessary to attempt a defense of the paleobiologists' position. I list below five categories of objection that have been raised repeatedly in recent years, and my answer to them.

1. What paleontologists categorize as species do not necessarily correspond with species as understood by biologists, for whom the key criterion is capacity to interbreed and produce fertile offspring. Only if there is close correspondence between morphology and genome is the paleontological categorization justified. This would imply that sibling species are extremely rare, whereas modern genetic work has shown that this is far from being the case, especially in groups such as frogs and rodents. Research in molecular biology has demonstrated that the genome is dynamic, exhibiting constant turnover, and a species in the true, genetic sense cannot persist for millions of years, as numerous examples of morphological stasis in the fossil record would suggest (Schopf, 1981; Hecht and Hoffman, 1986).

Paleontological species are indeed by necessity only morphospecies, but this is true also of numerous species recognized by biological taxonomists, for which the genetics is known only for a minuscule fraction; in some groups such as bivalve and gastropod molluscs, the shells provide better criteria for species distinctions than the soft parts. To dismiss morphology as a criterion of species distinction would be to throw out a very large neontological baby with the paleontological bath water. Correlation between morphology and genetics is considerable, though obviously less than perfect. In this respect it is no worse than many other data sources and its reliability depends on what questions are being asked. The most important point is that morphology offers valid information that the evolutionary synthesist disregards at his peril, and provides an essential link between the present and the past.

As for the observation about the dynamic genome, so much stressed by Schopf (1981) in his attack on the hypothesis of punctuated equilibria, this misses the key point, which is how to explain morphological stasis of species persisting for appreciable periods of geological time. A pertinent analogy can be drawn with banknotes (G. Dover, personal communication). There is a constant turnover with time of banknotes of a given currency, as old ones are worn out and replaced by new issue, but this process differs fundamentally from the far less frequent but more drastic change involved in altering the banknote design, which corresponds to a speciation event.

2. The stratigraphic record is too incomplete to allow a proper test to be made between the hypotheses of punctuated equilibrium and phyletic gradualism, which concern the tempo and mode of evolutionary change among fossil species. This objection received some support from the work of Sadler (1981), who elegantly demonstrated an inverse correlation between apparent sedimentation rate of stratigraphic sequences in a wide range of facies and the time span of sedimentation, which is most plausibly accounted for by invoking numerous intervals of nondeposition and/or erosion.

While it is true that the sedimentary record is never likely to be so complete as to allow one to trace the generation-by-generation changes that form the subject matter of population genetics, one cannot justifiably extrapolate from this undeniable limitation to the vastly longer time intervals concerned in distinguishing between the rival paleobiological hypotheses. A period of, say, 5000 years is more than long enough to account for gradual changes of the sort familiar to population geneticists, but is a mere geological instant. Phyletic gradualism postulates that gradual morphological changes in a given lineage persist for millions of years, whereas punctuated equilibrium postulates periods of stasis of this duration interrupted by relatively brief episodes when speciation takes place. Distinction between these fundamentally different postulates can readily be made in favorable circumstances, if care is taken in the choice of stratigraphic sections, with preference being given to those that independent criteria suggest are relatively complete, and for which there is a good fossil record in little-changing facies (Hallam, 1982; Schindel, 1982; Fortey, 1985).

3. Many punctuational changes in species successions could result from migration of replacing species from other geographic locations, rather than rapid evolution *in situ* (Hecht and Hoffman, 1986).

In favorable instances, however, which are many, it is possible to exercise geographic as well as stratigraphic control, and eliminate migration as a factor. This is particularly clear when there is a well-documented faunal provinciality, as in the Jurassic (Hallam 1982; Callomon, 1985). By careful study of species lineages based on bed-by-bed collection of large samples, plausible cases can be made for *in situ* evolution because of the small amount of species-to-species change (see, for instance, the various case histories documented in Cope and Skelton, 1985). When heterochronous change can be recognized, involving paedomorphosis and peramorphosis, straightforward ancestor-descendant relationships of species in a given region can be established with even greater confidence (Hallam, 1982; McNamara, 1982, 1986; McKinney, 1986).

4. Living organisms offer much information relevant to evolution that fossils fail to provide, such as soft-part anatomy, physiology, genetics and behavior.

This objection can be countered by pointing out that neontological information is also incomplete because it lacks the historical dimension vital to a comprehensive evolutionary understanding; living organisms can be considered to be a poor sample of Phanerozoic life. Paul (1982) makes a telling analogy with the study of human history. The historical record is meager compared with the contemporary literature, but it nevertheless gives a much better outline of the sequence of events than the most rigorous analysis of the most extensive contemporary records.

5. Fossils tell us nothing about the evolutionary process, for which we have to turn to genetics and ecology.

Without doubt there is a fundamental fascination involved in attempting to understand evolutionary mechanisms (Dawkins, 1986), but we should also recall the famous concluding paragraph of *The Origin of Species,* in which Darwin expresses wonder that the diversity of the organic world can have been produced from one or a few ancestors by the operation of several natural laws: "there is grandeur in this view of life. . . ." The preferential replication of genes by means of natural selection may well be a necessary condition for evolution to take place, but it is hardly a sufficient explanation for how the enormous diversity of life in space and time has come about. The study of evolution is as much about pattern as about process (Raup and Jablonski, 1986), and pattern can have an important bearing on process.

Patterns of Speciation

The article by Eldredge and Gould (1972) was deliberately polemical and tended to drive fellow paleontologists into two opposing camps, supporting either the punctuated equilibrium or phyletic gradualism model. More important, it stimulated a considerable amount of new data gathering and analysis of particular fossil groups as a result of which Gould and Eldredge (1977; Gould, 1986) have been happy to concede that the question is not in the category of "either/or" but "how much," in other words relative incidence. (There is even a third, intermediate, category proposed, termed "punctuated gradualism" [Malmgren *et al.*, 1983]). Several interesting questions are now being pursued, such as the following.

1. What is the relative incidence of punctuated equilibria and phyletic gradualism in different fossil groups and different environmental regimes?

McKinney (1985), for example, has proposed that there is a tendency for shallow-water benthic invertebrates to be dominated by punctuated patterns of speciation, whereas planktonic organisms of the pelagic realm are characterized by more gradualistic patterns. Banner and Lowry (1985) suggest that planktonic foraminifera show no dominance of one mode or the other, and the recent study of Sheldon (1987) on Ordovician trilobites, a shallow-water benthic group—a study which included exceptionally detailed morphometric analysis—was held to support the gradualistic model. Other patterns, bound up with ecology, physiology, and biogeographic distribution, could be suggested.

2. Accepting the punctuational model, are the relatively brief speciation events associated with an increase in morphological variability of the taxa in question suggesting perhaps the temporary weakening of normal developmental constraints?

This was proposed by Williamson (1981) on the basis of his morphometric study of an extraordinarily complete sequence of Neogene lacustrine, snails and bivalves in Kenya. Williamson's claim of genuine speciation events simultaneously affecting the fauna has proved highly controversial, and many feel he has not satisfactorily answered the counterclaim that the changes described are merely ecophenotypic (Hallam, 1985). Unfortunately, he has not yet published the full results of his analysis, so it is difficult to attempt an objective judgment.

3. Does long-term morphological stasis, lasting up to several million years, involve frequent oscillations about a mean or tightly bound stability?

This is another subject clearly demanding multivariate analysis of fossils from numerous levels in stratigraphic successions. Such an analysis of Neogene bivalve lineages by Stanley and Yang (1987) supported the oscillatory model.

Closely related to this question is whether long-term stasis can be accounted for by stabilizing selection rather that the operation of developmental constraints. Unsurprisingly, population geneticists have opted for the former (Charlesworth *et al.*, 1982; Lande, 1986). This implies either that the environment has remained stable in given instances for up to several million years, which seems highly unlikely, or that organisms have tracked changing environments. Such a subject can readily be put to the test by using an array of paleoecological, sedimentological, and geochemical techniques to infer the pattern of environmental change and its correspondence with the fossil record. For example, in a study of late Cenozoic marine ostracods, Cronin (1985) came up with intriguing and counterintuitive results: species maintain stasis during rapid high-frequency climatic oscillations (cf. Coope [1979] for similar results with Pleistocene beetles), whereas long-term climatic change disrupts stasis and catalyzes speciation. There is no way such a conclusion could have been predicted from exclusively biological studies. The subject of developmental constraints is of course an aspect of morphogenesis, which is perhaps the most elusive of all subjects relevant to evolution. It is most readily amenable to embryological research in conjunction with developmental genetics (Raff and Kauffman, 1983), but paleontology can also play an important role, as in the study of heterochronous patterns and trends (McNamara, 1982, 1986).

4. What is the relative incidence of cladogenesis and anagenesis in speciation events?

The traditional view of paleontologists has been that anagenesis, involving "pseudoextinction," has been the predominant mode, with a single ancestral species evolving more or less gradually into its descendant. The cladogenetic alternative embraced both by cladistic systematists, following Hennig (1966), and punctuationists such as Eldredge and Gould (1972) and

Stanley (1979), postulates relatively short-lived branching or splitting events allowing ancestor to coexist in time with descendant(s). A third possibility accepts punctuated equilibria but denies cladogenesis and can be called punctuated anagenesis (e.g., Hallam, 1982).

This question is of fundamental importance for a certain school of paleobiologists because of the critical role they assign to species selection, in conjunction with punctuated equilibria, in establishing the relative independence of macroevolution. The concept of species selection has been much discussed, and its meaning clarified by Vrba and Eldredge (1984), who claim that, whatever the other differences of opinion, the following four basic points are generally agreed on: punctuated equilibria rather than phyletic gradualism predominates in the fossil record; the directions of speciation events are random in relation to any long-term trend among species; species can be treated as individuals; and species selection is nonrandom sorting among species individuals. Related to species selection is the effect hypothesis of Vrba (1980, 1983), whereby differences between lineages in the characters of organisms and genome may incidentally determine a pattern of among-species evolution in a monophyletic group. Thus long-term directional tendencies among species through time may arise as incidental, nonadaptive consequences of normal Darwinian processes at the among-organism level. Effect macroevolution differs from species selection, however, in that causation is at the level of the organism, and emergent species characters need not be invoked (Vrba and Eldredge, 1984). Whether this difference can be recognized in the fossil record remains, however, open to questions.

It has been argued that species selection, if it has indeed operated in the past, can have played only an insignificant role in evolution because it utterly fails to explain fine-tuned adaptations. Selection at the level of the individual is bound to remain immensely more important because of the vastly greater frequency of opportunity for selection (Dawkins, 1982). An alternative approach to the subject is to test the model with reference to the fossil record. Both species selection and effect macroevolution demand the ubiquity of cladogenesis as a speciation mode, with anagenesis and pseudoextinction relegated to an at best insignificant role. If the analogy between Darwinian natural selection and species selection is to be maintained, there should have been at a given time interval, or stratigraphic time plane, a multiplicity of species within monophyletic groups from which to select. This is at least something that should be testable because species selection is dependent for its supporting evidence on the fossil record. Arguments about the biological validity of paleontologists' species are here irrelevant. The database of species "individuals" is of necessity the taxa distinguished by competent specialists of particular fossil groups. Levinton (1983), Hoffman (1985), and Hecht and Hoffman (1986) have pointed out that the documentary evidence for extensive cladogenesis and species selection is almost nonexistent or at best very limited. On the other hand, Levinton's statement that lineages, involving little or no cladogenesis, are characteristic of what can be confidently inferred from the fossil record is amply confirmed by the case histories discussed in Cope and Skelton (1985).

Heterochrony

The need for species selection or effect macroevolution arose from the requirement of explaining phyletic trends in the fossil record within the framework of punctuated equilibrium theory. An alternative explanation accepting anagenesis or the predominant speciation mode invokes an important role for heterochrony, which provides a developmentally feasible means of generating significant morphological change within lineages.

Heterochrony has been defined by Gould (1977, p. 2) as the "changes in relative time of appearance and rate of development of characters already present in ancestors." As such, it concerns the nature of the relationship between an individual's development (ontogeny) and evolutionary history (phylogeny). Heterochronous changes may be either paedomorphic—in which the adult descendant resembles the juvenile ancestor—or peramorphic—in which the juvenile descendant resembles the adult ancestor. In other words, paedomorphosis is expressed by a reduction, and peramorphosis by an increase, in morphological development through successive ontogenies (Alberch *et al.*, 1979). If more than two species are involved, trends my be recognized and respectively termed paedomorphodines and peramorphodines (McNamara, 1982). If the ancestral species undergoes more morphological changes during ontogeny than the descendant species, then the scope for phyletic change is limited and species morphology will eventually achieve a condition of stasis.

Paedomorphosis predominates over peramorphosis in documented instances (McNamara, 1986). This may reflect the greater ease of effecting such changes in morphogenesis (P. Alberch, personal communication). On the other hand, K. McNamara (personal communication) suggests that peramorphic changes may be as common but have been recorded less often because they are more easily overlooked. This is an empirical matter that should be resolvable by comprehensive analysis of as many fossil groups as possible. Relationships between heterochrony and changes in the physical environment, as determined by geological analysis, need to be studied in detail. McNamara (1982) assumes a direct relationship between paedo- and peramorphodines and environmental gradients, implying a straightforward adaptive response by the organisms in question. However, it is not apparent that the early Jurassic *Gryphaea* paedomorphodine records any such response to environmental change (Hallam, 1982). With regard to processes, it is important to establish, if possible, whether peramorphosis is a consequence of increase in growth rate or delay in the onset of maturity (hypermorphosis) and why its incidence might be less than paedomorphosis, which can occur by either a reduction in the rate of development (neoteny) or precocious sexual maturation (progenesis). The same considerations apply to phyletic size increase. Thus it was possible to demonstrate by growth band analysis that size increase in Jurassic *Gryphaea* was the result of greater longevity rather than more rapid growth (Hallam, 1982).

Phyletic Size Increase

One of the most widely recognized and discussed patterns of evolutionary change discernible in the fossil record is phyletic size increase, commonly known as Cope's Rule (Newell, 1949; Stanley, 1973; La Barbera, 1986). In a study of phyletic size increase in Jurassic ammonites and bivalves (Hallam, 1975), it became apparent that the rate of increase in ammonites was appreciably faster than in bivalves, in correspondence with their higher rate of taxonomic turnover. Although small ammonite and bivalve taxa frequently evolved from larger ones, this almost invariably seems to have taken place at an appreciably more rapid rate than phyletic size increase, which is characteristically gradual. Indeed, evolutionary size decrease is normally very abrupt in the stratigraphic record (Hallam, 1975, 1978). In other words, there is apparently a temporal asymmetry to the phenomenon of evolutionary size change.

A clue to the interpretation of this asymmetry is provided by the study of ammonite size increase in conjunction with facies analysis of the sedimentary cycles characteristic of much of the European Jurassic. According to facies interpretation of environmental change, the times of abrupt size decrease in a given lineage correspond to times of marine shallowing and regression, with a corresponding restriction of habitat and consequent increased environmental stress. Such stressful environments favor, in ecologists' parlance, *r* selection, with the premium being on early maturation and increased reproduction. At times of higher sea level and reduced stress, *K* selection is favored, its most characteristic expression being delayed maturity and consequently larger maximum size of organisms. The most dramatic evolutionary changes take place at times of regression, with preferential extinction of larger taxa and survival of smaller opportunists, which may in turn become phyletically larger and go extinct during the next regressive event. I first tentatively put forward this model a decade ago (Hallam, 1978), and it has since received support from ammonoid workers on both the Jurassic (Bayer and McGhee, 1985) and Carboniferous (Ramsbottom, 1981).

Since phyletic size increase is such a widespread trend in the animal kingdom, there must be manifestly one or more selective advantages of larger size. Among those proposed are: an improved ability to capture prey or ward off predators; a greater reproductive success; increased regulation of the internal environment; and increased heat regulation per unit volume (Newell 1949; Rensch, 1959; Odum, 1971; Stanley, 1973; Calder, 1984). A price must be paid, however, for such adaptive advantages. Because food resources are likely to remain approximately constant, population sizes must decrease, thereby increasing the probability of extinction (Hallam, 1975). The correlative later maturation and slower reproductive rate will serve to reinforce the extinction vulnerability.

Brown and Maurer (1986) have presented data for a variety of vertebrates and plants that indicate that large species utilize a disproportionately large share of resources within local ecosystems. Even though small species tend to have higher population densities, these are not sufficient to compensate for their lower rate of energy use per individual. Thus selection pressures give rise to Cope's Rule, which is the result of two opposing forces: one operating at the level of individuals within a population, the other at the level of species within ecosystems. Individuals of large size are favored by intraspecific selection because they can dominate resource use, and consequently leave more offspring than their smaller relatives. However, the size increase is, as pointed out above, accompanied by a higher probability of extinction because of smaller population size, lower population density, and slower population growth. The ammonite data can therefore be explained by a fascinating interaction of biotic and abiotic factors. During times of relatively low environmental stress, the biotic factors predominate and ammonite taxa tend to increase their size more or less gradually. During times of increased stress, such as produced by regression, abiotic factors predominate and the extinction rate increases, with the survival of smaller taxa being favored (Hallam, 1978).

Adaptive Trends

Besides small-scale phyletic trends involving species lineages, many larger-scale trends have been recognized by paleontologists, which can be given a plausible adaptive interpretation along conventional Darwinian lines. Among terrestrial vertebrates, the classic example of the evolution of mammals from reptiles (Kemp, 1982) comes most readily to mind. For marine invertebrates, one of the most striking stories to emerge recently concerns the decline through the late Mesozoic of poorly armored benthic molluscs and the corresponding increase of heavily armored forms, related by Vermeij (1977, 1987) to the contemporary radiation of predatory fish, crabs, and neogastropods, which implies a considerable measure of co-evolution. Unfortunately, the fossil record tells us little about what must have been one of the most outstanding examples of co-evolution, between angiosperms and insects.

Patterns of Phanerozoic Diversity Change

It is a striking fact that all the major animal body plans appeared very early in Phanerozoic history, between about 600 and 500 million years ago, with subsequent evolution being expressed by change at progressively lower taxonomic levels. The diversity of higher-order taxa has in consequence diminished through time (Valentine, 1977). Rather than being a mere taxonomic artifact, this appears often to be the consequence of the wide variety of "evolutionary experiments" that took place during the initial metazoan radiation at the end of the Precambrian and early in the Paleozoic, with only a minority of body plans proving viable in the long term. An excellent example is provided by the Phylum Echinodermata (Paul, 1977).

A quantitative analysis of Gould *et al.* (1987) has led to their making a generalization that clades (essentially equivalent to monophyletic groups) at the level of genera within families generally concentrate diversity early in their history. This is held to be true of a wide range of animal groups, including both marine invertebrates and terrestrial mammals. The main implication of this research is an intriguing one: that study of the evolutionary history of clades can give an objective measure of direction in time, independent of vague, culture-laden, and untestable notions such as "progress." A comparable study of family origination and extinction patterns by Gilinsky and Bambach (1987) has revealed that the pace of origination tends to decline significantly through time, whereas the pace of extinction stays more or less constant. This presumably accounts for the asymmetry in time recognized by Gould *et al.* (1987).

The database for Phanerozoic taxa has improved considerably in recent years as a result of the painstaking work of Jack Sepkoski, who has produced a compendium of marine families (Sepkoski, 1982) and is currently compiling generic data. Factor analysis led him to propose three successive faunas, labelled I, II, and III, and to generate a kinetic model (1979, 1981, 1984). This has stimulated similar work for terrestrial plants (Niklas *et al.*, 1985) and vertebrates (Benton, 1985). There has been lively controversy about the extent to which equilibrium models derived from ecological population studies can be applied to the interpretation of Phanerozoic diversity patterns. A study by Kitchell and Carr (1985) is especially illuminating here. The authors formulate and test a deductive model of Phanerozoic diversification using discrete mathematics, and find that it corresponds well with the pattern recognized by Sepkoski. Perturbations combined with evolutionary innovations and turnover have maintained the system at nonequilibrium throughout. Whereas other paleobiologists have warned against the tendency to see determinism in patterns where there may be none, Kitchell and Carr point out the opposite danger, of assuming that deterministic processes generate only orderly patterns. Mass extinction perturbations signify extrinsic perturbations to a stable system at nonequilibrium rather than oscillations of an unstable or chaotic system. Contrasts are drawn between "hedonist" and "stoic" faunas, illustrated respectively by Sepkoski's faunas I and III. Hedonist faunas are characterized by high rates of initial diversification and diversity-dependent negative feedback, and are therefore most sensitive both to increased diversity levels and perturbations. Stoic faunas have low rates in these parameters and are in consequence relatively insensitive to diversity levels and perturbations. Evidently it is the stoic rather than the meek that have inherited the earth.

The Motor of Evolution

The question of what drives evolution is a fundamental one, for which the fossil record in conjunction with geological data provides critically important evidence.

Darwin viewed biotic interactions—"the struggle for existence"—as being the major promoter of evolution. This is clearly indicated in the following passage from *The Origin of Species:*

> species are produced and exterminated by slowly acting causes, and not by miraculous acts of creation; and . . . the most important of all causes of organic change is one which is almost independent of altered and perhaps suddenly altered physical conditions, namely the mutual relation of organism to organism—the improvement of one organism entailing the improvement or the extermination of others.

This view has been uncritically accepted by generations of evolutionary biologists and has received its fullest modern formulation in the so-called Red Queen hypothesis of Van Valen (1973), named after the Lewis Carroll character who found it took all the running one can do to keep in the same place. It is thoroughly Darwinian in its emphasis on the paramount importance of biotic interactions. All species within a given adaptive zone compete intensively. A successful adaptive response by one species is assumed to occur at the expense of other species, which must either adapt by themselves speciating or become extinct, as the quality of their environment is reduced. This phenomenon leads to an endless chain of adaptive responses, and in the long run means that fitness and rate of extinction remain constant.

The alternative to the Red Queen model, termed the stationary model by Stenseth and Maynard Smith (1984), is that the prime motor of evolution is change in the physical environment, without which evolution could conceivably grind to a halt. The Phanerozoic fossil record can be used to put these alternative hypotheses to the test. The most valuable approach is to analyze the pattern of diversity change and replacement for particular groups with time. As noted above, this has now been done comprehensively to family level and to some extent also to generic level (Valentine, 1985; Raup and Jablonski, 1986). Besides more gradual changes, some of which may relate to co-evolution (Vermeij, 1987), a number of spectacular radiation and extinction events can be recognized, in organisms of widely different habitat and biology, which affect a high proportion of the Earth's biota at a given time. Such phenomena are often seen to correlate with major events in the physical environment, such as those bound up with plate tectonics, sea-level change, or climate (some would add the impact of extraterrestrial bodies), which argues strongly in favor of the stationary model (Hallam, 1983). For more detailed analysis, the rich record of Cenozoic calcarous and siliceous plankton from deep-sea cores provides very favorable material. Hoffman and Kitchell (1984) found that their data marginally supported the Red Queen model, whereas Wei and Kennett (1986) argued for the stationary model.

Research of this kind has raised the question of what kind of role competition might have played in evolution. The conventional Darwinian view is that adaptively superior organisms progressively outcompete their more ancient relatives, but the fossil record clearly indicates that mammals coexisted with dinosaurs for well over 100 million years as small, probably nocturnal creatures, and did not radiate significantly until after the dinosaurs went extinct at the end of the Cretaceous, thereby vacating a range of ecological niches. The dinosaurs in their turn radiated at the end of the Triassic, *after* their potential reptile competitors had gone extinct (Benton, 1983). This pattern is also a common one among marine invertebrates and suggests that competition is predominantly *preemptive* rather that *displacive* (Hallam, 1987, in press). Apparently it largely depends on who is first in the field. Thus there appears to be a major opportunistic element in evolution, not readily predictable from normal biotic interactions. This is illustrated particularly well by the history of marine reef communities, which are very complex and highly integrated biological systems. Detailed studies of the Phanerozoic record indicate that ancient reef communities are characterized by long periods of surprising stability punctuated by shorter episodes of more rapid change resulting from mass extinction (Fagerstrom, 1987).

Conclusions

The evolutionary debate in the last two decades between biologists and paleobiologists—at best refreshingly lively and stimulating, at worst unnecessarily acrimonious—has been characterized by a disproportionately large amount of rhetoric. Now that the dust has settled somewhat, it can be seen in retrospect that some of the early claims of revolutionary change were exaggerated, and that such changes as may be required can be encompassed broadly within a Darwinian paradigm. On the other hand, some biologists have been guilty of complacency and blinkered vision. Thus I have heard population geneticists maintain that they can explain any kind of speciation—punctuational or gradualistic, anagenetic or cladogenetic—with some theoretical model or other. But surely theories that can explain everything in effect explain very little, and fail to tell us what has actually happened in history. It is gratifying in this respect that one of our most eminent living evolutionary biologists, John Maynard Smith, has conceded that long-term morphological stasis, as revealed by fossils, was never predicted by biologists.

Again, while it is surely correct that we shall learn more about *process* from biological studies, it would be wrong to assume that process is necessarily more important than *pattern* in a properly comprehensive view of evolution, whatever the more reductionist biologists might claim. For many if not most people, the outstanding question about evolution remains the same as it was in Darwin's day: Given descent from a common ancestor, how did the extraordinary diversity of life in space and time come about? Part of the answer will come from a better understanding of morphogenesis in relation to molecular biology, but crucial evidence bearing on the subject can be obtained only from paleontology and geology. By scrutinizing evolutionary biological research in the context of what has apparently happened over long periods of earth history, we ought to be able to put it in perspective and be in a better position to distinguish the significant from

the trivial, and the working out of organizational principles from the historically contingent.

Alberch, S., Gould, S. J., Oster, G. F., and Wake, D. B., 1979, Size and shape in ontogeny
    and phylogeny, *Paleobiol.* **5**:296-317.
Banner, F. T. and Lowry, F. M. D., 1985, The stratigraphic record of planktonic foraminifera
    and its evolutionary implications, *Spec. Pap. Palaeont.* **33**:117-130.
Bayer, U. and McGhee, G. R., 1985, Evolution in marginal epicontinental basins: the role of
    phylogenetic and ecological factors (ammonite replacements in the German Lower and
    Middle Jurassic), in: *Sedimentary and Evolutionary Cycles* (U. Bayer & A. Seilacher, eds.),
    pp. 164-220, Springer-Verlag, Berlin.
Benton, M. J., 1983, Dinosaur success in the Triassic: a noncompetitive ecological model,
    Quart. Rev. Biol. **58**:29-55.
Benton, M. J., 1985, Patterns in the diversification of Mesozoic non-marine tetrapods and
    problems in historical diversity analysis, *Spec. Pap. Palaeont.* **33**:185-202.
Brown, J. H. and Maurer, B. A., 1986, Body size, ecological dominance and Cope's rule,
    Nature **324**:248-250.
Calder, W. A., 1984, *Size, Function and Life History*, Harvard University Press, Cambridge.
Callomon, J. H., 1985, The evolution of the Jurassic ammonite family Cardioceratidae, *Spec.
    Pap. Palaeont.* **33**:49-90.
Charlesworth, B., Lande, R., and Slatkin, M., 1982, A neo-Darwinian commentary on mac-
    roevolution, *Evolution* **36**:474-498.
Coope, S. R., 1979, Late Cenozoic fossil Coleoptera: evolution, biogeography and ecology,
    Ann. Rev. Ecol. System **10**:247-267.
Cope, J. C. W. and Skelton, P. W. (eds.), 1985, Evolutionary case histories from the fossil
    record, *Spec. Pap. Palaeont.* **33**:1-203.
Cronin, T. M., 1985, Speciation and stasis in marine Ostracoda: climatic modulation of evolu-
    tion, *Science* **227**:60-62,
Dawkins, R., 1982, *The Extended Phenotype*, Freeman, Oxford.
Dawkins, R., 1986, *The Blind Watchmaker*, Longman, Harlow.
Eldredge, N. and Gould, S. J., 1972, Punctuated equilibria: an alternative to phyletic
    gradualism, in: *Models of Paleobiology* (T. J. M. Schopf, ed.), pp. 82-115, Freeman, San
    Francisco.
Fagerstrom, J. A., 1987, *The Evolution of Reef Communities*, Wiley, New York.
Fortey, R. A., 1985, Gradualism and punctuated equilibria as competing and complementary
    theories, *Spec. Pap. Palaeont.* **33**:17-28.
Gilinsky, N. L. and Bambach, R. K., 1987, Asymmetrical patterns of origination and extinction
    in higher taxa, *Paleobiol.* **13**:427-445.
Gould, S. J., 1977, *Ontogeny and Phylogeny*, Harvard University Press, Cambridge.
Gould, S. J., 1982, Darwinism and the expansion of evolutionary theory, *Science* **216**:380-387.
Gould, S. J., 1985, The paradox of the first tier: an agenda for paleobiology, *Paleobiol.* **11**:2-12.
Gould, S. J. and Eldredge, N., 1977, Punctuated equilibria: the tempo and mode of evolution
    reconsidered, *Paleobiol.* **3**:115-151.
Gould, S. J., 1986, Punctuated equilibrium at the third stage, *System. Zool.* **35**:143-148.
Gould, S. J., Gilinsky, N. L. and German, R. Z., 1987, Asymmetry of lineages and the direction
    of evolutionary time, *Science* **236**:1437-1441.
Hallam, A., 1975, Evolutionary size increase and longevity in Jurassic bivalves and ammonites,
    Nature **258**:193-196.
Hallam, A., 1978, How rare is phyletic gradualism? evidence from Jurassic bivalves, *Paleobiol.*
    4:16-25.
Hallam, A., 1982, Patterns of speciation in Jurassic *Gryphaea*, *Paleobiol.* **8**:354-366.
Hallam, A., 1983, Plate tectonics and evolution, in: *Evolution from Molecules to Men* (D. S.
    Bendall, ed.), pp. 367-386, Cambridge University Press, Cambridge.
Hallam, A., 1985, Comment, *Biol. J. Linn. Soc.* **26**:341-343.
Hallam, A., 1987, Radiations and extinctions in relation to environmental change in the marine
    Lower Jurassic of north west Europe, *Paleobiol.* **13**:152-168.

Hallam, A., in press, Biotic and abiotic factors in the evolution of early Mesozoic marine molluscs, in: *Biotic and Abiotic Factors in Evolution* (R. M. Ross and W. D. Allmon, eds.), Chicago University Press, Chicago.

Hecht, M. K. and Hoffman, A., 1986, Why not neo-Darwinism? a critique of paleobiological challenges, *Oxford Surveys Evol. Biol.* **3**:1-47.

Hennig, W., 1966, *Phylogenetic Systematics*, Illinois University Press, Urbana.

Hoffman, A., 1985, Species selection, *Evol. Biol.* **18**:1-20.

Hoffman, A. and Kitchell, J. A., 1984. Evolution in a pelagic planktic system: a paleobiologic test of models of multispecies evolution, *Paleobiol.* **10**:9-33.

Kemp, T. S., 1982, *Mammal-like Reptiles and the Origin of Mammals*, Acad. Press, London and New York.

Kitchell, J. A. and Carr, T. R., 1985, Nonequilibrium model of diversification: faunal turnover dynamics, in: *Phanerozoic Diversity Patterns* (J. W. Valentine, ed.), pp. 277-310, Princeton University Press, Princeton.

La Barbera, M., 1986, The evolution and ecology of size, in: *Patterns and Processes in the History of Life* (D. M. Raup and D. Jablonski, eds.), pp. 69-98, Springer-Verlag, Berlin.

Lande, R., 1986, The dynamics of peak shifts and the pattern of morphological evolution, *Paleobiol.* **12**:343-354.

Levinton, J. S., 1983, Stasis in progress: the empirical basis of macroevolution, *Ann. Rev. Ecol. System.* **14**:103-137.

Levinton, J. S., 1988, *Genetics, Paleontology, and Macroevolution*, Cambridge University Press, Cambridge.

Malmgren, B. A., Berggren, W. A., and Lohman, G. P., 1983, Evidence for punctuated gradualism in the late Neogene *Globorotalia tumida* lineage of planktonic foraminifera, *Paleobiol.* **9**:377-389.

McKinney, M. L., 1985, Distinguishing patterns of evolution from patterns of deposition, *J. Paleont.* **59**:561-567.

McKinney, M. L., 1986, Ecological causation of heterochrony: a test and implications for evolutionary theory, *Paleobiol.* **12**:282-289.

McNamara, K. J., 1982, Heterochrony and phyletic trends, *Paleobiol.* **8**:130-142.

McNamara, K. J., 1986, A guide to the nomenclature of heterochrony, *J. Paleont.* **60**:4-13.

Newell, N. D., 1949, Phyletic size increase—an important trend illustrated by fossil invertebrates, *Evolution* **3**:103-124.

Niklas, K. J., Tiffney, B. H., and Knoll, A. H., 1985, Patterns in vascular land plant diversification: an analysis at the species level, in: *Phanerozoic Diversity Patterns* (J. W. Valentine, ed.), pp. 97-128, Princeton University Press, Princeton.

Odum, E. P., 1971, *Fundamentals of Ecology*, Saunders, Philadelphia.

Paul, C. R. C., 1977, Evolution of primitive echinoderms, in: *Patterns of Evolution as Illustrated by the Fossil Record* (A. Hallam, ed.), pp. 123-158, Elsevier, Amsterdam.

Paul, C. R. C., 1982, The adequacy of the fossil record, in: *Problems of Phylogenetic Reconstruction* (K. A. Joysey and A. E. Friday, eds.) pp. 75-117, Acad. Press, London and New York.

Raff, R. A. and Kauffman, T. C., 1983, *Embryos, Genes and Evolution*, Macmillan, New York.

Ramsbottom, W. H. C., 1981, Eustatic control in Carboniferous ammonoid biostratigraphy, in: *The Ammonoidea* (M. R. House and J. R. Senior, eds.), System. Ass. Spec. Vol. 18, pp. 369-388, Acad. Press, London and New York.

Raup, D. M. and Jablonski, D. (eds.), 1986, *Patterns and Processes in the History of Life*, Springer-Verlag, Berlin.

Rensch, B., 1959, *Evolution above the Species Level*, Columbia University Press, New York.

Sadler, P. M., 1981, Sediment accumulation rates and the completeness of stratigraphic sections, *J. Geol.* **89**:569-584.

Schindel, D. E., 1982, Resolution analysis: a new approach to the gaps in the fossil record, *Paleobiol.* **8**:340-353.

Schopf, T. J. M., 1981, Evidence from findings of molecular biology with regard to the rapidity of genomic change: implications for species durations, in: *Paleobotany, Paleoecology and Evolution* (K. J. Niklas, ed.), pp. 135-192, Praeger, New York.

Sepkoski, J. J., 1979, A kinetic model of Phanerozoic taxonomic diversity. II. Early Phanerozoic families and multiple equilibria, *Paleobiol.* **5**:222-251.

Sepkoski, J. J., 1981, A factor analytic description of the Phanerozoic marine fossil record, *Paleobiol.* **7**:36-53.

Sepkoski, J. J., 1982, A compendium of fossil marine families, *Milwaukee Publ. Mus. Contr. Biol. Geol.* **51**:1-125.

Sepkoski, J. J., 1984, A kinetic model of Phanerozoic taxonomic diversity. III. Post-Paleozoic families and mass extinctions, *Paleobiol.* **10**:246-267.

Sheldon, P. R., 1987, Parallel gradualistic evolution of Ordovician trilobites, *Nature* **330**:561-563.

Stanley, S. M., 1973, An explanation for Cope's Rule, *Evolution* **27**:1-26.

Stanley, S. M., 1979, *Macroevolution: Pattern and Process*, Freeman, San Francisco.

Stanley, S. M. and Yang, X., 1987, Approximate evolutionary stasis for bivalve morphology over millions of years: a multivariate, multilineage study, *Paleobiol.* **13**:113-139.

Stenseth, N. C. and Maynard Smith, J., 1984, Coevolution in ecosystems: Red Queen or stasis? *Evolution* **38**:870-880.

Valentine, J. W., 1977, General patterns of metazoan evolution, in: *Patterns of Evolution as Illustrated by the Fossil Record* (A. Hallam, ed.), pp. 27-58, Elsevier, Amsterdam.

Valentine, J. W. (ed.), 1985, *Phanerozoic Diversity Patterns*, Princeton University Press, Princeton.

Van Valen, L., 1973, A new evolutionary law, *Evol. Thoery* **1**:1-30.

Vermeij, G. J., 1977, The Mesozoic marine revolution: evidence from snails, predators and grazers, *Paleobiol.* **3**:245-258.

Vermeij, G. J., 1987, *Evolution and Escalation*, Princeton University Press, Princeton.

Vrba, E. S., 1980, Evolution, species and fossils: how does life evolve? *S. Afr. J. Sci.* **76**:61-84.

Vrba, E. S., 1983, Macroevolutionary trends: new perspectives on the roles of adaptation and incidental effect, *Science* **221**:387-389.

Vrba, E. S. and Eldredge, N., 1984, Individuals, hierarchies and processes: towards a more complete evolutionary theory, *Paleobiol.* **10**:146-171.

Vrba, E. S. and Gould, S. J., 1986, The hierarchical expansion of sorting and selection: sorting and selection cannot be equated, *Paleobiol.* **12**:217-228.

Wei, K.-Y. and Kennett, J. P., 1986, Taxonomic evolution of Neogene planktonic foraminifera and paleoceanographic relations, *Paleoceanography* **1**:67-84.

Williamson, P. G., 1981, Palaeontological documentation of speciation in Cenozoic molluscs from Turkana Basin, *Nature* **293**:437-443.

Arthur J. Boucot

Professor Hallam has skillfully summarized many of the current burning questions of paleobiology. Still, there is always room for more. In my view (Boucot, 1978, 1983), it is crucial to an understanding of the evolutionary process that we study the change in taxa within their evolving community context. I would, on this basis, seriously question the fifth item in Hallam's introduction about fossils being incapable of telling us anything about the evolutionary process. I feel that fossils *do* have the capacity to tell us certain key things about the evolutionary process, things that the genetics and ecology of living organisms are incapable of providing. I will now try to make clear just what I have in mind.

The fossil record has several unique attributes that are of potential interest to evolutionists. The attribute familiar to all is the time sequence of morphologies that permits us to infer varied phylogenies. Far less well known are the more aggregate properties of the fossil record. By "aggregate" I am thinking of the many major and minor changes, occurring somewhat abruptly on a geological time scale, in flora and fauna, *plus* the changing nature through time of what the paleontologist-geologist commonly terms "biofacies," but what the ecologist might well term "communities." I will elaborate on these aggregate properties in the following pages.

The publication of d'Orbigny's monumental synthesis (1849-52, 1850-52) made clear that the fossil record is divisible into a number of significant biostratigraphic units. He emphasized that *within* each of his units the fauna had an overall sameness, with many of his taxa extending in time from the bottom to the top of each particular unit. However, within each of these d'Orbigny-type units there are a number of individual biofacies, the term commonly used by the geologist, or communities, the term

commonly preferred by the biologist. I have referred (1983) to the major d'Orbigny-type units as "ecologic-evolutionary units."

Our problem as present-day students of evolution is to determine the nature of the changes occurring through time within the varied taxa present in each community. We need to consider whether there are significant changes in relative abundance between the taxa present in each community type through evolutionary time. We also need to pay attention to the initial, critical interval of community formation in terms of whether all taxa appear simultaneously or not, and if not, whether there is any order to their appearance in terms of their relative abundance. We need to pay attention to the opposite end of the interval, during the extinction interval, about just which taxa drop out first, whether most taxa drop out at about the same time, and whether there are any correlations between relative abundance and time of extinction.

We will not be able to decide whether the relatively fixed nature of the community types, which I term community groups, within individual ecologic-evolutionary units results from coevolutionary relations or is merely a result of individual taxa remaining in relatively stable environments that happen to coincide with the ecologic-evolutionary unit boundaries. This critical question needs to be decided by experiments made with living materials.

The individual ecologic-evolutionary units and their subunits have relatively abrupt boundaries, as stated above. These boundaries may correspond to major and minor extinction events, to major and minor adaptive radiations, and to dispersal events. Between these boundaries it needs to be emphasized that evolutionary changes in place —vicariance—is the modal form of evolution; the contention between dispersalists and vicariance followers is needless, for both processes are important, each in its place. We have little real understanding of just what are the population biologic and genetic controls involved with adaptive radiations, i.e., what happens during that geologically brief time interval when varied, very unrelated higher taxa radiate within a fixed number of community types (community groups). Examination of the current literature also makes it clear that we are far from reaching agreement about the causes of extinctions in any part of the record. One would think that we could at least do something very positive about dispersal events, but our overall ignorance of older paleogeographies even prevents much certainty on this score.

Community Groups

I have defined and discussed (1975, 1978) the term community group. A community group refers to the fact that within each ecologic-evolutionary unit there are a distinct, finite set of community types. Because the ecologic-evolutionary units are based on the widespread, abundant level-bottom marine benthos, one finds that the level-bottom community groups persist from beginning to end of each ecologic-evolutionary unit. However, the nonlevel-bottom community groups, such as those present in the reef complex of communities during those intervals when the reef complex is in existence— pelmatozoan thickets, sponge forests, bryozoan thickets, algal thickets, and the like—may have much shorter time ranges owing to their commonly later initiation, although they commonly share the same termination time as the associated level-bottom community groups.

An individual community group may be defined as a regularly recurring set of genera, regularly recurring through the time interval of the particular ecologic-evolutionary unit, in which the relative abundances of the co-occuring genera remain about the same, although far from identical. By this I mean that

abundant genera tend to remain abundant, common genera to remain common, and rare genera to remain rare, although there may be wide fluctuations within these limits owing to the many vagaries (larval success, predation, disease, local catastrophes, etc.) affecting the local success of varied organisms. Directing attention now to the individual genera of a particular community group (Boucot, 1983, Fig. 1), it is typical to observe that the abundant, the dominant genera commonly show little or no evidence for changes in morphology through time; they tend to be assigned to a single species. Contrariwise, the less abundant, less dominant genera tend to show modest changes in morphology that may be interpreted as moderate rates of species-level, phyletic evolution. And the rare genera, those commonly not found in a fauna unless a very large sample has been collected, tend to show evidence for far more change in morphology through time, i.e., for rapid rates of phyletic evolution. In other words, there appears to be an inverse relation between relative abundance of a genus and its species, and its rate of phyletic evolution. The taxonomic content of individual community groups shows little evidence for cladogenesis (branching-type evolutionary diversification), i.e., increasing diversity through time, or for decreasing diversity through time. One does not see evidence favoring immigration into or emigration out of particular community groups. Community groups manifest a kind of taxonomic monotony unless one is paying careful attention to species-level changes within a genus. All of this indicates that the ecosystem within any particular ecologic-evolutionary unit is not in some kind of continual environmental flux, with the environmental, physiological, and behavioral limits of the taxa continually changing. The paleontologist has been well aware of this situation since d'Orbigny's time. In conclusion, one could state that the element of fitness having to do with relative abundance between taxa undergoing relatively rapid phyletic evolution and those showing little or no evidence for significant morphologic change is zero, i.e., neutral (Boucot, 1978), and that the entire structure is undergoing strong stabilizing selection.

I have discussed evidence from the marine environment. What we know from the nonmarine, freshwater, and terrestrial environments is consistent with conclusions based on the marine environment.

The essentially very conservative behavior of virtually all taxa is emphasized by the very small number of exceptions. I would define "exceptions" to mean those instances where a genus can be shown to have really changed its environmental tolerances significantly over time. At present I can refer here to the few genera singled out by Arkell (1956, p. 616), Woodring (1960), Feldmann and Wilson (1988), and Cooper (1988). To me these are the exceptions that prove the rule.

Initial Diversification

The nature and pattern of initial community reorganization following an extinction event has not been studied (see Hansen, 1988; Harries *et al.*, 1988, for exceptions relevant to this discussion). However, it is apparent from stratigraphic range studies that there is an overall tendency for the more abundant, more cosmopolitan genera, commonly those that tend to survive extinction events, which are commonly more eurytopic (environmentally less specialized) in terms of occurring in more than one community group as well as in more varied shoreline to far offshore positions, to appear first. Following them are the increasingly more stenotopic (environmentally more specialized), more provincial taxa. These comments apply to the level-bottom community groups. Turning to the nonlevel-bottom community groups, it is well known that

they commonly appear considerably later in time than the level-bottom community groups (Boucot, 1983; Fagerstrom, 1987; Talent, in press). The reasons for this tendency for later appearance are unknown, and we have no hint whether this is a largely stochastic problem or one due to unrecognized causal factors. No study has been given to the order of taxic appearances within the nonlevel-bottom community types, any more than to the level-bottom community types, and whether it too seems to follow the pattern suspected for the level bottoms. Partly relevant to the above is Sorauf and Pedder's (1986) work indicating that the precursors of the Carboniferous coral genera and families appear in the later Famennian (latest Devonian) in a somewhat staggered, steplike manner.

We lack careful studies of initial diversification, adaptive radiation within communities following an extinction event. But Jarvis *et al.* (1988) do provide extensive clues in terms of stratigraphic range data both before and after the Cenomanian-Turonian (later Cretaceous) Oceanic Extinction Event in northern Europe that are well worth considering in this context. Their work emphasizes the gradual elimination of varied taxa prior to the extinction event, and their gradual addition following the extinction event.

Terminal Elimination

In the past decade an increasing amount of data has accumulated about the pattern of terminal extinction overall, but there has been little effort to work out the patterns of within-community extinction. It is clear from the studies of many workers in varied parts of the column that major extinctions, and presumably minor extinctions, follow a regular pattern of taxic eliminations. During an interval of several million years—possibly as much as three or four, but probably not much more—varied taxa belonging to any one trophic grouping or guild tend to drop out intermittently, until a final community crash (McLaren's biomass collapse; see 1970, 1983, 1985, wherein he emphasizes this terminal community-collapse aspect of extinction) in which the last, commonly the very abundant survivors, finally disappear. There has been discussion about whether these extinction-related disappearances occur in steps (Kauffman, 1984, 1986) or gradually over an interval of several millions of years. Until careful studies of extinctions from within specific community groups are carried out, the answer to this question will be uncertain. The stepwise mode of extinction, as contrasted with the gradual, may be largely an artifact of changing environments and accompanying communities occurring at any one place during the overall extinction interval. It is seldom the case that the overall environment and community group remain constant in any one place for as long an interval as several million years.

Recent papers with good examples that emphasize the gradual or stepwise extinction of taxa in the interval immediately prior to the terminal community collapse include Eckert (1988; Late Ordovician crinoids), Cocks (1988; Ashgillian brachiopods), Becker (1986; Frasnian-Famennian ammonoids), Stearn (1987; Frasnian-Famennian stromatoporoids), Copper (1986; Frasnian-Famennian brachiopods), McGhee (1988; Frasnian-Famennian brachiopods), Kauffman (1984, 1986; Cenomanian-Turonian and Maastrichtian-Danian mollusca), Hansen (1988; Maastrichtian mollusca), Johnson and Kauffman (1988; Cretaceous rudistids), and Lamolda (1988; Maastrichtian foraminifera). Somewhat contrary to the preceding are Sorauf and Pedder's (1986) conclusions that the end Frasnian extinction of most rugose coral genera (p. 1277) was a "sudden and dramatic event" and "extinguished a minimum of 42 of the 47 late Frasnian genera," with the additional comment that these were mostly abundant as individuals. The comment about abundance might indicate that these rugosans were mostly eurytopic types more subject to terminal community collapse than is commonly the case with most higher taxa, where the bulk of the genera are relatively stenotopic and uncommon.

These recent studies are a welcome change from the former, biostratigraphically crude compilations, emphasizing that *all* taxa involved in an extinction event failed at the same moment in time, because no attempt had been made to carefully sample, cm-by-cm, zone-by-zone, the final stage, or in all too many instances, the final series of a particular time interval terminated by an extinction event, although as a group they are not nearly as detailed as the cm-by-cm goal.

Patterns of Cladogenesis

Once the pattern of adaptive radiations and extinctions within evolving community groups is established, it becomes clear that the classic diagram indicating the time-random nature of cladogenesis is false. Rather, we must face a far more regular pattern of major cladogenesis (metacladogenesis), generation of new families and higher taxa, that occurs within an evolving community group context. The varied, taxonomically unrelated contents of a community group adaptively radiate, presumably following a quantum evolution mode, during the geologically brief interval when new community groups first appear, i.e., at the beginning of most ecologic-evolutionary units, or not at all during the subsequent duration of the community group within its ecologic-evolutionary unit.

The apparent randomness shown by many higher taxa during cladogenesis would seem to oppose this conclusion, the purely taxonomic conclusion versus the purely community ecologic. This apparent contradiction may be essentially eliminated *if* one restricts consideration to individual ecologic units, such as the level bottom, the reef complex of communities, pelmatozoan thickets, bryozoan thickets, sponge forests, and the like. Superimposing the family trees of the same and different groups from major, distinct ecologic units (such as the level bottom, reef complex of communities, pelmatozoan thickets, bryozoan thickets, etc.) can give rise to an appearance of randomness.

Another major contributor to this appearance of randomness are sampling artifacts due to taphonomy and rarity. By "taphonomy" I refer to those preservational factors that prevent organisms, such as most echinoderms, from commonly being preserved in the fossil record. Thus, the known time range of most fossil echinoderms reflects unusual preservation possibilities through time, and is far short of what community paleoecology suggests might have been their true time ranges. By "rarity" I refer to the common sampling problem involved with the fact that most samples are too small to obtain the species of rare genera, and consequently our information about their "known" time ranges is commonly far short of what community paleoecology suggests should be their true ranges.

The real pattern apparent when one takes both evolution and ecology into consideration is a trellis-like one in which cladogenesis affecting many unrelated groups is relatively co-occurring rather than random through time. This pattern is consistent with both d'Orbigny's work and Darwin's, although differing from Darwin's diagram in its regularity.

The cladogenesis being discussed here is of the metacladogenetic type (Boucot, 1978; diversification giving rise to truly major evolutionary changes, as when birds were derived from nonvolant reptiles, rather than the low-level monotonous derivation of individual species from very similar ancestral species, with little real change in overall morphology or other characters). The diacladogenetic (evolutionarily minor diversification in a morphologic and taxonomic sense) occurrences of the record commonly correlate with minor increases in levels of provincialism, such as the generation of the Isthmus of Panama for shallow marine creatures.

In connection with the two major evolutionary modes discussed here, it is well to point out that Krasilov (1969) some time ago also recognized the distinction between the minor, chiefly phyletic changes occurring within evolving communities, as contrasted with the major adaptive radiation events occurring at about the time when new community units are generated. He essentially follows Simpson (1953) in this regard in contrasting Simpson's quantum evolution with phyletic evolution. Simpson did not specifically spell out the within-community aspects of the problem, but was well aware of them. Schindewolf's (1950) awareness of the same problem is reflected in his terms "typogenesis" and "typostasis."

Ecologic-Evolutionary Unit History in Brief

I have previously (1983, 1987a) laid out something of the character of ecologic-evolutionary unit history. I defined (1983) 12 major units in the Cambrian-present interval. They are of unequal absolute time duration. It is important to recognize that most of these 12 major ecologic-evolutionary units may be subdivided into subunits of varying importance. The presence of such subunits is testified to by the biostratigraphic units into which the time interval is subdivided.

Conclusions

For those concerned with evolution, consideration of community evolution provides few answers to basic evolutionary mechanisms, but does give rise to a new set of basic problems. The evidence of community evolution, however, is consistent with the conclusion that the modal form is monotonous, lineal, phyletic evolution at the species level, for which there is little or no change in relative abundance between those taxa undergoing significant morphologic change (most commonly those characterized by small populations overall, which also happen to commonly be stenotopic and provincial), consistent with strong stabilizing selection and neutralism being active controls. It is clear that major adaptive radiation, metacladogenesis at the familial and higher levels, is not a random process through time *if* one restricts one's attention to a particular part of the ecosystem, such as the marine level bottom. Study of community evolution provides a more realistic view of phylogenetic patterns, the coordinated nature of adaptive radiations and extinctions, and the within ecologic-evolutionary unit generation of the nonlevel-bottom community complexes, but provides no real answers as to how these phenomena are controlled.

Oregon State University

Arkell, W. J., 1956, *Jurassic Geology of the World*, Oliver & Boyd.

Becker, R. T., 1986, Ammonoid evolution before, during and after the "Kellwasserevent"—review and preliminary new results, in: *Global Bio-Events*, Lecture Notes in Earth Sciences, 8 (O. H. Walliser, ed.), pp. 181-188, Springer-Verlang.

Boucot, A. J., 1975, *Evolution and Extinction Rate Controls*, Elsevier.

Boucot, A. J., 1978, Community evolution and rates of cladogenesis, *Ev. Biol.* **11**: 545-655.

Boucot, A. J., 1981, *Principles of Benthic Marine Paleoecology*, Academic Press.

Boucot, A. J., 1983, Does evolution take place in an ecological vacuum? II., *J. Paleo.* **57**: 1-30.

Boucot, A. J., 1987a, Phanerozoic extinctions: how similar are they to each other? in: Abstracts, Conference on Paleontology and Evolution: Extinction Events, III, *Jornadas de Paleontologia*, Bilbao, pp. 50-80.

Boucot, A. J., 1987b, The relative abundance through time of articulate brachiopods, and their utility for biogeographic purposes during the Phanerozoic, in: *Les Brachiopodes fossiles et actuels, Biostratigraphie du Paleozoique 4* (P. R. Racheboeuf and C. V. Emig, eds.), pp. 449-454.

Cocks, L. R. M., 1988, Brachiopods, in: *The Ordovician-Silurian Boundary* (M. K. Bassett and L. R. M. Cocks, eds.), Univ. Wales Press.

Cooper, M. R., 1988, A new species of the brachiopod genus *Aqulhasia* (Terebratulidinae: Chlidonophoridae) from the Uloa Formation, *Suid-Afrikaanse Tydskrif vir Wetenskap* **84**: 35-38.

Copper, P., 1986, Frasnian/Famennian mass extinction and cold-water oceans, *Geology* **14**: 835-839.

Eckert, J. D., 1988, Late Ordovician extinction of North American and British crinoids, *Lethaia* **21**: 147-167.

Fagerstrom, J. A., 1987, *The Evolution of Reef Communities*, Wiley Interscience.

Feldmann, R. M., and Wilson, M. T., 1988, Eocene decapod crustaceans from Antarctica, *Geol. Soc. Amer. Mem.* **169**: 465-488.

Hansen, T. A., 1988, Rate of molluscan response to the Cretaceous-Tertiary extinction, *Third Internat. Cong. Global Bioevents: Abrupt Changes in the Global Biota*, p. 17.

Harries, P. J., Kauffman, E. G., and Hansen, T. A., 1988, Models for survival and repopulation of the earth following mass extinction, *Third Internat. Conf. Global Bioevents: Abrupt Changes in the Global Biota*, p. 18.

Jarvis, I., Carson, G. A., Cooper, M. K. E., Hart, M. B., Leary, P. N., Tocher, B. A.,

Horne, D., and Rosenfeld, A., 1988, Microfossil assemblages and the Cenomanian-Turonian (late Cretaceous) Oceanic Anoxic Event, *Cret. Res.* **9**: 3-103.

Johnson, C. C., and Kauffman, E. G., 1988, Extinction patterns in Cretaceous reefs, *Third Internat. Conf. Global Bioevents: Abrupt Changes in the Global Biota,* p. 21.

Kauffman, E. G., 1984, The fabric of Cretaceous marine extinctions, in: *Catastrophes and Earth History* (W. A. Berggren and J. A. van Couvering, eds.), pp. 151-246, Princeton Univ. Press.

Kauffman, E. G., 1986, High resolution event stratigraphy: regional and global Cretaceous bio-events, in: *Global Bio-Events,* Lecture Notes in Earth Sciences, 8 (O. H. Walliser, ed.), pp. 279-335, Springer-Verlag.

Krasilov, V. A., 1969, Filogeniya i Sistematika, in: *Problemi Filogenii i Sistematiki. Materiali Simpoziya,* pp. 12-30, Vladivostok.

Lamolda, M. A., 1988, The Cretaceous-Tertiary boundary crisis at Zumaya (Northern Spain), *Micropaleontological Data: Third Internat. Conf. Global Bioevents: Abrupt Changes in the Global Biota,* p. 25.

McGhee, G. R., Jr., 1988, The Devonian mass extinction record in the eastern United States, *Third Internat. Conf. Global Bioevents: Abrupt Changes in the Global Biota,* p. 27.

McLaren, D. J., 1970, Time, life, and boundaries, *J. Paleo* **44**: 801-815.

McLaren, D. J., 1983, Bolides and biostratigraphy, *Bull. Geol. Soc. America* **94**: 313-324.

McLaren, D. J., 1985, Mass extinction and iridium anomaly in the Upper Devonian of Western Australia: a commentary, *Geology* **3**: 170-172.

d'Orbigny, A., 1849-52, *Cours elementaire de Paleontologie et de Geologie Stratigraphiques,* Masson, Paris.

d'Orbigny, A., 1850-52, *Prodrome de Paleontologie,* Masson, Paris.

Schindewolf, O., 1950, *Grundfragen der Palaontologie: Schweizerbart'sche,* Stuttgart.

Simpson, G. G., 1953, *Major Features of Evolution,* Columbia University Press.

Sorauf, J. E., and Pedder, A. E. H., 1986, Late Devonian rugose corals and the Frasnian-Famennian crisis, *Can. J. Earth Sci.* **23**: 1265-1287.

Stearn, C. W., 1987, Effect of the Frasnian-Famennian extinction event on the stromatoporoids, *Geology* **15**: 677-679.

Talent, J. A., in press, Organic reef-building: episodes of extinction and symbiosis? *Senck. Lethaea.*

Woodring, W. P., 1960, Paleoecologic dissonance; *Astarte* and *Nipa* in the Early Eocene London Clay, *Am. J. Sci.* **258-A**: 418-419.

Antoni Hoffman

Professor Hallam has given a broad overview of the potential of paleontology to contribute to the understanding of biological evolution or, to be more precise, to the understanding of macroevolution; for it is by now fairly obvious that both patterns and processes of microevolution generally are beyond the temporal resolution achievable in the fossil record. I largely agree with Hallam's assessment of successes as well as failures of the efforts undertaken recently by paleontologists toward this goal. I believe, however, that a couple of points should be emphasized more strongly. I shall here briefly discuss what I view as the main failure and the major success of modern paleontological research.

I fully concur with Hallam's view that an adequate understanding of biological evolution, which all evolutionary biologists strive to grasp, must entail both the process and the pattern of evolution. It also must encompass organic as well as biotic evolution, to employ the distinction made by Williams (1966): organic evolution refers to changes in structure, function, and behavior of organisms through time, whereas biotic evolution refers to changes in taxonomic and ecologic composition of clades and biotas (from local communities up to the global ecosystem, or biosphere) on the geological time scale.

Insofar as the pattern of biotic evolution is concerned, paleontology has undoubtedly much to say about it. In fact, paleontologists alone can really contribute to the knowledge of this pattern. The geological time scale simply is inaccessible to other evolutionary biologists. As to the pattern of organic evolution, comparative biological analysis of both anatomic and molecular data can tell us much about phylogenetic relationships among various living taxa. Yet no phylogenetic reconstruction can safely neglect extinct relatives of the taxa under consideration, if only because taking them into account may change the ingroup-outgroup context and, consequently, the polarity interpretation of character states and the entire topology of phylogenetic relationships. In this perspective, problematic fossil taxa may be of paramount importance for recognition of the pattern of organic evolution, since they represent the branches of the tree of life that we do not know at all where to fit. Paleontology, of course, must remain the only source of information about extinct organisms, and hence it makes a unique and necessary contribution to phylogenetic reconstruction.

It is also the only source of information about the actual pathways of phylogeny—that is, about at least some of the phenotypic transformations that really took place on the way from the unknown common ancestor of related living taxa to their present form and function. This information can only exceptionally be deemed adequate, but we have nothing more suitable to this end. Paleontological research is also the only way to get an insight into the relationship between environmental events and evolutionary phenomena in the history of particular organic groups. It provides data about the ecological context of the evolution of life, and hence, it puts constraints on hypothetical evolutionary scenarios that are to depict the course of evolution. Briefly, paleontology is at the core of historical biology, and its practitioners are the historians of life on Earth. The study of the fossil record is indispensable for reconstruction of the historical pattern of life, and insofar as such reconstruction is necessary for an adequate understanding of biological evolution, paleontology is as much a part and parcel of evolutionary biology as is population genetics or evolutionary ecology.

So far so good, and no disagreement with Hallam. In the last two decades, however, many paleontologists have explicitly sought to achieve a much grander goal. Niles Eldredge, Stephen Jay Gould, David M. Raup, Thomas J. M. Schopf, J. John Sepkoski, Steven M. Stanley, and Elisabeth S. Vrba have shaped this research tradition. They have attempted to contribute to the understanding of biological evolution something more than only a reconstruction of the historical pattern of life. They have also searched for regularities in this pattern—both of organic and of biotic evolution—which would demand as explanation some specifically macroevolutionary laws, irreducible to the laws of microevolution that are within the domain of neontological study. These macroevolutionary laws should describe the operation of some macroevolutionary processes as causally different from the processes induced by interaction between the genetic evolutionary forces and environment. Punctuated equilibrium can serve as an example, since under one of the interpretations of this concept, it has suggested that the pattern of morphological evolution entails a clear-cut bimodality of evolutionary rates (fast rates at speciation and nearly zero rates, or almost full stasis, at all other times) and that this pattern implies a causal distinction between speciation and ordinary microevolution by natural selection. Other examples include the theories of species selection, mass extinctions, and diversity-dependent taxonomic diversification in the Phanerozoic.

It is, I think, clear that the aim of these theories has always been not only to describe the pattern but also to interpret the process of macroevolution. But it should be unambiguously stated that no order has thus far been discovered in the historical pattern of life, as represented by paleontological data, which would demand specifically macroevolutionary laws as explanation. No such regularity has been found in the pattern of morphological evolution, since both punctuated and gradual patterns and also their intergradations seem to occur in nature. No convincing example of species selection has been documented.

Neither in the case of mass extinctions, nor in that of taxonomic diversification in the Phanerozoic, can the null hypothesis of a stochastic nature of these patterns be rejected. I have recently discussed the available evidence (Hoffman, 1989) and do not wish to repeat this discussion here. One point must be made clear, however: there is, and there can be, no evidence to prove that macroevolutionary processes, which are causally distinct from microevolutionary ones, are absent from the causal plexus of biological evolution. But the point of the matter is that no positive evidence for their action has been demonstrated—in spite of very intense search and, in fact, many claims to the contrary. The absence of such evidence is what I regard as the main failure of the last two decades of research in evolutionary paleontology. This failure is certainly counterbalanced by the substantial raising of standards in paleontological research, caused by the need to evaluate and test macroevolutionary theories and by the large amounts of fascinating data on the history of life amassed in the course of this research.

The main success of evolutionary paleontology in the last two decades, as I see it, is the emphasis on the fundamental role the changes in physical-chemical environment have always played in the history of life on Earth. There is no doubt in my mind that, within the neo-Darwinian conceptual framework, the environment has for long been given an appropriate place in the causal plexus of biological evolution. Neo-Darwinism, as I understand it, views evolution as a result of the interaction between microevolutionary genetical forces (natural selection, genetic drift, molecular forces) and environment. This interaction, of course, always takes place within a framework given by the biological constitution of each evolving species—the structure of its genome and the nature of its developmental program,

which are shaped by the species' phylogenetic history. The role of environment is here evident at each step; for it is the interaction between genes and environment that produces the phenotype, and it is the interaction between phenotypes and environment that triggers the microevolutionary forces of natural selection and genetic drift. Yet for the sake of simplicity, geneticists often leave the environment out of their models of microevolution. This practice may lead to the mistaken view that biological evolution is a purely autonomous process, driven solely by intrinsic biological forces. The history of life on Earth—as reconstructed by paleontology—and the history of the global ecosystem—as reconstructed by geology and geochemistry—show beyond any reasonable doubt that this view is incorrect.

At least two different lines of argument can be developed to this end. One is indeed being developed by Hallam, who points out that many organic groups began to radiate only after their potential competitors had gone extinct; thus, extinction often seems to liberate the ecospace necessary for new taxa to evolve. Emiliani (1982) coined the term "extinctive evolution" to describe this situation. Whether this is the norm in the history of life on Earth is hard to judge on the basis of the rather scarce data that we have, but it certainly is not an exception. (Contrary to Hallam and also Wei and Kennett [1986], I would argue that the distinction between the Red Queen and the Stationary models of Stenseth and Maynard Smith [1984] and Hoffman and Kitchell [1984] does not directly refer to this problem. It primarily addresses the question of what happens to evolution in the absence of environmental change, whereas both these models affirm that a change in effective environment will indeed result in both organic and biotic evolution.)

The other line of argument concerns changes in the boundary conditions imposed by the physical-chemical environment upon evolutionary processes. Consider, for example, the well-known trend toward development of ever more elaborate skeletal structures composed of calcium carbonate in various marine organisms during the Phanerozoic. One explanation for this trend puts emphasis on skeletons as primarily defensive devices against shell-crushing predators; it portrays the trend toward increased thickness and complexity of skeletal structures as a result of the arms race between predators and their prey (Vermeij, 1987). An alternative explanation, however, views development of calcitic or aragonitic skeletons primarily as a detoxification mechanism under excessive calcium concentration. It therefore interprets the trend toward heavier skeletons of marine organisms, along with its episodic ups and downs, primarily as a response to the changes in calcium concentration in the ocean (Kazmierczak *et al.*, 1985).

Consider also the case of oxygen concentration in the atmosphere, which is obviously of vital significance for many organisms. The traditional view is that although the primordial atmosphere was anoxic and the later buildup of oxygen was due to the photosynthetic activity of the biosphere, the present levels of oxygen were achieved long ago and generally maintained ever since by a system of geochemical feedbacks. Yet some new data clearly indicate that the oxygen levels in the atmosphere underwent some really dramatic changes during the Phanerozoic. Around the Permo-Triassic transition, an enormous shift in stable carbon isotope composition of the seawater took place between 1 and 2 million years (Gruszczynski and Malkowski, 1987), which can only be explained by rapid oxidation of huge amounts of organic matter. Calculations show that the amounts of the oxidated organic matter must have been two orders of magnitude greater than the total living biomass

today. During the process, a corresponding amount of oxygen must have been taken away from the atmosphere, thus dramatically decreasing the oxygen concentration in the air. This was probably one of the environmental events that caused the Permo-Triassic mass extinction.

In the paleontological perspective, there can be no doubt that events of this kind had a tremendous impact on the historical pattern of biological evolution. To my mind, the emphasis on this aspect of the causal plexus of evolution—which evolutionary biologists often tend to gloss over—is one of the major successes of modern paleontology.

Polish Academy of Sciences

Emiliani, C., 1982, Extinctive evolution, *J. Theor. Biol.* **97**:13-33.

Gruszczynski, M. and Malkowski, K., 1987, Stable isotopic records of the Kapp Starostin Formation (Permian), Spitsbergen, *Pol. Polar Res.* **8**:201-215.

Hoffman, A., 1989, *Arguments on Evolution*, Oxford University Press, New York.

Hoffman, A. and Kitchell, J. A., 1984, Evolution in a pelagic planktic system: apaleobiologic test of models of multispecies evolution, *Paleobiology* **10**:9-33.

Kazmierczak, J., Ittekott, V., and Degens, E. T., 1985, Biocalcification through time: environmental challenge and cellular response, *Palaont. Z.* **59**:15-33.

Stenseth, N. C. and Maynard Smith, J., 1984, Coevolution in ecosystems: Red Queen evolution or stasis? *Evolution* **38**:870-880.

Vermeij, G. J., 1987, *Evolution and Escalation*, Princeton University Press, Princeton.

Wei, K.-Y. and Kennett, J. P., 1986, Taxonomic evolution of Neogene planktonic foraminifera and paleoceanographic relations, *Paleoceanography* **1**:67-84.

Williams, G. C., 1966, *Adaptation and Natural Selection*, Princeton University Press, Princeton.

Jeffrey S. Levinton

Evaluating the Data Base of Paleontology

The field of paleontology rests on the foundations of complete collections and descriptions of fossils, accurate environmental reconstruction, and accurate dating of fossil materials. Most paleontologists realize that weaknesses in these three areas have usually prevented the resolution of major disputes. The current controversy surrounding so-called mass extinctions is a perfect example. In the past, claims of large-scale extinctions were based on qualitative evidence alone, and the great boundaries of geological time were established at the geological horizons where major fossil groups disappeared. Now, there is a call for much more accurate and quantitative evaluations. Raup and Sepkoski (1984), for example, have presented evidence for a periodicity of extinctions, and this periodicity has been related to extraterrestrial events. Needless to say, many have challenged this claim, and the arguments have turned around mainly the following:

- The accuracy of the geological time scale.
- The statistical methods used to evaluate the data base.
- The efficacy of the taxonomic data base.

The general accuracy of the geological time scale is not in great dispute, but we have focused on some specific problems only since the debate began. The estimated time of some boundaries differs substantially between different authors, but this was never of particular importance before this debate. Differences of as much as 5 my are substantial when one is claiming a 26-my periodicity. I shall not comment on the statistical aspects of the dispute, except by quoting a television commentator who once recounted a claim of increased reading scores in Iowa. He said that there was a "statistically significant, that is to say, very small, increase." It is often difficult to judge among statistical techniques, but I believe Raup and Sepkoski have nevertheless been successful in defending the conclusion that there is some periodicity in the data (see Raup and Sepkoski, 1988; Stigler and Wagner, 1988).

The issue of taxonomic structure is most intriguing, since it exposes one of the great weaknesses of the paleontological taxonomic data base, so universally employed in studies of diversification and extinction. To understand the problem fully, one must refer back to the first studies of taxonomic overturn and evolution. In his *Principles of Geology*, Charles Lyell (1831-3) first employed the rate of replacement of fossil taxa to help establish a geological time scale (see Rudwick, 1972). He examined the rate at which fossil taxa disappeared as he sampled the geological column toward the Recent. By this approach he was able to detect a large missing portion of the geological record in Great Britain. Eighty years later, a number of paleontologists began to use range charts of fossil taxa to examine the rates of expansion and contraction. Preston Cloud (1948) used the data base of the 1940s to show that many unrelated groups tended to expand and contract together. This method has been refined over the years, and the same conclusion has been reached recently with a more complete data base and a more sophisticated battery of statistical tests (Raup and Boyajian, 1988).

Simpson's use of the approach exposed a major problem with interpreting geologic range charts of taxa. Simpson (1944) looked at taxonomic longevity and reckoned it to be an estimate of the rate of phyletic evolution. Since mammal taxa of a given rank had shorter geological ranges, they must have evolved more rapidly than mollusks. If taxa appear and disappear rapidly, then Simpson reckoned that character evolution must have also been rapid.

Some major criticisms can be leveled at the data base used by Raup and Sepkoski (1984, 1986). First, some proportion of the generic ranges used are invalid, since the taxa under consideration don't become extinct, but rather evolve into other genera. Thus a series of five geologically successive taxa, with ranges of 10 my each, may actually be only one continuous 50-my lineage that evolves phyletically. Boucot (1988) argues that much of the brachiopod fossil record involves such "pseudoextinction." If so, then the end of a taxon's range does not constitute an extinction, so much as a phyletic evolutionary event. If this is true, then Simpson was essentially correct. Taxonomic overturn is the equivalent of phyletic evolution. Simpson did not accept this entirely since he accepted the notion of cladogenesis, but at least phyletic evolution would contribute substantially to the determination of the geologic ranges of taxa. One must also consider the large number of monotypic taxa that are recorded from single occurrences. Surely, their true geologic range is underestimated (Patterson and Smith, 1987).

If this criticism is legitimate, then one must look at the Raup and Sepkoski extinction data quite differently. The periodic "disappearance" of taxa may just be the periodic evolution of characters that are used to define taxa. This somehow takes the luster away from those various cosmic and extravagant global catastrophes that pepper the covers of magazines, both technical and popular. It does not, however, obviate us from explaining why there is a periodicity in the first place.

The second taxonomic criticism stems from the construction of taxa in the first place. Patterson and Smith (1987) have argued that many of the taxa used by paleontologists are not monophyletic. They are not taxa that have derived from a single ancestor. It then seems nonsensical to plot the comings and goings of such artificial constructs. In the worst case, a taxon derived from a subterminal branchpoint in a large clade may be accorded a rank equal to that of the ancestral clade. If this is done, it is possible to have the entire ancestral clade become "extinct," even if the derived clade in fact is a survivor. Because many paleontological taxa are constructed from shared primitive characters (i.e., are paraphyletic), much extinction is merely the death of certain characters, as opposed to being the death of monophyletic groups (Smith, 1988).

Even if the taxa are monophyletic (i.e., derived from a single ancestral species), the question of rank becomes an issue. Is it legitimate to compare taxa of the same rank (e.g., geological ranges of superfamilies) among widely divergent groups (e.g., comparing mammals with mollusks)? Second, can one estimate diversity of taxa at one level by counting those at another level? Van Valen (1984) argued that the family level is equivalent to the adaptive zone of Simpson. By extension, families of widely differing groups should have a commonality of response. Alternatively, one might be able to calibrate the meaning of taxonomic level by a quantitative comparison among phyla and taxonomic levels (Van Valen, 1973). While some criteria might be imagined that could be used to choose which taxonomic level is comparable with another in two different phyla, this approach seems fraught with difficulties. If the rate of taxonomic overturn was only explained by the rate of character evolution, and if all characters in all groups were comparable, then one might imagine comparing, for example, families of mammals and mollusks. But how does one compare number of teeth on a bivalve hinge with the relative size of cranial elements?

The relationship of diversity to taxonomic level is also suspect. The number of marine-fossilizable taxonomic orders suggests a gradual increase over the

Phanerozoic to a plateau (Sepkoski, 1978). But a completely different picture obtains when families and genera are considered (Raup and Sepkoski, 1986). In bivalve mollusks, the respective rates of appearance of families and super-families correlate strongly through the Mesozoic, but then become decoupled in the Tertiary (Levinton, 1988, p. 390). This stems from the different responses at different taxonomic levels. Ordinal diversity, for example, seems to track the number of body plans, whereas generic diversity is more probably a measure of species diversity. Sepkoski (1984) argues that family and generic level taxa estimate species numbers.

This discussion suggests that the taxonomic data base must be better understood before we can argue just what "appearance" and "extinction" really mean. In all fairness to Raup and Sepkoski and to others who have investigated appearance-extinction patterns, some of these problems would only cloud non-random patterns (but see Stigler and Wagner, 1988). There is still, therefore, something important to explain.

Space does not permit me to discuss the issue of environmental reconstruction. It is clear that extinctions can by and large not be predicted (or, more properly, retrodicted) from lithologic evidence without the records of the organisms themselves. The periodic extinction theory, for example, requires some form of major extraterrestrial—or as yet unknown terrestrial—force to drive the extinctions. But some of the extinctions are truly catastrophic, whereas others were unknown until Raup and Sepkoski identified them through statistical analysis (again, the statistics are used to spot a very small change). While his generalization may be too broad, Stanley (1984) has made a more complete case from which one might use geological and paleontological evidence to predict extinctions from drops in temperature. In any event, the

lack of precision of environmental reconstruction makes it difficult to determine the extremity of the milieu that organisms faced at any given time. Even the famous end-Cretaceous event cannot be defined very well in terms of temperature change, water turbidity, and atmospheric clarity. This leaves us with a dangerous circularity: Extinctions and other organismal changes make us search for evidence of environmental change, and we tend to exaggerate those environmental changes associated with biotic extinctions.

Paleontology's Important Contributions to Evolutionary Biology

One often has to justify one's research and even one's field to granting agencies and to university administrations. But the crux of a field's importance is its central contributions to the larger scheme of knowledge and science. For a variety of reasons, paleontologists have been put on the defensive and have been asked to justify their field. Some of this can be explained by the gradual demise of soft-rock geology in American universities. Fossils were once the only way to date rocks, but now they constitute just one of a battery of techniques. Fossils, moreover, give only a qualitative estimate of age even though, ironically, that estimate may be of a finer scale than radiometric dating. Paleontologists also feel a sort of inferiority relative to their neontologist cousins, who work with living, breathing organisms that live and die in our lifetime, replete with DNA, salivary chromosomes, colors, and soft parts.

One controversy of recent years has demonstrated that both paleontology and neontology can be deficient. Only the Rip Van Winkles among us have failed to notice the punctuated equilibrium controversy, stimulated by Eldredge and Gould (1972). To address the controversy, it would be very useful to have a firm understanding of the patterns and rates of speciation. While some evidence can be marshalled to address the controversy, the time scale of speciation seems to be too great for neontological investigation and much too short for paleontological investigation (Levinton 1988).

I have argued (Levinton 1988) at some greater length that paleontology and neontology each has its own unique contributions to evolutionary biology, but I would like to summarize here a few conclusions derived from paleontological research that could not have been gleaned from any investigation on neontological materials.

1) Mass Extinctions. The history of life has not been one of smooth taxonomic overturn, as originally envisioned by Charles Lyell. Rather, major parts of the world biota have become extinct over time scales very short relative to the entire of Phanerozoic history. It seems unlikely that these mass extinctions were caused by localized failures of certain taxa to adapt to changing conditions. Rather, the environmental changes seemed to overwhelm approximately simultaneously the survival capacities of many independent taxa. This is not to say that mass extinction is random; taxa with certain ecological characteristics have survived preferentially.

2) Diversity of Early Taxa. While still controversial and difficult to document quantitatively, the earliest part of the Phanerozoic seems to be a time when many widely divergent body plans appeared, but only a fraction survived. The Echinodermata show a large diversity of body plans in the Cambrian, but these soon pare down to relatively few. The same can be said of shelled animals seemingly related to mollusks. Adolph Seilacher has suggested that the Vendian soft-bodied faunule is phylogenetically unique, and constitutes an early evolutionary radiation unrelated to the rest of the Invertebrata. While this can be debated, the Vendian forms certainly add to the early diversity. As much as

this claim seems to be obvious, it has been suggested uncritically by many and is about to enter the folklore of paleontology before critical testing. I urge the reader to examine Runnegar (1986) and Smith (1988) for excellent critical discussions of the data for mollusks and echinoderms, respectively.

3) Lack of Subsequent Evolution at Higher Levels. As Simpson (1944) and Valentine (1969) both concluded, the fossil record shows that evolution was rapidly divergent at first, at the phylum level, but later taxonomic divergence occurred only at lower levels. The Permian extinction may have eliminated the overwhelming majority of marine-fossilizable species, but no new phylum evolved into the subsequent void. The same can be said for the end-Cretaceous event.

It may be argued that the claim that "phyla appear first" is just an artifact of taxonomy, that more inclusive taxa appear earlier simply because that is how we construct taxa. I believe that this is erroneous. The basic body plans that differentiate the phyla do seem to have appeared early, and later evolution seems to consist only of elaborations of these early themes. Besides, the phyla were defined before the details of the fossil record were understood very well. Echinoderms were separated from mollusks long before anyone knew that both appear first in the earliest part of the Phanerozoic. I have proposed a theory of commitment (Levinton, 1988, Chapter 9) that predicts increasing fidelity to basic developmental patterns, owing to natural selection, developmental constraints, and genetic constraints.

4) Documentation of Intermediate Forms. The fossil record has been an essential tool in documenting the means by which evolutionary transitions occurred between major different body plans. It is unimaginable how one could reconstruct the transitions to the mammalian organization without the early Mesozoic fossil record. The links among echinoderm groups similarly are opaque without recent discoveries of several fossil groups (see Smith, 1984). While it is true that credible genealogies can often be established without fossils, the richness of data on morphological transitions will be forever missing without paleontological data.

5) Gradual Evolution of Bauplans. In some cases, we can identify a complex of characters that contribute to the difference of organization of one major body plan versus another. One of the crucial questions is whether these changes came in concert, or whether they are the result of a long and complex building process. In the case of the mammals and angiosperms, the evidence seems to militate in favor of gradual buildup (Levinton, 1988, Chapter 7).

I wish I could add to the list some other contributions, such as an accurate reconstruction of environmental history, the pattern of speciation, or rates of phyletic evolution. We may make material progress in those areas some day, but we are not nearly there as yet. Nevertheless, these generalizations and unique strengths of paleontology cannot be ignored by evolutionary biology. Paleontology has become noticed in the last 20 years, thanks to the successful efforts of an enthusiastic group of investigators. I doubt that the field of evolutionary biology will ever again ignore the great strengths of fossils and their stewards.

SUNY at Stony Brook

Boucot, A. J., 1988, Periodic extinctions within the Cenozoic, *Nature* **331**: 395-396.

Cloud, P. E., 1948, Some problems and patterns of evolution exemplified by fossil invertebrates, *Evolution* **2**: 322-350.

Eldredge, N. and Gould, S. J., 1972, Punctuated equilibria: an alternative to phyletic gradualism, in: *Models in Paleobiology* (T. J. M. Schopf, ed.), pp. 82-115, Freeman, Cooper, San Francisco.

Levinton, J. S., 1988, *Genetics, Paleontology, and Macroevolution*, Cambridge University Press, New York.

Patterson, C. and Smith, A. B., 1987, Is the periodicity of extinction a taxonomic artefact? *Nature* **330**: 248-251.

Raup, D. M., and Boyajian, G. E., 1988, Patterns of generic extinction in the fossil record, *Paleobiology* **14**: 109-125.

Raup, D. M. and Sepkoski, J. J., Jr., 1984, Periodicity of extinctions in the geologic past, *Proc. Natl. Acad. Sci. USA* **81**: 801-805.

Raup, D. M. and Sepkoski, J. J., Jr., 1986, Periodic extinction of families and genera, *Science* **231**: 833-836.

Raup, D. M. and Sepkoski, J. J., Jr., 1988, Test for periodicity of extinction, *Science* **241**: 94-96.

Rudwick, M. J. S., 1972, *The Meaning of Fossils*, Macdonald, London.

Runnegar, B., 1986, Molecular palaeontology, *Palaeontology* **29**: 1-24.

Sepkoski, J. J., Jr., 1978, A kinetic model of Phanerozoic diversity. I. Analysis of marine orders, *Paleobiology* **4**: 223-251.

Sepkoski, J. J., Jr., 1984, A kinetic model of Phanerozoic taxonomic diversity. III. Post-Paleozoic families and mass extinctions, *Paleobiology* **10**: 246-267.

Simpson, G. G., 1944, *Tempo and Mode in Evolution*, Columbia University Press, New York.

Smith, A. B., 1984, Classification of the Echinodermata, *Palaeontology* **27**: 431-459.

Smith, A. B., 1988, Patterns of diversification and extinction in early Paleozoic echinoderms, *Palaeontology* **31**: 799-828.

Stanley, S. M., 1984, Temperature and biotic crises in the marine realm, *Geology* **12**: 205-208.

Stigler, S. M. and Wagner, M. J., 1988, Test for periodicity of extinction, *Science* **241**: 96-99.

Valentine, J. W., 1969, Patterns of taxonomic and ecological structure of the shelf benthos during Phanerozoic time, *Palaeontology* **12**: 684-709.

Van Valen, L., 1973, Are categories of different phyla comparable? *Taxon* **22**: 333-373.

Van Valen, L., 1984, A resetting of Phanerozoic community evolution, *Nature* **307**: 50-52.

Molecular Biology and Evolutionary Theory: The Giant Panda's Closest Relatives

Stephen J. O'Brien
National Cancer Institute

A primary goal of evolutionary biology is the correct reconstruction of phylogenetic history that would establish ancestral relationships between living and extinct species. This exercise can be conceptually divided into three components: the derivation of an evolutionary "tree" that relates divergence nodes for ancient splits between evolutionary lineages; the calibration of the tree with elapsed time for each of the divergence nodes; and the interpretation of existing form and function of species in the context of evolutionary divergence and perhaps adaptation to a particular niche. Evolution and the sister discipline of taxonomy have remained largely in the purview of morphologists, ethologists, and physiologists since formal descriptive biology began. In 1962 E. Zuckerkandl and Linus Pauling introduced a new approach, one that studies the evolving genes and their protein products (1). Since then the field of "molecular evolution" has made a number of insightful advances, but has also raised some fascinating questions about the tempo and mode of molecular and morphological evolution.

The application of molecular data to the questions of evolutionary divergence is made possible by the emergence and application of the molecular clock hypothesis, a simple yet very powerful concept. The hypothesis is based on the premise that the genetic material (DNA) of reproductively isolated species diverges continuously over time because of random mutations in chromosomal DNA that are passed on to subsequent generations. These mutations often occur in the coding regions of DNA that determine the amino acid sequence of a protein. So mutational changes between two related species can be studied by examining either DNA or the protein products of a gene sequence.

As species evolve, these substitutions continue to accumulate and, with increased time, the extent of sequence divergence becomes greater. The mutational differences are mostly evolutionary "noise," but have the advantage of being proportional to the time elapsed since the existence of a common ancestor of two species. Further, for any individual molecular metric, the time of divergence can be calibrated by measuring the same metric between species whose time of divergence has been established geologically (for example, the time of separation of the Old and New World occurred approximately 25-35 million years ago). Thus, by measuring one or more molecular metrics between two taxa, a relative estimate of their evolutionary distance and their time of divergence can be estimated. The use of the molecular clock has been elegantly applied to primate radiations and other evolutionary metrics by V. Sarich, A. Wilson, C. Sibley, and their colleagues, and it now is an established method of evolutionary theory (2-6). The reader is referred to Wilson *et al.* (6) and Thorpe (7) for a technical discussion of the molecular clock hypothesis, and to Gribbin and Cherfas (8) for an excellent popular description of the contributions of molecular evolution to sorting out the evolutionary history of mankind.

Molecular data and the associated molecular clock hypothesis have not been applied to evolutionary questions without controversy. Critics of the methods argue that different DNA sequences evolve at very different rates in the same lineage and that homologous DNA sequences often evolve at different rates in different lineages (7). This leads to a perception of a clock that is sometimes uneven, misses a beat occasionally, and is not such a terrific timekeeper. It turns out that this flaw is not fatal because it is possible to check the rate of sequence evolution by a "relative rate test" (2, 6). Perhaps more important, the rate differential will affect limb lengths, but probably not the topology (position of the nodes) in an evolutionary tree. So although the molecular clock is not perfect, even its harshest critics agree that the amount of potentially valuable information present in the genetic material is enormous. For example, mammals contain about 3.2 billion evolving nucleotide base pairs in a linear array in their germ cells. Furthermore, critics might also agree that mutational accumulation is cumulative and proportionate to the time elapsed since two measured species shared a common ancestor.

A variety of molecular methods have been used for phylogenetic inference in the past 25 years (9-11). In parallel with the derivation of comparative molecular data, a number of mathematical algorithms have been developed that are useful for deriving topologies from genetic distance as well as from unweighted unit character data sets (12-17a). We reasoned that the multi-faceted molecular approach would be beneficial to a longstanding evolutionary puzzle: the phylogeny of the giant panda, the red panda, and the bears. First, the strategy would provide new data to a question that has been debated for a century. Second, it would allow us to compare the data sets derived from several molecular methods for the same group to each other and to similar data sets from a related mammalian group, anthropoid apes and man. Third, if a verifiable consensus relationship were derived, then knowledge of this would allow a retrospective evaluation of the molecular methods as well as the morphological characters that led to alternative interpretations in the past. The results of our analysis, which we will review here, were strikingly concordant in their predicted topologies (18-20). The only ambiguity the data could not resolve was the relationship among four recently evolved species of ursine bears. The results reveal several noticeable limitations (and strengths) about the application of these methods to phylogenetic inference.

The Background

The giant panda, *Ailuropoda melanoleuca*, was first described to the West by the French missionary-naturalist Père Armand David in 1869. David recognized the giant panda as a scientific novelty and he dispatched a description of this new species, which he termed *Ursus melanoleuca* (which means black-and-white bear), to his colleague Alphonse Milne-Edwards, son (and later successor) of the director of the Paris Museum of Natural History (21). The following year, after examining skins and skeletal material David sent, Milne-Edwards decided that several osteological and dental characteristics were not typically ursid (bearlike) but more closely resembled the giant panda's smaller Chinese cousin, the lesser or red panda, *Ailurus fulgens*. Since these and other characters had placed the red panda in the raccoon family, Procyonidae, Milne-Edwards concluded that the giant panda was really a giant procyonid that had developed certain bearlike traits by evolutionary convergence (22). This scientific exchange marked the beginning of a century-old debate regarding the correct phylogenetic positions of both the giant and red pandas (Table 1).

Although the giant panda certainly looks like a bear, it has some unique characteristics and habits that are unusual for bears. First, the giant panda, like the red panda, is largely herbivorous, subsisting on a diet of bamboo shoots, stems, and leaves. Their bamboo diet has led to some specialized or derived morphological adaptations, some of which are apparent in the panda's Miocene (≥ 10 million years old) progenitors. The giant panda's teeth are large with low flat cusps; its skull and jaw are massive with enlarged jaw muscles for extra grinding power. The giant panda has relatively massive forequarters, which account for its ambling gait. The animal has a sixth digit on the forepaw, resulting from an evolutionary extension of the radial sesamoid wrist bone to an awkward but functional opposable thumb. The combination of these characters leads one to the conclusion that the giant panda is specialized for sitting on its hindquarters for long periods of time eating bamboo.

The giant panda has other features that are atypical for bears, but are not related to its diet. The male genitalia are tiny and posteriorly directed in a manner similar to the procyonids. The panda does not really behave like a bear either. Certain alpine bear species exhibit a type of annual hibernation, whereas the panda does not. This may also be related to diet because pandas cannot store enough energy from bamboo, a relatively inefficient energy source. Ethologists have used vocalizations to demonstrate phylogenetic relationships; here again, the panda and bears differ. Bears roar or growl, while the giant panda "bleats," a rather unbearlike

Table 1. This table presents a summary of the conclusions of the taxonomic and systematic treatises relating to the giant panda published since 1869. Of 42 citations, 18 supported placement of the giant panda in Ursidae, 13 in Procyonidae (raccoon family), and 11 in *Ailuropodidae* or *Ailurinae* (separate family). Specific references can be found in (26, 29, 34, 56). Edwin Colbert interpreted the controversy in 1938 (57) as follows: "So the question has stood for many years, with the bear proponents and the raccoon adherents and the middle-of-the-road group advancing their several arguments with the clearest of logic, while in the mean time the giant panda lives serenely in the mountains of Szechuan with never a thought about the zoological controversies he is causing by just being himself."

Taxonomic Assignments of the Pandas

Date	Giant Panda	Red Panda	Basis	Author
1869	Ursidae	———	Morphology	Pere Armand David
1870, 1874	Procyonidae	Procyonidae	Osteological characters and dentition similar to lesser panda	H. Milne-Edwards
1870, 1875	Ursidae	———	Intracranial cast; skeletal morphology	P. Gervais
1885	Procyonidae	Procyonidae	Skull architecture, dental morphology	St.-G. Mivart
1891	Ursidae	Procyonidae	Review of mammals' similarity to fossil ursid, Hyaenarctos	W. H. Flower
1895	Ursidae	Procyonidae	Skeletal morphology similar to fossil ursid Hyaenarctos	H. Winge
1901	Procyonidae	Procyonidae	Skeletal and dental morphology	E. R. Lankester
1901	Procyonidae	Procyonidae	Skull and limb morphology	R. Lydekker
1902	Ursidae	Procyonidae	Review of mammals	F. E. Beddard
1904	Ursidae	Procyonidae	Similarity to fossil ursid Hyaenarctos	M. Webber

Date	Giant Panda	Lesser Panda	Basis	Author
1913	Ursidae	———	Dental and osteological morphology	K. S. Bardenfleht
1921, 1928	Ailuropodidae	Ailuridae	Review of procyonid taxonomy	R. I. Pocock
1936	Procyonidae	Procyonidae	Skull and dental morphology	W. K. Gregory
1936	Procyonidae	Procyonidae	Visceral anatomy	H. C. Raven
1943	Ursidae	Ursidae	Morphology of auditory region and ossicles	W. Segall
1945	Procyonidae	Procyonidae	Review of mammals	G. G. Simpson
1946	Ursidae	———	Brain topology	F. A. Mettler and L. J. Gross

1951	Procyonidae	Procyonidae	Review of mammals	J. R. Ellerman and T. C. S. Morrison-Scott
1955	Procyonidae	———	Review of vertebrates	E. Colbert
1956	Ursidae	———	Precipitin test, serum proteins	C. A. Leone and A.L. Wiens
1964	Procyonidae	———	Review of mammals	E. P. Walker
1964	Ursidae	Procyonidae	Comparative anatomy 50 different systems	D. D. Davis
1966	Procyonidae	Procyonidae	Ethological characters	D. Morris
1964, 1966	Procyonidae	Procyonidae	Karyology, cytology	R. E. Newnham and W. M. Davidson
1971	Ailuropodidae	———	Anatomy	N. Kretozoi
1973	Ursidae	Ursidae	Immunological distance	V. Sarich
1973	Procyonidae	Procyonidae	Review of Carnivores	R. F. Ewer
1974	Ailuropodidae	———	Morphology, dentition, ethology	C. Chu
1974	Ailuropodidae	———	Fossil evidence, cranial and dental morphology	T. K. Wang
1978	Ursidae	———	Review	D. Starck
1979	Ailuropodidae	Ailuridae	Review of paleontological, morphological, serological, karyological and ethological characters of giant panda	V. E. Thenius
1980	Ailuropodidae	Procyonidae	Banded karyology	D. Wurster-Hill and M. Bush
1980	Ursidae	———	Dentition serology	Q. B. Hendey
1981	Ursidae	———	Serology	W. Pan, L. Chen, and N. Xiao
1981	Ailuropodidae	Ailuridae	Review of mammals	J. F. Eisenberg and H. Setzer
1983	Ursidae	Procyonidae	Review of mammals	R. M. Nowak and J. L. Paradiso
1984	Procyonidae	Procyonidae	Review of mammals	B. Bertram
1985	Ailuridae	Ailuridae	Behavior, reproduction	G. Schaller
1985	Ursidae	Procyonidae	Ridges on the hard palate	M. Eisentraut
1985	Ursidae	———	Globin sequence	G. Braunitzer et al.
1986	Ailuropodidae	Ailuridae	Globin sequence	D. A. Tagle et al.
1986	Ailuropodidae	———	Comparative anatomy	Consortium Beijing Zoo, Beijing Agricultural University, Beijing Natural History Museum

vocalization that is more reminiscent of sheep or goats.

The history of phylogenetic and taxonomic assignments of the giant and red pandas has been less than reassuring. Over the last century, there have been over 40 different systematic treatises directed toward the two pandas, some with new information, but many that reinterpreted previous data. With almost equal frequency, it has been concluded that the giant panda is: a specialized bear, Ursidae; a specialized member of Procyonidae; neither, but constitutes a separate Carnivore family, Ailuropodidae, comprised of only the giant pandas, or shared with the red panda (see Table 1).

The systematic arguments were multifaceted, the data were apparently contradictory, and the debates were often aligned along national or cultural camps. In the same year that Milne-Edwards opted for procyonids, P. Gervais examined the brain morphology and joined the bear camp (23). In 1885 St. George Mivart reviewed the classification of arctoid (bear- and doglike) carnivores and placed the giant panda in Procyonidae because he found its similarities to the red panda inescapable (24). Mivart's conclusions were reaffirmed by an impressive collection of British and American naturalists over the next century. The prolific British taxonomist, R. I. Pocock, was the first to suggest that the giant panda deserved separate ranking and thereby raised the panda to its own family status, Ailuropodidae (25).

In 1964 D. Dwight Davis, then curator of mammals at Chicago's Field Museum of Natural History, published an extraordinary monograph based upon the gross anatomy of Su Li, a captive male panda who died in 1938 at the Brookfield Zoo (26). Davis's opus, which Stephen Jay Gould recently characterized as "our century's greatest work of comparative anatomy" (27), neatly described some 50 organ systems. His taxonomic conclusions were resounding: "the giant panda is a bear and . . . very few genetic mechanisms—perhaps no more than half a dozen—were involved in the primary adaptive shift from *Ursus* to *Ailuropoda*" (26). Davis's conclusions were quickly accepted by such authorities as Gould and Ernst Mayr, who considered the matter finally settled (27, 27a). But others did not agree, and with good reason. Davis's analysis, although lengthy, was largely anatomical but did not follow standard principles of systematics. His critics argued that many of the traits he marshalled were irrelevant for phylogenetic concerns, since traits shared by bears and pandas were found in many other carnivores as well (28-30). By his own admission, Davis simply concluded a priori that the giant panda was a bear and assumed this throughout his text, making no attempt to present comparative data because ". . . this became so difficult, I gave up." Gould recently remarked that "Davis's personal tragedy must reside in his failure to persuade his colleagues" (27).

R. F. Ewer, in her excellent monograph on Carnivora (30), agreed with a comprehensive review of the panda's ancestry published in 1966 by Ramona and Desmond Morris, mammal curators at the London Zoo (29). Based on both behavior and morphology, the Morrises concluded that the giant panda was a procyonid. More recently, ethologists John Eisenberg

(30a) and George Schaller and colleagues (30b) independently argued for separate family status, as did several paleontologists (C. Chu, T. Wang, W. C. Pei, E. Thenius) who examined the meager fossil record of ursids and procyonids (31-34). The first banded chromosomal study lent support to that view, since pandas have 42 largely metacentric (biarmed) chromosomes while most bears have 74 largely acrocentric (single-armed) chromosomes, a dramatic difference (35).

Finally, in 1986 a text on the anatomy of the giant panda that was just as daunting as Davis's was published in China (36). A consortium of zoologists from the Beijing Zoological Gardens and the associated universities presented 600 pages of anatomical data based on 27 specimens. They concluded that "the giant panda is different from the bear . . . we are in favor of assigning an independent family for the giant panda." Suffice it to say that 120 years after its first description to Western naturalists, the panda's origins remain controversial.

In retrospect, it seems like this controversy was hardly a trivial issue, but one of meaningful consequences to a wider understanding of evolutionary processes. How much morphological or molecular change has occurred in this lineage? What were the driving forces of speciation, of morphological divergence? How widely divergent were the panda's or bear's ancestors in the distant past? The giant panda may not care whether it is a bear, a raccoon, or a solitary member of an ancient family (see legend to Table 1), but our ability to perceive and interpret biological changes that occurred in the past is diminished without this kind of understanding.

The dilemma of the panda's ancestry also provided an excellent opportunity to examine how effective different types of biological characters are in providing information about how organisms are related. The reason is that the methods and measures of phylogenetic inference come in two packages. The first (called homologous traits) are similarities between taxa that are related by descent; that is, characters that were inherited from a recent common ancestor. Evolutionary relatedness is, in large part, measured by counting up the number of shared homologous characteristics that occur in different species. The second kind of characters (termed analogous traits) owe their similarity to evolutionary convergence. These traits are morphological or behavioral similarities that may be a selected response to a common environmental condition (e.g., prey base, predators, pathogens). An example of convergence is the development of flying ability in birds, bats, and insects. Because analogous (convergent) characters have no basis in common descent, they actually confound the deductive process and mislead the naturalist. The confusion between homology and analogy represents the crux of the paradox that fueled the earlier disputes.

A common difficulty in identifying homologous morphological and anatomical traits is that their genetic basis is rarely well understood. For example, a small change in a morphological trait may involve large amounts of reorganization at the gene level, while other more complex traits (like the development of the panda's thumb) may actually involve a rather small

Table 2
Species and Sources

Code	Species	Common Name	Source	Sex	Director	Veterinarian
AME	*Ailuropoda melanoleuca*	Giant panda	National Zoo Wash., DC	♂	T. Reed	M. Bush
AFU	*Ailurus fulgens*	Red panda	National Zoo Wash., DC	♂	T. Reed	M. Bush
TOR	*Tremarctos ornatus*	Spectacled bear	Baltimore Zoo Baltimore, MD	♀	B. Rutledge	M. Cranfield
UAR	*Ursus arctos*	Brown bear	Shrine Circus Omaha, NE	♂	————	L. Philips
UAM	*Ursus americanus*	Black bear	Minnesota Zoo Minneapolis, MN	♀	K. Roberts	F. Wright
UTH	*Ursus (Selenarctos) thibetanus*	Asiatic black bear	San Antonio Zoo San Antonio, TX	♀	L. DeSabio	K. Fletcher
UMAL	*Ursus (Helarctos) malayanus*	Malayan sun bear	Henry Doorly Zoo Omaha, NE	♂	L. Simmons	L. Philips
UMAR	*Ursus (Thalarctos) maritinus*	Polar bear	National Zoo Wash., DC	♂	M. Robinson	M. Bush
UUR	*Ursus (Melursus) ursinus*	Sloth bear	National Zoo Wash., DC	♀	M. Robinson	M. Bush
PLO	*Procyon lotor*	Raccoon	CRC, Front Royal National Zoo	♂	M. Robinson	M. Bush

amount of genetic change. Dwight Davis had suggested exactly this, but his conclusions were speculative since the accurate weighing of characters without a demonstrated genetic basis is virtually impossible.

The Molecular Methods

In order to study the DNA and encoded proteins of the pandas and their relatives, we collected blood samples and small skin biopsies from all the species listed in Table 2. Blood samples were separated by centrifugation into erythrocytes, leukocytes, and plasma. The skin biopsy was digested with trypsin plus collagenase and used to establish a primary tissue culture line (37). DNA and/or soluble proteins were extracted from each of the materials and employed in the methods listed in Table 3. Each method produced a measure of "evolutionary distance," a quantitative estimate of DNA sequence divergence between measured species. Matrices of these distance values were used to construct phenetic topologies using evolutionary algorithms presented in Table 4. In addition, the electrophoretic data (allozyme and 2-dimensional gel electrophoresis, 2DE) were also treated as unweighted unit-character data sets. In this treatment, each electrophoretic form (allele or fixed difference between species) is considered as a discrete character that was present or absent. The character matrix was analyzed using the Wagner method contained in the PAUP (phylogenetic analysis using parsimony) computer package of Dr. D. Swofford (17). This algorithm derives unrooted minimum-length phylogenetic trees based on the principle of parsimony. Roots of trees were identified as the midpoint between extreme taxa, in this case bears and raccoons.

The first molecular method we used was DNA hybridization of unique cellular DNA (Figure 1), a commonly used procedure for measurement of phylogenetic affinity (4, 5, 18, 38). Briefly, DNA from one species is labelled by growing skin fibroblast cells in a medium containing radioactive DNA precursors. DNA from a second related species is unlabelled or "cold." Both DNAs are extracted and sheared by sonication to pieces of about 400 nucleotides in length, and heated to "melt" the original double-stranded DNA hybrids to single-strand fragments. A mixture of the two melted DNAs is allowed to reanneal. The amount of hybrid DNA molecules is measured by collecting radioactive hybrid molecules on a filter or by chromatography. Two measures of sequence homology are obtained from this procedure: first, the percent hybridization between species A and species B; and second, the difference between the midpoints of the melting profile between heterologous DNA hybrids and that of homologous DNA. This latter measurement, called ΔT_m, is proportional to the amount of base-pair differences between the two DNA samples. Because all the single-copy cellular DNA is used (the repetitive DNA is removed before mixing), the procedure gives an estimate of the percent divergence of the over one billion base pairs of single-copy sequence in the mammalian genome.

The second molecular metric used was isozyme genetic distance (18,39,40). In this procedure, extracts of soluble enzymes from different

Table 3
Metric of Evolutionary Distance Employed

	Procedure	Basis	Data set
I.	DNA hybridization	Melting curve, ΔT_m	Distance matrix
II.	Genetic Distance (Nei) Isozymes	N = 50 isozymes	Distance matrix and cladistics
III.	Genetic Distance 2D gel fibroblast proteins	N = 261 proteins	Distance matrix and cladistics
IV.	Immunological Distance	Albumin, Transferrin	Distance matrix
V.	Karyology	G-trypsin banded High resolution 800 band stage	———

Table 4
Phylogenetic Algorithms

Algorithm	Computer Program	Reference
1. UPGMA	Biosys PHYLIP	(17a)
2. MATTOP	MATTOP	(15)
3. FITCH-MARGOLIASH	PHYLIP	(12,16)
4. DISTANCE WAGNER	PAUP	(13,17)
5. NEIGHBORLINESS	NEIGHBORLINESS	(14)

tissues (erythrocytes, leukocytes, fibroblast cultures) are separated by gel electrophoresis and stained histochemically (Figure 2). The mobility of homologous enzymes from the different species (Figure 3a) is compared and an estimate of the extent of mutational accumulation in the primary stucture of up to 50 proteins is determined. M. Nei and others developed very useful mathematical formulae for estimating the extent of allelic mutational substitution at a group of loci between populations (39,40). The genetic distance estimate, D, is defined as the average number of gene differences per locus between individuals in two test populations. Within the limits of certain assumptions relating to the electrophoretic resolution and relative rates of amino acid substitution, the genetic distance values increase proportionately with the time the compared populations have been reproductively isolated.

Our third method was to compute genetic distance from a different class of cellular proteins, those resolved by 2DE (20). Like the isozyme procedures, this method measures the extent of protein migration on electrophoretic gels (Figure 2), but it has the advantage of resolving over 300 radio-labelled fibroblast proteins on a single gel (Figure 3b).

The fourth molecular method involved data collected and published previously in a classic paper by Vincent Sarich (41). Sarich, who pioneered the use of immunological distance as a method for phylogenetic resolution, tested the giant panda and its relatives in 1972 (2,3,41). The procedure he employed measures amino acid differences between homologous serum proteins (e.g., albumin) from two species based on displacement of immunological titration curves in a micro-complement fixation assay for antibody. Briefly, several rabbits were immunized with purified albumin from the giant panda. The sera were then pooled and titered against giant panda albumin. In an evolutionary distance determination, albumin from another species (e.g., a raccoon) is first preincubated with titered antiserum against the giant panda albumin. Then, the adsorbed serum is retested against giant panda albumin. The remaining antibodies bind to the giant panda albumin in an amount quantitatively related to the amount of immunological difference. The displacement of immunological titration curves is proportional to the sequence divergence between the albumin genes of the two species. When several antisera are prepared, a matrix of immunological distances can be used as above for estimating evolutionary distances. Sarich generated such immunological distance matrices with two proteins, albumin and transferrin (41).

The Solution

The results of each of our different evolutionary measurements have been published elsewhere (18-20) and will be summarized briefly here. The evolutionary distances derived from each method were by and large concordant in the topology that was produced. Different clustering or phylogenetic algorithms for the same data sets in general produced the same tree. Uncertainties within certain data sets were apparent regardless of the algorithm

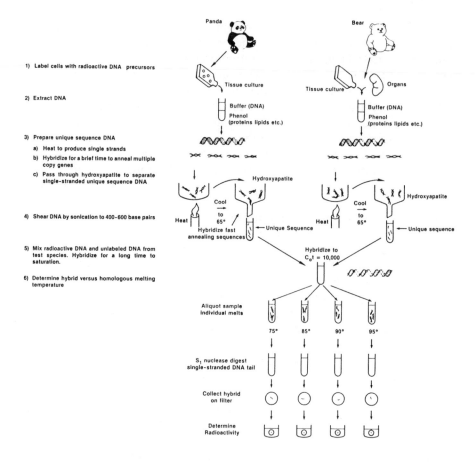

1) Label cells with radioactive DNA precursors

2) Extract DNA

3) Prepare unique sequence DNA

   a) Heat to produce single strands

   b) Hybridize for a brief time to anneal multiple copy genes

   c) Pass through hydroxyapatite to separate single-stranded unique sequence DNA

4) Shear DNA by sonication to 400–600 base pairs

5) Mix radioactive DNA and unlabeled DNA from test species. Hybridize for a long time to saturation.

6) Determine hybrid versus homologous melting temperature

Figure 1. DNA hybridization procedure for estimating thermal stability from a gradual melt of heterologous DNA hybrids. The validity of a data matrix derived by molecular methods like DNA hybridization can be tested in three ways (18). The first test is reciprocity; that is, Δ Tm values using species A as the labelled DNA and species B as the cold DNA should have a low variance from the values obtained when species B is labelled and species A is cold. The second test is the relative rate test. This test demands that a species which is outside the group being studied should have an equal molecular distance from all the species in the studied group. For example, we used a dog as an "out-group" and this showed an equivalent distance from bears, procyonids, and pandas. If that had not occurred, it would indicate that the "molecular clock" was not running on time in that lineage. The third test is based on the prediction that a data set which is an accurate reflection of evolutionary distance between taxa should obey the triangle inequality. That is, for distances between any three taxa in the matrix, one distance cannot exceed the sum of the remaining two. If this condition is met the data are said to be "metric." Unfortunately, some distance estimates (e.g., Nei genetic distance) are non-metric for theoretical reasons and cannot be tested. Compliance of a molecular distance data set to these three tests is taken as evidence that the matrix will produce the correct evolutionary relationship.

100

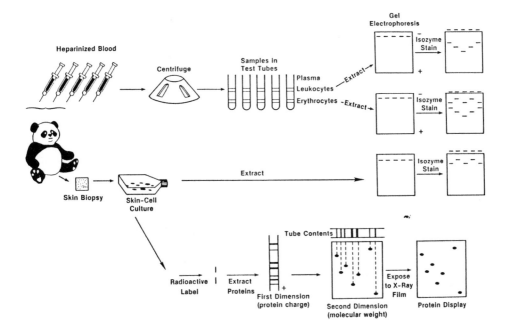

Figure 2. Two electrophoretic methods for measuring genetic distance are illustrated. In one method, fresh blood is treated with heparin to prevent clotting so that different components (white cells, red cells, and plasma) can be separated by centrifugation. In addition, a skin biopsy from the animal is digested with trypsin and collagenase and used to establish a tissue culture cell line. Soluble enzymes from extracts of blood components and the cell lines are subjected to electrophoresis; that is, they are exposed to an electric field that causes them to migrate through a gel matrix, after which they are visualized by specific stains for enzyme reaction products. Enzymes that have accumulated a single amino acid difference migrate to a different position from those that have not. By comparing mobility at some 50 homologous isozyme systems between two species, an estimate of the frequency of identical gene products is achieved. The genetic distance is the negative logarithm of this value and increases proportionally with evolutionary time. Three tissues (red cells, white cells, and tissue culture cells) are used to resolve tissue-specific enzymes and to provide duplications of equivocal results in one tissue. In the second method, radioactively labelled proteins from skin cell cultures are exposed to electric fields that separate them in two dimensions. Proteins are separated first on the basis of electric charge and then on the basis of molecular weight. Finally, the gels are exposed to X-ray film which reveals hundreds of proteins whose position can be compared between different species. Genetic distance based on shifts of the presumed homologous protein gene products are computed exactly like the isozyme genetic distance and calibrated with evolutionary time.

and were often resolved using other methods. The one area that was not resolved was the relationship among the ursine bears (genus *Ursus*), which diverge rather closely in time from a common ancestor 6 to 10 million years before the present (mybp). A consensus tree based upon the combination of results from each of the four molecular methods is presented in Figure 4.

Once we found that the four different molecular topologies were in agreement, our next task was to place a time scale on the evolutionary tree. This turned out to be a difficult problem. Although the carnivore fossil record is unusually good and has been studied intensively, even the commonly accepted dates for divergence of these families can vary by as much as 25 to 50 percent (30,42,43,43a). For example, geological dates for the time of procyonid-ursid divergence range from 30 to 50 million years ago. A strategy we have used for setting our molecular clock was to take advantage of the demonstration that the primate and carnivore clocks appear to run at the same rate (44-46). Because the primate radiations have been studied rather extensively, we reasoned that the species pairs that had the same distance for a particular metric within the two orders shared a common ancestor at approximately the same time in their evolutionary history. Further, that time in the carnivores might be precisely identified by the primate time scale that has been calibrated by numerous authors from both paleontological and molecular perspectives (2-8).

We performed the same three molecular analyses on the hominoid primates and used Sarich and Wilson's data on the same group using immunological distance (2). Our primate results confirmed precisely what others have reported (2-5), so we could now compare primate and carnivore molecular phylogenies (presented in Figure 4). For calibration of the primate phylogenies we used the time scale based on paleontologist Peter Andrews's estimated date of human-orangutan divergence at approximately 13 million years ago (47). The derived primate topology places the time of human-Old World monkey divergence at 25 to 35 million years ago, which agrees with generally accepted paleontological dates of these events. Because the four seemingly independent molecular methods were highly consistent within the carnivore radiations, we integrated the results and drew a consensus molecular phylogeny that included the definitive aspects of each phylogeny (Figure 4).

Briefly, between 30 and 50 million years ago, the progenitors of the modern ursids and procyonids split into two lineages. Within 10 million years of that event, the procyonid group split into Old World procyonids (represented today by the genus *Ailurus,* the red panda) and the New World procyonids (raccoons, coatis, olingos, and kinkajous). The red panda and giant panda clearly do not share a common ancestor after the ursid-procyonid split, emphasizing that the morphological similarities of the pandas are probably the result of convergence or parallel retention of ancestral characters. At about the same time as the gibbons split from great apes (18 to 25 million years ago), the ancestors of the giant panda diverged from the ursid line. This event was nearly 20 million years after the initial divergence of the ursid and procyonid lines. At the time that the orangutan

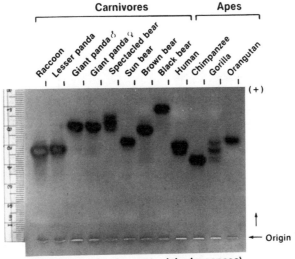

PGD (6-phosphogluconate dehydrogenase)

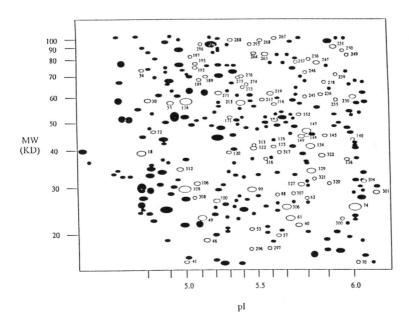

Figure 3. (a) Electrophoretic migration is shown for one isozyme, 6-phosphogluconate dehydrogenase, using extracts of tissue culture cells. The raccoon and red panda enzymes have
identical mobilities, while the giant panda and the brown bear share the same mobility which
is distinct from the raccoon. The spectacled bear is a heterozygote; i.e., there are two genetic
forms—one is the same as the giant panda and the other species. Both the sun bear and the
black bear have unique electrophoretic forms not seen in the other species. The hominoid
ape tissues were run in the same gels. (b) Diagrammatic representation of 2DE gel patterns
of bears, pandas, and procyonids. Open ellipses vary between species; closed ellipses represent
invariant proteins (20).

103

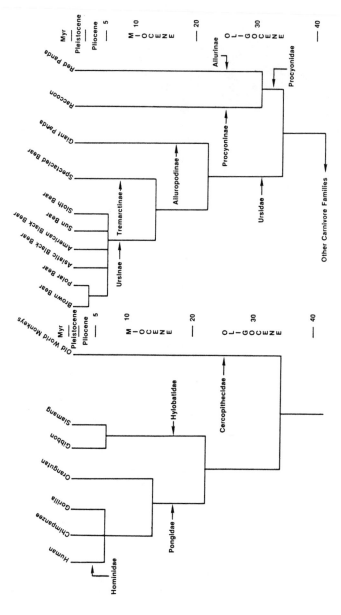

Figure 4. A consensus molecular phylogeny of the bear family, the giant and red pandas, and raccoon. This tree is a subjective compromise of the results of four different molecular methods: 1) DNA hybridization, 2) isozyme genetic distance, 3) 2D gel electrophoresis of fibroblast proteins, and 4) immunological distance. Each of these methods gave a similar evolutionary tree and they differed largely by length of the limbs. The primate tree was built using the same four methods: first, to demonstrate that our laboratory's molecular data gave us the same answers that other molecular laboratories were producing, and second to provide an index of calibration dates. Because the molecules we have studied seem to evolve at rates which were similar in primates and carnivores (44-46), we simply aligned the molecular scale of the carnivores with the primates and used the time scale of primate evolution to date the carnivore divergence nodes.

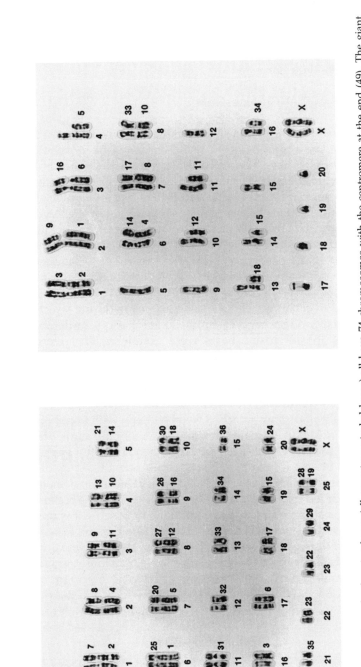

Figure 5. The recently evolved ursine bears (all except spectacled bears) all have 74 chromosomes with the centromere at the end (49). The giant panda has 42 chromosomes, each with a centromere in the middle (18). (a) When chromosomes of the brown bear (*Ursus arctos*) and giant panda (*Ailuropoda melanoleuca*) were compared, it became clear that nearly every large chromosome of the brown bear could be aligned with a giant panda chromosome arm. The left chromosome of each pair is the giant panda chromosome. The numbers below each pair refer to giant panda chromosomes. The numbers on the right of each pair identify brown bear chromosomes. Where no clear homolog exists with a bear chromosome, the panda chromosome is shown by itself. The giant panda seems to have developed its chromosome pattern by the relatively simple process of chromosome fusion at the centromere during its evolution off the main bear lineage. (b) Comparison of G-banded chromosomes of spectacled bear, *Tremarctos ornatus* and *Ursus arctos*. The left chromosome of each pair is the spectacled bear chromosome. The numbers below each pair refer to spectacled bear chromosomes. The numbers to the right of each pair identify brown bear chromosomes.

diverged from the African ape-human line (13 to 16 million years ago), the earliest true bear, *Tremarctos* (spectacled bear), split from the ursid line. The genus *Ursus* began its radiation into the ursine bears (brown, black, and sun bears) 6 to 10 million years ago.

The Chromosomes

Our final analysis of the giant panda's phylogeny concerned what we originally thought would be a conflicting character, chromosome morphology. The six ursine bears all have 74 single-armed (acrocentric) chromosomes with the centromere at one end, while the giant panda has 42 mostly biarmed (metacentric) chromosomes. Earlier cytologists had thought that this was an irresolvable difference that argued against any recent heritage of the bear and giant panda (35,48). Because we were suspicious of this conclusion, we took another look. One of us (W. G. N.) had recently developed some special techniques for producing high resolution G-banding patterns in carnivore chromosomes by transforming all primary cultures with a retrovirus and subsequently synchronizing the cells (37). Just before metaphase, there is a period of maximum chromosome extension during which cells could be harvested to produce banded chromosomes of exquisite detail.

When karyotypes of the six ursine bears were examined, they were virtually identical (49). The surprise came when we compared bear chromosomes to those from the giant panda. It turned out that most of the giant panda's chromosome arms had an identical banding pattern to individual ursine bear chromosomes (Figure 5a) (18). Giant panda chromosomes were actually pairs of bear chromosomes attached head to head with common centromeres. So what looked like a major chromosome reorganization was actually quite a simple fusion of ancestral bear chromosomes in the evolutionary line leading to the giant panda.

A similar but independent chromosome fusion event also must have occurred in the line that led to the spectacled bear (Figure 5b). The reason is that the spectacled bear karyotype is also comprised of biarmed fusions of acrocentric chromosomes found in the bears, but none of the fusion combinations seen in the spectacled bear are the same as the combinations found in the giant panda (49). Similar chromosomal reorganizations, termed Robertsonian translocations, often have been suggested to be important in establishment of reproductive isolation during speciation events. It is tempting to hypothesize that the extensive chromosomal fusion may have played an adaptive role in the evolution of both the panda and spectacled bear lineages.

In order to fit the chromosome pattern of the red panda into this picture, one should first understand that much of the carnivore order is characterized by a rather conservative karyotype composed of metacentric chromosomes. For example, each of the 37 species of cats has either 18 or 19 pairs of mostly biarmed chromosomes, and 15 of these chromosomes are invariant throughout the Felidae family (50,51). Furthermore, most of these conserved Felidae chromosomes are also present in several other carnivore families (procyonids, mustelids, hyaenids) either intact or only slightly variant (52,53). For this reason, it is useful to consider that the continued transmission of a conservative "carnivore karyotype" is preserved more or less intact in several families. Canids and ursids are exceptions to the rule because they both experienced a dramatic chromosome fissioning early in their evolution. We can still align the dog and bear chromosome arms to certain segments of the primitive carnivore karyotype, but none of the ancestral carnivore fusion combinations is seen in modern dogs or bears (49,54). In these families the chromosome arms were shuffled and in many cases (as in the giant panda) reattached in different ways.

The banded chromosomes of the red panda are very similar to the primitive carnivore karyotype that is also seen in the procyonids (50). Fourteen chromosomes of the red panda are strikingly homologous to chromosomes found in several procyonids, and ten of these are identical to conserved carnivore chromosomes. Only two of the red panda's banded chromosomes had recognizable counterparts in the bears or giant panda. The simplest interpretation of these karyological results seems to affirm the molecular topologies; that is, the red panda and the procyonids possess a shared primitive carnivore karyotype, suggesting they diverged at an evolutionary mode apart from the bear-giant panda divergence. The ursid line apparently evolved in conjunction with a global chromosomal fissioning away from the carnivore karyotype, resulting in a shared derived karyotype organization in bears and giant panda. This chromosomal fissioning persisted in the ursine bears but was reorganized by centromere fusion twice: once in the giant panda line and again after the split leading to the spectacled bear.

Some Implications

The molecular data had told us that the giant panda's ancestors split off the ursid lineage 10 to 20 million years after the ursid-procyonid divergence, while the red panda split from the New World procyonids very near this time point. But how can we reconcile this conclusion with the many morphological and behavioral characteristics offered by several authors as evidence of an evolutionary distinction between bears and the giant panda? In retrospect, it is important to emphasize first that Dwight Davis not only stated but meticulously detailed the fact that the vast majority of morphological characters actually affirmed the affinity of bears and the giant panda (26). Second, many of the characters that giant pandas share with the red panda are related to the observation that both species are largely herbivorous (29,30). Apparently, most of these traits (e.g., grinding teeth, massive skull, extra thumb, behavioral similarities) are really analogous or convergent— the misleading kind for phylogenetic inference. Both species apparently acquired the derived traits in parallel as an adaptive response to their diet. Other traits shared in the two pandas could simply be homologous primitive carnivore characters retained in pandas but arbitrarily lost in bears and New World procyonids.

An important consideration in solving phylogenetic puzzles is the information derived from the fossil record. There are about 50 described fossils of the giant panda dispersed throughout China and Southeast Asia during the Pleistocene geological period (31-34). Unfortunately, they are largely indistinguishable from modern pandas and tell us little except that the panda's feeding adaptations were evident by one or two million years ago. The only earlier fossil that may be placed on the giant panda lineage with some certainty is a piece of mandible (*Agriarctos kretozo*) from a late Miocene site in Europe (34,54). V. E. Thenius, who discovered the fossil, pointed to its incipient molarization of premolars as a precursor to the giant panda robust dentition. Thenius had suggested that the giant panda split from the ursid line 15 to 20 million years ago and that *Agriarctos* was on the panda line. Before that split, an early Miocene (about 20 to 25 million years ago) fossil genus *Ursavus* is thought to be the earliest ursid specimen. The placement of these fossils fits nicely with the molecular phylogeny we have derived.

The development of a consensus phylogeny of the giant and red pandas that is consistent from several biological perspectives now allowed us to make some taxonomic recommendations. The derived panda relationships indicated two possible options: place the giant and red panda each in different families separate from each other and from Ursidae and Procyonidae; or place the giant panda in Ursidae and the red panda in Procyonidae, preferably with subfamily status for both. The second option was chosen primarily because it acknowledges the relatively recent divergence of the giant panda from the ursid line and the definitive though somewhat older split of the red panda from the procyonid lineage. Molecular and fossil evidence had indicated that most carnivore families split from the main stock more than 40 million years ago (55a). Hence, the giant panda (which split 18 to 25 million years ago) is placed in Ailuropodinae, a subfamily of Ursidae, while the red panda is the single member of Ailurinae, a subfamily of Procyonidae (18).

A rather important outcome of the data here reviewed is the opportunity to compare directly the topology and rates of different molecular methods within the same group. We attempt this in Table 5 by presenting the approximate calibrated dates of five major divergence nodes as estimated from five molecular data distance matrices (18,20,41). These values were obtained by making three presumptions: first, molecular evolution in carnivores and primates proceeds at an equivalent rate (44-46); second, the divergence date of orangutan from the ancestors of humans occurred about 13 myr ago (47); and third, molecular evolution is proceeding in a fashion that is directly proportionate to elapsed time. The first presumption has been tested in several contexts and appears to be reasonably accurate. The human-orangutan divergence date is still under intense debate (for discussion, see Sibley and Alquist [5]); however, the usual estimated range is 10-18 mybp. The comparative data presented in Table 5 belie the *direct* proportionality of all the molecular estimates with elapsed time since each data set gives substantive departure from precise quantitative agreement.

Table 5

Estimated Date of Divergence Nodes in Ursid-Procyonid
Taxa by Four Molecular Methods of Evolutionary Distance

			Genetic Distance		
		DNA		*Allozyme**	
Divergence node	*AID*	*Hybridization*	*2DE*	*1985*	*1988*
Ursine bear radiation (Uam-Umar)	6.5	9.3	4.4	6.01	7.2
Spectacled bear-ursine	6.5	12.2	10.5	9.6	15
Giant panda-ursine	15	17.1	18.2	33.8	22
Lesser panda-raccoon	52	54.8	17.1	23.5	28
Procyonidae-ursidae	45	54.3	22.4	32.6	32.3

*Distances are expressed in myr before the present and are calibrated according to an estimated divergence of orangutan from other great apes of 13 mybp (see text). Allozyme results are independent data sets from (18, 19) this report. Data for DNA from (18); AID from (41).

For example, the dates of the ursine radiation node and the ursid-procyonid divergence node both differed by 100 percent between 2DE estimates and DNA hybridization estimate (Table 5). The divergence nodes in the middle of the topologies (closer to the calibration date of 13 myr) show better agreement between methods.

We interpret the lack of agreement in dating of divergence nodes despite excellent topological similarity to suggest that each method has a different relationship to elapsed time. For each method then, that relationship is not a simple direct proportionality between methods or with evolutionary time. For this reason, it seems important to employ several independent methods (molecular, morphological, and paleontological) to reconstruct the correct phylogenetic interpretation of this or any other group.

While this study was progressing, it was difficult not to be impressed with the power of molecular and cytogenetic data, especially when multiple methods are employed, in resolving evolutionary relationships. The importance of this is evident in resolving evolutionary convergence, in conservation applications, and in unravelling the evolutionary significance of biological adaptation and speciation. The derivation of the panda's ancestral tree was not the only insight these studies produced. In addition, we discovered an outline of the relative divergence times of several other ursid and procyonid species—e.g., the giant panda results from an ancient split and need not be a punctuated event as the polar bear speciation seems to be (20). We were able to compare various phenetic and phylogenetic algorithms for building trees and, equally important, to compare various molecular approaches to bear phylogeny—each approach with its own inherent biases and relationship with absolute time. By using the primate data matrices, we could compare the same molecular methods in that distantly related family. Finally, once a consistent molecular topology for any group is available, the interpretation of morphological form and function can be more readily achieved (55a).

Conclusion

The field of molecular evolution is over 25 years old. The discipline is comprised of two distinct components: the collection of molecular data that can be used for phylogenetic inference and the development of evolutionary algorithms for interpreting these data. Both areas have matured substantially, and as a result the use of molecular data is today considered a critical element of most evolutionary discussions. We have used a variety of molecular technologies (DNA hybridization, genetic distance using homologous proteins, immunological distance, mitochondrial DNA maps, and cytological/syntenic homology) to study genome evolution in mammals. These studies have permitted the development of consensus molecular phylogenies of several carnivore families including ursids, felids, and canids. In this article we illustrated the rationale and methods of molecular evolution as they have been applied to the evolution and systematics of ursids (bear family), the giant and red pandas, and the raccoon family of Carnivora. A general agreement of different molecular methods for the same group provides credence to both the derived evolutionary trees, as well as to the efficacy of the methods for evolutionary inference.

1. Zuckerkandl, E. and Pauling, L.: Molecular disease, evolution, and genetic heterogeneity. In Kasha, M. and Pullman, B. (Eds.): Horizons in Biochemistry. New York, Academic Press, 1962, pp. 189-225.

2. Sarich, V. and Wilson, A. C.: Immunological time scale for hominoid evolution. Science 158: 1200-1203, 1967.

3. Sarich, V. M. and Wilson, A. C.: Rates of albumin evolution in primates. Proc. Natl. Acad. Sci. USA 58: 142-148, 1967.

4. Sibley, C. G. and Ahlquist, J. E.: The phylogeny of the hominoid primates, as indicated by DNA-DNA hybridization. J. Mol. Evol. 20: 2-15, 1984.

5. Sibley, C. B. and Ahlquist, J. E.: DNA hybridization evidence of hominoid phylogeny: Results from an expanded data set. J. Mol. Evol. 26: 99-121, 1987.

6. Wilson, A. C., Carlson, S. S., and White, T. J.: Biochemical evolution. Annu. Rev. Biochem. 46: 573-639, 1977.

7. Thorpe, J. P.: The molecular clock hypothesis: Biochemical evolution, genetic differentiation, and systematics. Annu. Rev. Ecol. Syst. 13: 139-168, 1982.

8. Gribbin, J. and Cherfas, J.: The Monkey Puzzle. Reshaping the Evolutionary Tree. New York, Pantheon Books, 1982.

9. O'Brien, S. J., Seuanez, H. N., and Womack, J. E.: On the evolution of genome organization in mammals. In R. J. MacIntyre (Ed.): Molecular Evolutionary Genetics (Monographs in Evolutionary Biology Series). New York, Plenum Press, 1985, pp. 519-589.

10. Nei, M.: Molecular Evolutionary Genetics. New York, Columbia University Press, 1987.

11. Ayala, F. (Ed.): Molecular Evolution. Sunderland, MA, Sinauer Associates, 1976.

12. Fitch, W. M. and Margoliash, E.: Construction of phylogenetic trees. Science 155: 279-284, 1967.

13. Farris, J. S.: Estimating phylogenetic trees from distance matrices. Am. Naturalist 106: 645-668, 1972.

14. Fitch, W. M.: A non-sequential method for constructing trees and hierarchical classifications. J. Mol. Evol. 18: 30-37, 1981.

15. Dayhoff, M. O.: Survey of new data and computer methods of analysis. Atlas of protein sequence and structure. In Dayhoff, M. O. (Ed.): National Biomedical Research Foundation, Washington, DC (Suppl 2). Washington, DC, Natl. Biomedical Res. Foundation, 1976, pp. 1-8.

16. Felsenstein, J.: Distance methods for inferring phylogenies: A justification. Evolution 38: 16-24, 1984.

17. Swofford, D. L.: Phylogenetic Analysis Using Parsimony (PAUP), version 2.3. Champaign, IL, Illinois Natural History Survey, 1985.

17a. Sneath, P. H. A. and Sokal, R. R. (Eds.): Numerical Taxonomy: The and Practice of Numerical Classification. San Francisco, W. H. Freeman and Co., 1973, 573 pp.

18. O'Brien, S. J., Nash, W. G., Wildt, D. E., Bush, M. E., and Benveniste, R. E.: A molecular solution to the riddle of the giant panda's phylogeny. Nature 317: 140-144, 1985.

19. O'Brien, S. J.: The ancestry of the giant panda. Sci. Am. 257: 102-107, 1987.

20. Goldman, D., Rathna Giri, P., and O'Brien, S. J.: The phylogeny of the bears, giant panda and procyonids as indicated by one- and two-dimensional protein electrophoresis. Evolution, in press.

21. David, A.: Extrait d'une lettre du meme, datee de la Principaute Thibetaine (independente) de Mou-pin, le 21 Mars 1869. Nouv. Arch. Mus. His. Nat. Paris, Bull., 5, 1869, pp. 12-13.

22. Milne-Edwards, A.: Note sur quelques mammiferes du Thibet oriental. Ann. Sci. Natl., Zoo., ser. 5, art. 10, 1870, 1 p.

23. Gervais, P.: Memoire sur les formes cerebrales propres aus carnivores vivants et fossiles. Nouv. Arch. Mus. Hist. Nat. Paris, (1) 6, pp. 103-162, 1870.

24. Mivart, St. G.: On the anatomy, classification, and distribution of the Arctoidea. Proc. Zool. Soc. London, 1885, pp. 340-404.

25. Pocock, R. I.: The external characters and classification of the Procyonidae. Proc. Zool. Soc. London, 1921, pp. 389-422.

26. Davis, D. D.: The giant panda: A morphological study of evolutionary mechanisms. Fieldiana Zool. Mem. 3 (Chicago Natural History Museum), 1964.

27. Gould, S. J.: Fuzzy wuzzy was a bear. Andy pandy too. Discover (February): 40-48, 1986.

27a. Mayr, E.: Uncertainty in science: Is the giant panda a bear or a raccoon? Nature 323: 769-771, 1986.

28. MacIntyre, G. and Koopman, K. Book Review—The giant panda. A morphological study of evolutionary mechanisms. Quant. Rev. Biol. 42: 72-73, 1967.

29. Morris, R. and Morris, D.: 1981. The giant panda. (Revised by J. Barzdo.) New York, Penguin Books.

30. Ewer, R. F.: The Carnivores. Ithaca, New York, Cornell University Press, 1973, 409 pp.

30a. Eisenberg, J. F. Cited in Collins, L. R. and Page, J. K.: Ling-Ling and Hsing-Hsing, Year of the Panda. Garden City, Anchor Press/Doubleday, 1973.

30b. Schaller G. B., Jinchu, H. Wenshi, P., and Jing, Z.: The Giant Pandas of Wolong. Chicago, University of Chicago Press, 1985.

31. Chu, C.: On the systematic position of the giant panda *Ailuropoda melanoleuca* (David). Acta Zool. Sinica 20: 174-187, 1974.

32. Wang, T.-K.: Taxonomic status of the species, geological distribution and evolutionary history of *Ailuropoda*. Acta Zool. Sinica 20: 191-201, 1974.

33. Pei, W.-C.: A brief evolutionary history of the giant panda. Acta Zool. Sinica 20: 188-190, 1974.

34. Thenius, E.: Zur systematischen und phylogenetischen Stellung des Bambusbaren: *Ailuropoda melanoleuca* David (Carnivora, Mammalia). Z. Saugetierk. 44: 286-305, 1979.

35. Wurster-Hill, D. H. and Bush, M.: The interrelationship of chromosome banding patterns in the giant panda (*Ailuropoda melanoleuca*), hybrid bear (*Ursus middendorfi* x *Thalarctos maritimus*), and other carnivores. Cytogenet. Cell Genet. 27: 147-154, 1980.

36. Beijing Zoo (Competent Authority), Beijing University, Beijing Agricultural University, Beijing Second Medical College, Beijing Natural History Museum, and Shaanxi Zoology Institute. Morphology of the Giant Panda: Systematic Anatomy and Organ-Histology. Beijing, China, Science Press, 1986.

37. Modi, W. S., Nash, W. G., Ferrari, A. C., and O'Brien, S. J.: Cytogenetic methodologies for gene mapping and comparative analyses in mammalian cell culture systems. Gene Anal. Tech. 4: 75-85, 1987.

38. Benveniste, R. E. and Todaro, G. J.: Evolution of type C viral genes: evidence for an African origin of man. Nature 261: 101-108, 1976.

39. Nei, M.: Genetic distance between populations. Am. Naturalist 106: 283-292, 1972.

40. Nei, M.: Estimation of average heterozygosity and genetic distance from a small number of individuals. Genetics 89: 583-590, 1978.

41. Sarich, V. M.: The giant panda is a bear. Nature 245: 218-220, 1973.

42. Savage, D. E. and Russell, D. E.: Mammalian Paleofaunas of the World. Reading, MA, Addison-Wesley, 1983.

43. Eisenberg, J. F.: The Mammalian Radiation. An Analysis of Trends in Evolution, Adaptation and Behavior. Chicago, University of Chicago Press, 1981.

43a. Flynn, J. M. and Galiano, H.: Phylogeny of early Tertiary Carnivora, with a description of a new species of *Protictis* from the middle Eocene of Northwestern Wyoming. Am. Mus. Novitates No. 2632: 1-16.

44. Benveniste, R.: The contributions of retroviruses to the study of mammalian evolution. In MacIntyre, R. J. (Ed.): Molecular Evolutionary Genetics (Monographs in Evolutionary Biology Series). New York, Plenum Press, 1985, pp. 359-417.

45. Kohne, D. E., Chiscon, J. A. and Hoyer, B. H.: Evolution of primate DNA sequences. J. Hum. Evol. 1: 627-644, 1972.

46. Sarich, V. M.: Pinniped origins and the rate of evolution of carnivore albumins. Syst. Zool. 18: 286-295, 1969.

47. Andrews, P.: Fossil evidence on human origins and dispersal. Cold Spring Harbor Symp. Quant. Biol. 51: 419-428, 1986.

48. Newman, R. E. and Davidson, W. M.: Comparative study of the karyotypes of several species in carnivora including the giant panda (*Ailuropoda melanoleuca*). Cytogenetics 5: 152-163, 1966.

49. Nash, W. G. and O'Brien, S. J.: A comparative chromosome banding analysis of the Ursidae and their relationship to other Carnivores. Cytogenet. Cell Genet. 45: 206-212, 1987.

50. Wurster-Hill, D. H. and Gray, C. W.: Giemsa banding patterns in the chromosomes of twelve species of cats (Felidae). Cytogenet. Cell genet. 12: 388-397, 1973.

51. Wurster-Hill, D. H. and Gray, C. W.: The interrelationship of chromosome banding patterns in procyonids, viverrids, and felids. Cytogenet. Cell Genet. 15: 306-331, 1975.

52. Wurster-Hill, D. H. and Centerwall, W. R.: The interrelationships of chromosome banding patterns in canids, mustelids, hyena and felids. Cytogenet. Cell Genet. 34: 178-192, 1982.

53. Modi, W. S. and O'Brien, S. J.: Quantitative cladistic analyses of chromosomal banding data among species in three orders of mammals: Hominoid primates, felids and arvicolid rodents. In Gustafson, P. (Ed.): Stadler Symposium. New York, Plenum, in press.

54. Wayne, R. K., Nash, W. G., and O'Brien, S. J.: Chromosomal evolution of the Canidae: II. Divergence from the primitive carnivore karyotype. Cytogenet. Cell Genet. 44: 134-141, 1987.

55. Kurten, B.: Reply to "A molecular solution to the riddle of the giant panda's phylogeny." Nature 318: 487, 1986.

55a. Wayne, R. K., Benveniste, R. E., Janczewski, D. N., and O'Brien, S. J.: Molecular evolution within the carnivore order. In Gittleman, J. L. (Ed.): Carnivore Behavior, Ecology and Evolution. New York, Cornell University Press, in press.

56. Jarofke, D. and Ratsch, H.: A bibliography of the giant panda (*Ailuropoda melanoleuca*). In Klos, H.-G. and Fradrich, H. (Eds.): Proceedings of the International Symposium on the Giant Panda, 1984. Berlin, Bongo, 1985, Vol. 10, pp. 209-228.

57. Colbert, E. H.: The panda: a study in emigration. Nat. Hist. 42, 33-39, 1938.

Malcolm C. McKenna

O'Brien summarizes a number of recently applied molecular and karyological tests of the phylogenetic position of the giant panda, *Ailuropoda melanoleuca*. He concludes that the giant panda is a member of the bear family Ursidae and that the red (lesser) panda, *Ailurus fulgens*, is a member of the raccoon family Procyonidae. I find a number of his arguments to be questionable even though I concur with his placement of the giant panda with the bears.

Firstly, "studies of molecular evolution" began long before the work of Zuckerkandl and Pauling (1962). In the first half of this century serologists like G. H. F. Nuttall, A. Boyden, and W. C. Boyd were early students of molecular evolution. Studies of molecular evolution did not begin with protein sequencing.

Secondly, O'Brien assumes that mutations in the protein-coding regions of the genome passed on to subsequent generations by DNA accumulate randomly without significant modulation by selection, and that therefore clocklike behavior occurs. However, while wholly random accumulation and therefore approximately clocklike behavior might hold for introns and pseudogenes not under selection, this is clearly not the case for protein-forming mutations in mammals (McKenna, 1987; Filipski, 1988). A study of the @A-crystaline sequence in *Spalax ehrenbergi*, the blind mole rat (Hendriks *et al.*, 1987), shows that selection is operative at the protein-forming level. *Spalax ehrenbergi* retains the eye lens but doesn't see. With vision no longer important, nine amino acid residues have mutated from the original condition, five of which (at loci 12, 29, 53, 60, and 163) do so nowhere else among sequenced tetrapods (McKenna, 1987). Thus, normally in tetrapods the protein sequence of @A-crystaline is under selection sufficient to keep its sequence rather conservative at most loci and completely so at some. Mutations may be more or less random, but their incorporation into the protein-forming part of the gene pool is selection-modulated and unlikely to provide a very accurate molecular clock. The credibility of phenetic analyses rests on clock accuracy.

Thirdly, O'Brien states that times of biological divergence are established geologically. Actually, this need not be the case. *Minimum* times can of course be estimated from paleontological range data, but actual times can be older than well-known plate tectonic or other geologically established barriers to gene flow. Although I do not know what O'Brien means by "separation of Old and New World" at 25 to 35 mybp, if this date implies the separation of lineages leading to *Homo* and to cercopithecids as he states, then what and where was the geologic event that caused it?

Fourthly, O'Brien believes that the phylogenetic position of the giant panda has remained a serious problem, only now yielding to new fields of inquiry. Morphologists familiar with Davis's (1964) data have generally concluded that the giant panda is a modified bear, although the secondary literature has been equivocal (Mayr, 1986). Elsewhere (Flynn and Wyss, 1988) O'Brien has been criticized for being overly impressed by phylogenetically uninformative symplesiomorphies (shared primitive characters) and autapomorphies (unique characters). A review of O'Brien's Table 1 shows that various authors do indeed differ in their taxonomic expression of the pandas' affinities. Several citations are of essentially casual opinions, several are from textbooks or other secondary literature, and most reflect phenetic rather that cladistic analysis. For several reasons these views should not be given equal weight. For instance, those authors favoring separate families Ailuridae and Ailuropodidae actually sidestepped the issue (Mayr, 1986) by emphasizing accumulated autapomorphous characters rather than phylogenetically significant synapomorphous (shared-derived) char-

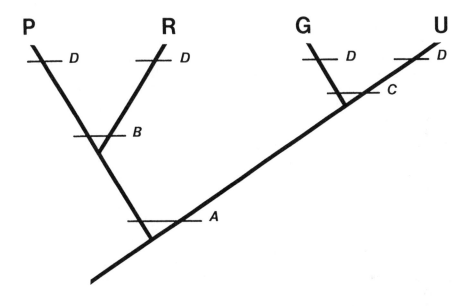

Figure 1. Simplified cladogram of procyonids (P), lesser (red) panda *Ailurus fulgens* (R), giant panda *Ailuropoda melanoleuca* (G), and remaining ursids (U). A: arctoid carnivore synapomorphies. B: 4 chromosomal synapomorphies mentioned by O'Brien et al. (1985). C: numerous synapomorphies mentioned by Davis (1964); possession of 74 single-armed (acrocentric) chromosomes (further modified by giant panda to 42 bi-armed [metacentric] chromosomes). D: various autapomorphies producing phenetic distance information but not genealogical information. If this cladogram applies, then the common term "panda" and the formal term "Ailuropodidae" are expressions of polyphyly when applied jointly to *Ailurus fulgens* and *Ailuropoda melanoleuca*. Phenetic studies of isozyme genetic distance and DNA-DNA hybridization (O'Brien *et al.*, 1985) only weakly suggest that *Ailurus* is a procyonid, whereas Sarich's (1973) phenetic work on albumins and transferrins suggests that it is a branch from the basal Ursidae.

115

acters that might indicate a uniquely shared common ancestry with either bears or raccoons. Placing either panda in a monotypic family does not change the topology of a depicted phylogeny. Moreover, how many authors favoring a raccoon alliance of the giant panda were actually basing their conclusions on uninformative plesiomorphous (shared-primitive) characters? In other words, did they really mean "relatively plesiomorphous arctoid carnivore" when they wrote "procyonid"? Although the giant panda has been confused with procyonids by phenetic analyses emphasizing plesiomorphous characters, cladistic analysis of the same data suggests that, rather than new fields of inquiry, merely more effective methods of analysis are required (Figure 1). Despite overly enthusiastic claims that "molecular studies" have solved problems of homology vs. homoplasy (Gould, 1985), these problems still seem to bedevil all levels, from ethology to gene sequencing. Cladistic analysis can be applied in place of phenetic methods in some instances, but until and even when "molecular studies" have reached the point where statistically significant fractions of the genome have been sequenced in many organisms, we can expect conflicting molecular results (McKenna, 1987). We should view "solutions," "proofs," "demonstrations," and the like with healthy skepticism, whether they are generated by students of comparative anatomy or of comparative chemistry.

American Museum of Natural History

Davis, D. Dwight, 1964, The giant panda, a morphological study of evolutionary mechanisms, *Fieldiana: Zoology Memoirs,* vol. 3, pp. 1-339.

Filipski, J., 1988, Sequence-based phylogeny in eukaryotic genomes, *Nature* **334:** 571-572.

Flynn, J. J. and Wyss, A. R. (Letter to the Editor), *Scientific American,* June 1988, pp. 8-9.

Gould, Stephen J., 1985, A clock of evolution, *Natural History* **94:** 12-25.

Hendriks, W., Leunissen, J., Nevo, E., Bloemendal, H., and de Jong, W. W., 1987, The lens protein @A-crystallin of the blind mole rat, *Spalax ehrenbergi:* evolutionary change and functional constraints, *Proceedings of the National Academy of Sciences USA* **84:** 5320-5324.

McKenna, Malcolm C., 1987, Molecular and morphological analysis of high-level mammalian interrelationships, in: *Molecules and Morphology in Evolution: Conflict or Compromise?* (C. Patterson, ed.), pp. 55-93, Cambridge University Press, Cambridge.

Mayr, Ernst, 1986, Uncertainty in science: is the giant panda a bear or a raccoon? *Nature* **323:** 769-771.

O'Brien, S. J., Nash, W. G., Wildt, D. E., Bush, M. E., and Benveniste, R. E., 1985, A molecular solution to the riddle of the giant panda's phylogeny, *Nature* **317:** 140-144.

Sarich, Vincent, 1973, The giant panda is a bear, *Nature* **245:** 218-220.

Zuckerkandl, E. and Pauling, L., 1962, Molecular disease, evolution, and genetic heterogeneity, in: *Horizons in Biochemistry* (M. Kasha and B. Pullman, eds.), pp. 189-225, Academic Press, New York.

Human Fossil History and Evolutionary Paradigms

David Pilbeam
Harvard University

Despite the old joke, I am not sure there ever was a time when there were more paleoanthropologists than hominid fossils, but both the hominid and the archaeological records have grown by several orders of magnitude in the last 50 years, and paleoanthropology has changed greatly (Cartmill *et al.*, 1986). *Apes, Men, and Morons* by Earnest Hooton was published in 1937, and while no single book can capture the full range and flavor of opinion of half a century ago, it is a reasonable sampler of paleoanthropological thinking at the dawn of the New Synthesis. The study of human evolution did not actually enter the modern biological world until two decades after the 1930s, but Hooton's book does have a foot in two worlds: one of orthogenetic typology, and what we would call racism and sexism; the other one in which population genetics and behavioral ecology are becoming important, humans are closest to African apes, and the middle Miocene is indeed 14 million years old. Since then so much has changed. Paleoanthropologists today, especially those in graduate school, are regularly exposed to the full range of modern evolutionary anthropology: geology, evolutionary theory, socioecology and sociobiology, molecular and population genetics, phylogenetic analysis, functional anatomy, archaeology, and ethnology. The quality of the best work done in the field, broadly defined, is as high as that in any other area of evolutionary biology.

Paleoanthropology is not a coherent discipline like physics. It is rather a question: What happened in human evolution, and why? A question about an odd mammal group that was never very diverse and that now has only one surviving lineage. Because it is a question of compelling interest to many of us, because it is multidisciplinary, because it is fun, it is pursued with often obsessive vigor. Paleoanthropologists are consumers, rather than producers, of major theoretical insights, but very lively consumers. Molecular phylogenetics, primate behavior studies, functional anatomy, and the geochronology of young sediments, to name but a few, have all benefited from intimate contact with paleoanthropology.

What follows is a brief review of the fossil and archaeological record, which obviously cannot be comprehensive, along with some discussion of its interpretation. First, there is a brief description of what happened. Second, a look at particular problems or issues from three different perspectives: taxonomy, phylogenetic relationships, and behavioral reconstruction. Each gives us a complementary view of the impact of "evolutionary theory" on paleoanthropology. A third perspective is through the eyes of the story-teller. It is healthy that we now recognize that narrative accounts of human evolution have often served the function of origin myths and that they can contain a substantial nonscientific or ideological component.

A Narrative Account of Hominid Evolution

Genetic comparisons clearly show that humans are odd African apes (Goodman, 1963; Sarich and Wilson, 1967). There is less consensus on whether, among African hominoids, chimpanzees are more closely related to humans or to gorillas, although it is agreed that the Asian apes—orang-utans and gibbons—are successively more distantly related. Hooton believed this in 1937. However, by the 1950s the consensus was that the great apes (chimpanzee, gorilla, orangutan) formed a monophyletic group, Pongidae (Clark and Leakey, 1951). But the comparative genetical analyses of the late 1950s and 1960s effectively eliminated that possibility. There is, as yet, no direct fossil evidence of the very earliest hominids or their immediate predecessors, but enough is known of the hominoid fossil record between 15 and 7 my and of the hominid record later, in the Pliocene, to provide at least approximate answers to four questions about hominid origins: when, where, what, why? (Pilbeam, 1986; Kelley and Pilbeam, 1986). Hominids probably evolved in the latest Miocene around 5 to 7 mya in Africa. Their initial adaptations probably involved a shift to a significantly bipedal positional repertoire from a more quadrupedal, apelike pattern, and the reduction in size of male canine teeth (coupled with slight morphological changes in the canines of both sexes). Why these changes occurred is much less clear, and there have been many suggestions (Isaac, 1983). Even with an adequate fossil record, answers to the question "why" may well remain hard to resolve.

Hominids are not well sampled until a little under 4 mya, with *Australopithecus afarensis* from Hadar in Ethiopia (Johanson and White, 1979) and Laetoli in Tanzania (Leakey, *et al.*, 1976). Only a few fragmentary specimens are known from sites older than 4 my and younger than 7 my that could be hominid (Ward and Hill, 1987). The *A. afarensis* sample probably represents one species, although arguments have been made for two (Senut and Tardieu, 1985). If only one species, it was slightly more dimorphic than the gorilla or orangutan, with female body weight averaging over 30 kgs and males more than twice as heavy (Leutenegger and Shell, 1987). Brain size was no larger than that of chimpanzees (Holloway, 1983), while cheek teeth were much larger relative to body size (McHenry, 1984). Tooth crowns had thick enamel, incisors were large, and canine crowns low and morphologically intermediate between apes (tusklike) and later hominids (chisellike) (Johanson and White, 1979). Although arms were longer and legs shorter than in *Homo*, hindlimb anatomy clearly shows that bipedalism was a significant fraction of the positional repertoire (McHenry, 1986; Latimer *et al.*, 1987). Forelimb length and joint morphology show that *A. afarensis*, although bipedal when moving on the ground, could have climbed easily in trees in search of food, to rest, and to avoid predators (Sussman, Stern, and Jungers, 1984). In complete contrast, it has also been proposed that *A. afarensis* was effectively identical to *Homo* in positional behavior without any major arboreal component (Johanson and Edey, 1981; Latimer *et al.*, 1987). At the least it can be said that the bipedalism of *Australopithecus*, if not as efficient energetically as that of *Homo*, was more efficient than the terrestrial locomotion of any ape. The anatomy of hands shows both that they were not used in moving on the ground and that they were adapted to a range of implement-using behaviors: tools were probably used frequently, though there is no evidence that stone flakes were made (Marzke, 1983). *A. afarensis* is known definitely so far only from east Africa. Associated faunas and other evidence suggest habitats ranging from woodland and gallery forest to open bushland, essentially the range of relatively open habitats found in east Africa today (Bonnefille, 1984).

After about 2.5 mya the number of contemporaneous hominid species lineages increases to two, three, and possibly even four (Delson, 1987). These species are included now in three genera, *Australopithecus*, *Paranthropus*, and *Homo*. There was some variation in body size, although none of the species seems to have exceeded modern human body weights (Leutenegger and Shell, 1987). All were bipeds and all had small brains, though these were larger than those of *A. afarensis* (Holloway, 1978). Both *Australopithecus* and *Paranthropus* have relatively larger cheek teeth than any living hominoids, *Paranthropus* perhaps even more than *Australopithecus*. The main difference among australopithecine species involves relative tooth size and proportions, masticatory muscle mass, and facial morphology (Tobias, 1967). Some species, *Paranthropus boisei* and *P. robustus*, for example, had relatively enormous, low-cusped, thick enamelled cheek teeth, small canines and incisors, deep, flat, and buttressed faces, and very large temporal, masseter, and pterygoid muscles (Grine, 1986). Much attention has been paid to inferring diet in these species (Walker, 1981). They were probably eclectic feeders, with the bulk of their diet being plant foods. Occlusal surface microwear indicates that relative to *Australopithecus*, *Paranthropus* included more small, hard objects such as nuts and tough fruits in its diet (Grine and Kay, 1988). It seems likely, by analogy with chimpanzees (Goodall, 1986), that australopithecines may have occasionally hunted small animals.

Precise relationships among australopithecines are not unanimously

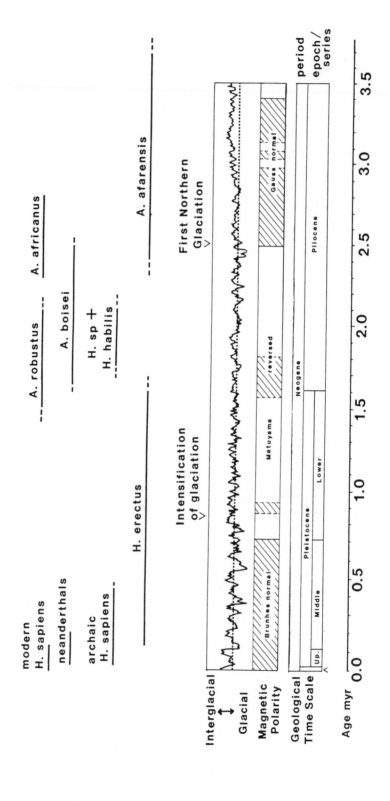

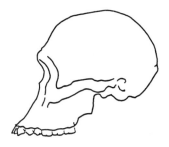

A. africanus

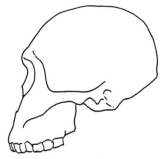

H. habilis

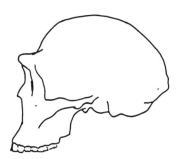

H. erectus

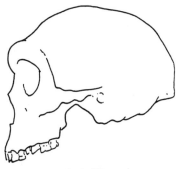

archaic *H. sapiens*

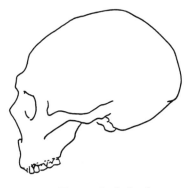

H. neanderthalensis

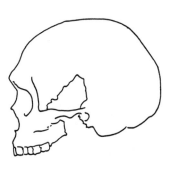

H. sapiens

agreed upon (Delson, 1987), although differences in relationships have little effect for the most part upon the likely sequence of inferred behavioral events during this phase of hominid evolution. Perhaps more interesting are changing views on the quality or complexity of australopithecine behavior. During the 1950s a case was made that *Australopithecus* was an omnivorous, aggressive, and predatory form with social organization and subsistence behavior similar to those of humans (Dart, 1953). By the early 1980s this view had changed considerably, *Australopithecus* as well as *Paranthropus* frequently being interpreted as more herbivorous and apelike both in subsistence behavior and social organization (Binford, 1983).

Hooton mentioned the australopithecines in 1937 but did not believe them to be directly relevant to the mainstream of human evolution. It took at least another decade before they were so considered. His main attention focused on the Pleistocene evolution of *Homo*.

An important behavioral change for hominids occurred by around 2 mya (perhaps as much as 2.4 mya), and is reflected in the appearance of an archaeological record in the form of stone flakes, concentrations of stone artifacts, broken bones representing food refuse, and mixtures of stones and bones (Isaac, 1971). At approximately the same time a new hominid species appeared, *Homo habilis* (Leakey *et al.*, 1964). First described in 1964, *H. habilis* has had a checkered history, largely because it consists of relatively incomplete or single specimens rather than associated material (Day, 1986). If indeed only one species is represented, considerable variation in brain size and cranial and postcranial anatomy is documented (Stringer, 1986; Lieberman *et al.*, 1988). At least some specimens had brains significantly larger than those of australopithecines, and some postcranial bones show resemblances to later *Homo* species. As with the australopithecines, behavioral interpretations of *H. habilis* have swung like a pendulum (Binford, 1983). First, it was inferred to be like modern humans in significant features of subsistence and social behavior; more recently, both subsistence and social behavior were, in important features, thought to be unlike modern humans. At the least, *H. habilis* diets are thought to have included more animal parts than those of any australopithecine (Bunn and Kroll, 1986). There is no consensus as to the selective advantage of larger brains.

It is worth making the general point here that it is easier with all forms of historical reconstruction to say when an historical state was *like* the present than to specify how it might have been *un*like the present.

More evolved hominids appeared in Africa before 1.5 mya and have been called *H. erectus*, although the species was first recognized and is best represented by material from east Asia between 1 and 0.5 mya old (Day, 1986). Relative to *H. habilis*, *H. erectus* brain volume was larger, face and jaws smaller, and cranial shape more elongated; postcranially there may have been only minor differences (at least in the few comparable parts). Almost concurrently the African archaeological record documents a change: the production of large symmetrical flakes known as bifaces (Stringer, 1984).

The succeeding million-plus years are sampled for hominids in such a way that only average trends can be documented. By 200 to 300 tya most hominids are generally described as archaic *Homo sapiens*, although it must be emphasized that, except for brain size, there are few differences from *H. erectus*. Body size and postcranial morphology show little change, and neither does the archaeological record. Brain volume does increase, but it is impossible to decide at present what the trajectory of evolutionary change was, and the case has been made both for stasis and for gradual change (Rightmire, 1981; Wolpoff, 1984). It has also been argued that, taxonomically, this segment of the sequence is significantly under-split (Tattersall, 1986; Stringer and Andrews, 1988).

By the beginning of the late Pleistocene, marked around 130 tya by an abrupt change from full glacial to full interglacial conditions (Roberts, 1984), it is clear that major changes *had* occurred. Northern latitudes of Eurasia were the home of the neanderthals, a large-brained *Homo* species with very characteristic cranial and postcranial morphology (Boaz *et al.*, 1982; Stringer, 1984; Stringer and Andrews, 1988; Trinkaus, 1986). They are best known between 70 and 34 tya in western Europe, although neanderthal features are present in some European hominids older than 130 ty, presumably ancestors of later populations. Neanderthals disappear after about 34 tya. Anatomically modern humans are known from sub-Saharan Africa during the last interglacial (*sensu lato*) between 75 and 130 tya, with at least some being older than 100 ty in South Africa. In Ethiopia they may be as old as 125 ty, while in Israel they are almost 100 ty old. Their presumably more archaic ancestors are only poorly known. Anatomically, modern humans and neanderthals can now be seen as contemporaneous within the Old World for a long time. It is possible that southwest Asia was close to the boundary between the two populations, because there is evidence in Israel for the alternation of the two populations during the Late Pleistocene (Boaz *et al.*, 1982; Stringer and Andrews, 1988).

Throughout their range, neanderthals are associated with Mousterian archaeological assemblages (e.g., Binford, 1983). There has been a great deal of debate on the meaning of differences between Mousterian industries and those associated with anatomically modern humans from about 40 ty on—the Upper Paleolithic (found in northern Eurasia, southwest Asia, north Africa) and the Late Stone Age (Africa) (White, 1982). The consensus among archaeologists is that nonmodern behaviors are implied by the Mousterian, although the exact nature and extent of differences are unclear (Klein, 1973). Of considerable current interest is the fact that early anatomically modern humans between about 125 and 40 ty are also associated with Mousterian assemblages, or with their African equivalent, Middle Stone Age industries. For a least 60 percent and probably more like 75 percent of the time after modern humans appeared, they were producing tools barely distinguishable from those of their neanderthal contemporaries (Singer and Wymer, 1982).

Comparative genetic studies of modern human populations have undergone something of a resurgence in the last few years. A variety of analyses of serum proteins (Nei, 1985), nuclear DNA (Wainscoat *et al.*, 1986), and mitochondrial DNA (Stoneking *et al.*, 1986; Cann *et al.*, 1987) mostly agree in showing a pattern of relationships in which European and Asian populations are similar to each other while African groups are more distant from both. In addition, in some of the systems studied, African populations are more variable than the others. The genetic patterns can be read as implying that modern humans evolved, probably sometime in the middle Pleistocene, from a geographically relatively restricted population. Some have argued that Africa was the original place of origin (Stringer and Andrews, 1988), although genetic data alone do not allow us to make unambiguous inferences about this (Giles and Ambrose, 1986; Greenwood, 1986; Excoffier *et al.*, 1987). Such a view is compatible with the fossil record, but that record is sufficiently poor in Asia to make strong inferences at the moment impossible. However, a tentative consensus would see modern humans evolving late in the middle Pleistocene of Africa, and spreading out of Africa several times over the past 100 ty or so (Stringer and Andrews, 1988).

Complementary Perspectives

As I noted earlier, paleoanthropologists have mostly been consumers of theoretical insights rather than producers, but there are at least three areas in which the New Synthesis and succeeding developments have had important impacts on paleoanthropology. First, there is the realization that taxonomy at the species level can only proceed within a population framework that explicitly recognizes variability. Second, evolutionary relationships require for their determination at least the confident recognition of homology. And third, behavioral reconstruction depends upon the plausible recognition and interpretation of functionally useful characters. The following three sections explore these issues in greater detail.

Taxonomy

In Hooton's account, little attention was paid to species-level taxonomic arguments (alpha taxonomy) because there were few kinds of hominoids represented by more than a handful of individuals. That situation has happily changed for hominoids in general and hominids in particular. Decisions about alpha taxonomy are of fundamental importance, and the next few paragraphs include some of the more critical current taxonomic issues.

The studies upon which the following taxonomic comments have been based are for the most part qualitative, or if quantitative they are rarely explicitly formal and probabilistic. All taxonomic attributions in fossil species assume some basic similarity between past and present morphological patterns, and all operate by making comparability judgments that are, in one form or another, a kind of analysis of variance (Pilbeam and Zwell, 1972). How are fossil specimens to be sorted, given our understanding of within- and between-groups morphological and metrical variance in species populations, as it presumably reflects genetic variability? What is generally lacking is an explicit model, appropriately quantified, against which contingent hypotheses can be framed. For example, given assumptions about variability based upon observations of the world, what probabilities can be assigned to particular taxonomic hypotheses about past species? This approach is desirable because assumptions and inferential procedures are made explicit, and therefore conclusions can be clearly linked to data input and modified as new information becomes available (Pilbeam, 1978).

The Miocene hominoid record is expanding steadily (Kelley and Pilbeam, 1986). Some early Miocene (24-17 my) African species are well documented, both for body parts sampled and sample sizes for particular parts (especially teeth and jaws). *Proconsul africanus* from Kenya is well known cranially and postcranially (Clark and Leakey, 1951; Walker and Pickford, 1983), but other broadly contemporaneous apes are also increasingly well known (Leakey, 1988). Middle and late Miocene hominoids (17-5 mya) are, with the exception of *Oreopithecus* (Harrison, 1986), not so well sampled. The best known of the remainder, *Sivapithecus*, is hardly better represented than *Paranthropus robustus*, the least well-known australopithecine (Kelley and Pilbeam, 1986; Pilbeam, 1986). However, enough teeth and jaws of enough species are known to raise some very interesting taxonomic questions, with potentially important biological consequences.

It is plausible to infer that some Miocene hominoids exhibited a degree of tooth size dimorphism at the limit of or in excess of that seen in the most dimorphic living primates (Kelley, 1986a, b). In several cases where reasonable fossil samples are known—for example, Lufeng, China (ca 7 my), Haritalyangar, India (ca 7.5 my), the Potwar Plateau, Pakistan (ca 8.8 my), Ravin de la Pluie, Greece (ca 9 my), and Rudabanya, Hungary (ca 10 my)—the following pattern is found. For any given cheek tooth, linear measurements fall into a bimodal rather than a unimodal distribution, even in large samples. This would not be expected for mixed-sex samples of living primates, even from the most size dimorphic species. Where specimens contain canines and can be sexed, it is possible to compare means for samples of males and females. Such samples are almost invariably small, but imply similar conclusions. Either the average difference between male and female tooth size (molars and premolars) in at least some Miocene hominoids exceeds that in living species, or samples actually contain two morphologically very similar species with an unusual pattern of canine representation. If the former turns out to be the case, we shall need to consider carefully the biological implications.

Similar taxonomic issues arise among the australopithecines. Does the *Australopithecus afarensis* material represent one species (Johanson and

White, 1979), as dimorphic as or more than *Gorilla* or *Pongo,* or are two species sampled (Olson, 1985)? Implications both for behavioral reconstruction and phylogenetic analysis are clear. How many australopithecine species are represented at Sterkfontein and Kromdraai (traditionally one at each) (Clarke, 1985)? What is the taxonomic status of WT17000, originally assigned to *Paranthropus boisei,* but possibly representative of a new species (Walker *et al.,* 1986)? A question of considerable current interest, following almost a quarter century of debate, concerns the taxonomy of *Homo habilis* (Stringer, 1986; Lieberman *et al.,* 1988). Earlier argument centered around two issues: the validity of the taxon and its generic status. Most recently, interest has been revived in alpha taxonomy. How many species are represented, one or two? Two seems now somewhat more likely, although there is disagreement over the partitioning of the sample. How specimens are sorted obviously determines characteristics of the taxa, which will influence other critical issues: temporal and geographical distribution, phylogenetic relationships, and behavioral reconstruction.

The taxonomy of more derived species of *Homo* (*H. erectus* and so-called archaic *H. sapiens,* including neanderthals) is also in a state of stimulating flux (Tattersall, 1986). In Hooton's time this part of the hominid tree was complex, but the postwar trend was strongly toward a simple pattern with a single lineage exhibiting gradual change, with arbitrary, temporal, taxonomic boundaries. Sample size is too small and temporal control too imprecise to decide the issue unequivocally, but it is at the least plausible that several species are involved, both time-successive and overlapping, implying a more complex phylogenetic pattern than has been considered in four decades (Stringer, 1984). Growing out of the preceding set of issues is the question of *Homo sapiens* (*sensu lato*) taxonomy (Stringer, 1984; Stringer and Andrews, 1988). Specifically, what is the status of the neanderthals? Given their morphological, temporal, and geographical coherence, and their substantial (relative to modern human inter-population variability) difference from modern humans (Howells, 1972; Trinkaus, 1986), formal species distinction might be supportable. Proposed intermediates between *H. sapiens* and *H. neanderthalensis* are fragmentary, and the case for either hybrids between contemporaneous populations or phyletically transitional forms is ambiguous. In addition, other nonmodern later Pleistocene "archaic *H. sapiens*" hominid specimens remain to be classified.

These kinds of taxonomic decisions are indispensable to many other analyses and inferences. One particularly important issue concerns tempo and mode of evolution, which can only be determined if alpha taxonomy is of acceptable quality (Tattersall, 1986). The hominid fossil record is effectively inadequate to make firm choices, at reasonable levels of plausibility, concerning stasis versus gradual change, nor are there any relevant data on speciation. These issues have been most controversial with relevance to Pleistocene *Homo* species. With appropriate caveats, my personal preference is that there were probably several rather than few species involved, and most change is unlikely to have been "gradual."

Prior to the 1950s nomenclatural cleanup, there were many hominid generic and species names. After the 1960s at most two generic names were recognized, *Australopithecus* and *Homo*, with few species. Current thinking about morphological, and by implication behavioral, diversity is leading us back toward more generic names. And although most Pleistocene hominid species are likely to remain in *Homo*, the shift there toward more species in recognition of real biological diversity has implications for both phylogenetic relationships and behavioral reconstruction.

Evolutionary Relationships

The second major area of concern for paleoanthropologists is that of phylogenetic reconstruction, involving the recognition of morphological homology and polarity, and hence of evolutionary relationships. Here the debate in paleoanthropology, as with the systematics of all other groups, has been transformed by two developments. First, the cladistic approach: that is, the recognition that homologous similarity is of phylogenetic utility only if it is derived homology (e.g., Ridley, 1986). Second, the growth of numerous comparative genetic studies, often called "molecular," using data from DNA and proteins (Nei, 1987). These two developments have wrought something of a revolution. There are now areas of strong consensus concerning hominoid relationships, but areas of important controversy remain. I shall discuss briefly three general issues: living hominoid relationships; relationships among australopithecines and early *Homo*; and those among the late species of Homo—*H. sapiens*, *H. neanderthalensis*, and other "archaic *H. sapiens*."

Almost all possible relationships among extant Hominoidea have been proposed at one time or another on the basis of morphological character analysis. Hooton followed Keith (1911) in favoring a close link between *Homo* and *Pan*, with *Gorilla*, *Pongo*, and *Hylobates* successively more distant. But by the 1950s the consensus, at least in the English-speaking world, had shifted in favor of a monophyletic Pongidae, with *Homo* being more an outgroup (e.g., Clark and Leakey, 1951). The first modern "molecular" studies—the qualitative phenetic comparisons of Goodman (1963) using a range of hominoid serum proteins compared immunologically—clearly showed *Pan*, *Gorilla*, and *Homo* to be most similar and by inference monophyletic, with *Pong*, more different. The argument that this pattern arose because of accelerated molecular evolution in *Pongo* was effectively refuted by Wilson and Sarich's quantitative data set based on immunological analyses of albumin, which enabled them to show using the "rate test" that the amounts of difference in albumin structure between *Pongo* and, respectively, *Homo*, *Pan*, and *Gorilla* were subequal, while differences among the three were also subequal but clearly smaller (Sarich and Wilson, 1967; Sarich, 1983). This uniform patterning of phenetic differences implied some underlying regular process of change. This in turn was used to argue, given certain assumptions about the fossil record, that hominids had evolved later (5 mya) rather than earlier (15-30 mya). Regardless of arguments over timing, a consensus emerged quite rapidly that *Pan, Gorilla,* and *Homo* were indeed monophyletic (Sarich and Cronin, 1975).

Earlier amino acid sequencing of proteins supported, weakly, a *Pan-Homo* link (Goodman and Tashian, 1975; Nei *et al.,* 1985), but the debate has gathered strength more recently with the appearance in the past few years of DNA data (Weiss, 1987). It now seems clear from both phenetic and phylogenetic analyses that *Pan, Gorilla,* and *Homo* are indeed monophyletic, but beyond this there is as yet no consensus, opinion being divided between a *Pan-Homo* link (for example, Holmquist *et al.,* 1988), and *Pan-Gorilla* (for example, Andrews and Martin, 1987). The two splitting events that produced the three lineages were clearly close together, and therefore intrinsically difficult to resolve unambiguously. Although the disagreements have been seen as "molecular" versus "morphological," there are in fact both kinds of data adduced to support both hypotheses, and both phenetic and phylogenetic techniques used on both sides (e.g., Andrews and Martin, 1987; Groves, 1986). What would be useful now is a pause to review criteria for deciding, if possible, which evidence and which analytical techniques can be judged, on the basis of objective criteria, to be most useful.

What difference would it make to the likely morphology of the last common ancestor whether *Pan-Homo* is closest, or *Pan-Gorilla*? Either way, the ancestor of hominids and apes is likely to have been a large, stiff-backed, long-armed, short-legged, arm-swinging arboreal form that was also a quadrupedal climber-walker both in the trees and on the ground. At least some knuckle-walking or fist-walking is likely in either case. Neither the amount of change from ancestor to early hominid nor the proximate reasons for change are likely to be greatly different regardless of precise ancestral morphology. It is also comforting for a paleontologist to be able to state that, in this instance, the recovery of relevant fossils will contribute significantly to a resolution of this problem.

Another major area in which phylogenetic relationships have been somewhat controversial involves the Plio-Pleistocene hominids. Arguments have focused around the position of *Australopithecus africanus* (Johanson and White, 1979; Skelton *et al.,* 1986), the monophyly of *Paranthropus* species, the monophyly of *Homo* and *Paranthropus* (Wood and Chamberlain, 1987), and the relationships of early *Homo* (Chamberlain and Wood, 1987). These species represent a modest adaptive radiation with a time depth of just a few million years, temporally equivalent to that of *Macaca* or morphologically to a broader subset of papionines. Cladistic analyses using both parsimony and compatibility approaches agree above all in demonstrating the extent of homoplasy in the characters used in analyses (or the extent to which homology is difficult to recognize and polarity difficult to determine) (Chamberlain and Wood, 1987). This is a case where the lack of any objective criteria for evaluating incongruent morphological similarity sets is a severe problem (Ridley, 1986; Sarich, 1988).

One of the most interesting phylogenetic questions concerns the relationships of early *Homo* specimens, and here there is a very important interaction between alpha taxonomy and phylogenetic analysis. If *H. habilis* is a single species, it is the sister taxon of *H. erectus* and subsequent *Homo* species (Chamberlain and Wood, 1987). However, if the *habilis* sample represents two species the situation is changed, but potentially in different ways depending upon how the sample is partitioned. One intriguing possibility links *Homo* sp. (the non-*habilis* sample) to *H. erectus*, with *H. habilis* (*sensu strictu*) more distant (Chamberlain and Wood, 1987). If correct, this would imply that brain volumes significantly larger than those of australopithecines evolved not once but twice. In this case, deciding which taxonomic and phylogenetic relationships are most plausible will have a major impact on broader phylogenetic and biological hypotheses.

The third important area in which species relationships are currently under intense scrutiny involves modern human populations and more archaic species, including *H. neanderthalensis*. Did anatomically modern humans have an origin in a relatively restricted area, from which populations subsequently dispersed, replacing (in some unspecified and currently unknowable manner) anatomically more archaic and presumably genetically different hominids (Stringer and Andrews, 1988; Wolpoff *et al.*, 1988)? Or did modern human adaptations spread throughout a widespread species that always maintained genetic cohesion (Wolpoff *et al.*, 1984, 1988)? The question is now being addressed using both molecular and morphological data. Most genetic data support a dichotomy between African populations and those of Europe and Asia, although some data suggest other relationships. Given the similarity of the populations and the relative recency of the events, more independent genetic data are needed before definitive conclusions can be drawn about place and time of origin. Recent paleontological and geochronological work shows that the oldest reasonably well-dated anatomically modern humans come from sub-Saharan Africa, where they apparently exceed 100 ty (Stringer and Andrews, 1988), and from Israel, where they are probably a little under 100 ty old (Valladas *et al.*, 1988). This is clearly older than for other well-sampled regions, although much of Asia is effectively unsampled. Anatomically modern *H. sapiens* and neanderthals coexisted therefore for almost 100 ty (Boaz *et al.*, 1982). Given phenotypic differences, relatively marked genotypic differences are plausible. A reasonable hypothesis is that modern humans evolved from non-neanderthal archaic humans perhaps in Africa, and much later replaced neanderthals and other archaics elsewhere with little or no introgression (Stringer and Andrews, 1988; but see Wolpoff *et al.*, 1988).

Phylogenetic reconstruction is an important area of evolutionary biology. Fundamental to future progress will be a better understanding of the nature of genetic change (the "neutralist" versus "selectionist" debate) and greater insight into the mapping of genotypic and phenotypic change. This should lead to clearer criteria for defining "characters," and to the possibility of evaluating morphological differences and similarities in a (sometimes) more easily interpretable genetic currency.

Behavioral Reconstruction

The principal challenge in behavioral reconstruction is the recognition of adaptations and other functionally useful characters, which remains as critical an issue as in Darwin's time. Over 20 years ago, Williams (1966) articulated clearly the need for a scientific study of adaptation. While a trait or feature may often have a readily apparent function, what is frequently unclear is whether the function is primary or secondary (is the trait an adaptation or an exaptation in Gould and Vrba's [1982] terminology), or even whether it is epiphenomenal. Paleoanthropologists have rarely recognized the complexity of these issues, although many of the quintessential human features with which we are concerned (brain size, language, bipedalism) are in fact slippery and elusive when it comes to tracking their adaptive histories.

A fair amount of energy has been invested in discussing the behavioral causes of hominid origins. Given the absence of direct fossil evidence for the common ancestor of apes and humans, ambiguity arising from disagreements about the precise relationships among *Pan*, *Gorilla*, and *Homo*, and the distinct possibility that several million years of earliest hominid history remains unsampled, it is not surprising that "what happened" can be approached only very generally, while "why it happened" must remain even more speculative (Pilbeam, 1986). At the least, explanations will have to deal with the evolution of bipedalism, either in a single and presumably major rapid change or in a series of steps (Rose, 1984). Explanations for the evolution of bipedalism have covered a wide range of possibilities, most of them emphasizing the selective importance of carrying objects (tools, food, or weapons) (Isaac, 1983). An interesting recent suggestion proposes that, for a ground-trekking hominoid, bipedalism could be an energetically more efficient locomotor pattern than chimp- or orang-type quadrupedalism (Rodman and McHenry, 1980). This makes a plausible primary adaptation, to which other functions would have been added subsequently.

Abundant fossil evidence is now available for the australopithecines, along with much clearer understanding of taphonomic processes relevant to their accumulation. There has been a resurgence of interest in their behavioral reconstruction that flows from activity in at least three areas: primate behavioral biology and socioecology, especially of apes; functional anatomical research, using living species as models; and renewed interest in physiological processes relevant to life history parameters (e.g., Chivers *et al.*, 1984; Smuts *et al.*, 1986; Kinzey, 1987). The earliest behavioral reconstructions of *Australopithecus* by Dart (1953) inferred both highly aggressive within-group behavior and a high degree of predation on other species. Tools were thought to be used and made, and social-subsistence behavior was reconstructed as "proto-human" (with home bases, division of labor, food sharing, and so forth). Analysis of tooth eruption sequences seemed to show a delayed human pattern, in contrast to that characteristic of apes (Mann, 1975). Much of this inferential edifice was built on bone accumulations from the South African australopithecine caves.

Subsequent reinterpretation of the same data (Brain, 1981) showed that the hominids were prey rather than predators and that large carnivores were the primary bone accumulators. Soon after this dethronement, studies of tooth microwear in the australopithecines suggested a diet primarily of plant food (Walker, 1981; Grine, 1981). Also, expanded knowledge of behavioral biology of living apes had seemed to show a relatively low level of aggression (Goodall, 1971). So the australopithecines became more apelike and took on the demeanor of peaceful lotus eaters. However, more recent data on primate behavior, particularly of African apes, suggests to the contrary that levels of intraspecific aggression are high (Goodall, 1986; Fossey, 1983), and it is probable therefore that australopithecine behaviors included intraspecies aggression in addition to affiliative behaviors (Wrangham, 1987). New analyses of enamel development and tooth-eruption patterns indicate a uniquely australopithecine but basically ape grade, implying more rapid maturation and life history patterns unlike those of modern humans (Smith, 1986; Beynon and Wood, 1987; Conroy and Vannier, 1988). Relative brain size also implies this (Holloway, 1978; McHenry, 1986).

Although inferences about particular species clearly reflect the adequacy of alpha taxonomy, at least some australopithecine species seem to have been very dimorphic in body size (Leutenegger and Shell, 1987). Given that they are likely to have fed and moved to a significant extent on the ground, what can be said of their general social organization? We can proceed using the "exclusionary approach" mentioned earlier: given our understanding of socioecological principles, particularly as they apply to living catarrhines, and our understanding of behavioral-physiological-morphological links, what can be ruled *out* in the way of behavioral organization? (See Smuts *et al.*, 1986 for general references to the following discussion.) If monogamy, territoriality, brachiation, and minimal body-size dimorphism are functionally lined in gibbons, then arguments for monogamy in very dimorphic early hominids are problematic. An orang-type, relatively asocial pattern also seems unlikely, because it apparently reflects the constraints of large body size in a highly arboreal context (Rodman, 1984). The malefocused polygyny of mountain gorillas is evidently made possible by ubiquitous and evenly distributed food resources, which are perhaps unlikely for australopithecines. The human-type pattern, best characterized by the term "marriage" rather than "monogamy" or "pair-bonding" and dependent on language and culture, seems unlikely for a number of reasons. An initial analysis might conclude that, because australopithecines were more size dimorphic than chimps, they are also unlikely to have had a chimplike, male-bonded behavioral organization, *contra* speculations from behavioral biology (Wrangham, 1987). However, this is not necessarily so. Rodman (1984) has proposed that the relatively low degree of chimpanzee dimorphism can be explained by energetic constraints on males posed by the requirements of monitoring a large territory for critical resources such as food and mates and against males of adjacent groups. If it is also the case, as argued by Rodman and McHenry (1980), that chimpanzee knuckle-walking quadrupedalism is energetically more costly than australopithecine bipedalism can plausibly be inferred to have been, early hominoids could indeed have had a broadly chimpanzee-like social organization. Bipedalism would thus "permit" hominid males to be larger than chimpanzee males for equivalent amounts of trekking.

The behavioral reconstruction of *Homo* species is especially challenging. New features such as enlarged brains, more derived postcranials, and more elaborate manipulative-technological capabilities indicate behavioral changes from an australopithecine pattern beyond a general ape grade of complexity. The degree to which particular species of *Homo* resembled modern *H. sapiens* in social, subsistence, mating, and other critical behaviors is currently one of the more interesting and vigorously debated issues in paleoanthropology. The extent to which early *Homo* species were hunters or scavengers, how much meat they ate and how frequently, whether food was shared, how space was organized and environmental resources monitored, whether single places were foci for a range of important activities, are all at present unclear, although considerable progress is being made toward clarifying how they might be approached as research questions. Until a decade ago, a consensus probably existed for the view that early *Homo* species were behaviorally rather modern. Now the consensus does not exist, and at least some argue vigorously for the opposite conclusion (e.g., Binford, 1983).

Within the broader *Homo* debate, no issue is more fascinating than that concerning the very large-brained species, *Homo sapiens* and *Homo neanderthalensis*. For much of this century there has been a range of opinions on the mode of human origins (narrowly restricted or broadly distributed) and the interrelated issue of the behavior of neanderthals (primitive or essentially human). Recent opinion covers essentially an equivalent spread of positions, although by the early 1980s a loose consensus had emerged (Trinkaus, 1986). Thus, over the period from 100 ty to 20 ty, both morphological and archaeological change were thought to map behavioral change, essentially in synchrony, and to document the evolution about 40 ty ago of fully modern human behavior probably based on language-mediated symboling. An archaic morphology, typified by neanderthals, was believed to reflect nonmodern subsistence, manipulative, positional, and social behaviors. Archaeological residues, especially Mousterian industries associated with neanderthals, were also thought to indicate nonmodern behaviors. The association of a few anatomically modern humans with late Mousterian industries and a neanderthal with the very earliest French Upper Paleolithic in what was believed to be a brief overlap period were interpreted within either replacement or transitional frameworks.

This particular consensus is now badly dented because of several recent developments. But first I shall review a little more fully some inferences about neanderthal behavior derived from morphology. In a number of features, neanderthals and modern humans are similar. Body mass, brain size, and degree of body size dimorphism all resemble humans (Trinkaus, 1986). Biomechanical analyses of male and female femora show differences similar to those found in modern human hunter-gatherer populations, in contrast to modern agricultural and sedentary populations (Ruff, 1987). However, neanderthals differ from even the most robust modern humans in many morphological features, several of which suggest bio-behavioral differences (Trinkaus, 1986). For example, facial prognathism and anterior tooth wear in neanderthals show that paramasticatory activities were very important. Tooth-eruption patterns and osteon densities in long bones suggest that skeletal maturation was a little more rapid and longevity shorter than in modern humans. Skeletal and, by inference, muscle mass were high in neanderthals, considerably beyond anything seen in modern humans. Finger proportions differed, and distal limb segments were shorter in neanderthals. Facial dimorphism was more marked in neanderthals, indeed in all nonmodern hominids, suggesting perhaps different patterns of social-sexual signalling. Many neanderthal specimens preserve evidence of trauma or damage, and some show incisions, some of which may be cut marks (Russell and LeMort, 1986). These and other morphological features have been interpreted as indicating a behavioral system in neanderthals that was nonmodern and, in important ways, less biologically efficient (Trinkaus, 1986).

The morphological differences between neanderthals and modern humans, which presumably had a genetic basis (they are present in very young individuals), considerably exceed those found among modern human populations (Howells, 1972). Many of them imply neanderthal behavioral patterns that were both nonmodern and "primitive." The archaeological differences between Mousterian and Upper Paleolithic industries, paralleling those between the African Middle and Late Stone Age, also imply behavioral differences, although degree and kind are debated. Whatever the nature of the difference, it is widely although not unanimously agreed that there was a difference and that it was in the direction of "less complex" or "more primitive" for Mousterian and Middle Stone Age (Klein, 1973, 1983; Deacon and Thackeray, 1983).

Given all this, some new hominid discoveries are surprising and paradoxical. Anatomically modern humans from Qafzeh (92 ty), from Klasies River (probably older than 100 ty) (Stringer and Andrews, 1988), and from Omo Kibish Formation (perhaps 130 ty) (Day and Stringer, 1982) demonstrate contemporaneity between neanderthals and moderns for a substantial time period (Boaz et al., 1982), and all are associated with Mousterian or Middle Stone Age archaeological assemblages. In the case of the Mousterian, the assemblages are indistinguishable from those produced by neanderthals (Valladas et al., 1987, 1988). Does this imply no behavioral differences between early modern humans and neanderthals? If so, why the anatomical differences? If neanderthals were behaviorally "modern," why the morphological differences from moderns? Why did neanderthals disappear after a long period of "coexistence?" Were there bio-behavioral differences, as well as or in contrast to cultural differences, between earlier (Mousterian/ Middle Stone Age) and later (Upper Paleolithic/Late Stone Age) anatomically modern humans? These and other questions are among the most interesting faced by paleoanthropologists today.

Concluding Remarks on Narratives

Having covered many of the significant issues in hominid evolution at least once, I want to turn finally to the issue of narrative. All popular accounts of human evolution and all textbooks tell stories. The stories always vary in detail but, for any particular historical time, they tend to be roughly equivalent. Even more technical papers frequently tell, or are embedded in, some smaller portion of a story. Because narratives have basic forms regardless of subject matter, and because many paleoanthropologists often have, explicitly or implicitly, broader messages in mind, it is worth considering what goes into the construction of paleoanthropological accounts. Narratives of human evolution preceded any hominid fossil record (Latour and Strum, 1986; Perper and Schrire, 1977. Cartmill, 1983; Landau, 1984), and even the earliest scientific accounts were noted for the influence of "nonscientific" data. Marx noted in a letter to Engels: "It is remarkable how Darwin recognises among beasts and plants his English society with its division of labor, competition, opening up of new markets, 'invention,' and the Malthusian 'struggle for existence.' It is Hobbes' *Bellum omnium contra omnes.*" Landau has documented the often considerable extent to which paleoanthropological narrative in the late nineteenth and early twentieth century resembled a Hero story (Landau, 1984). In 1937, Hooton was no exception to this grand tradition:

> We must conceive these generalized precursors of man and the African great apes as large primates with projecting jaws and only moderately large brains, who progressed through the trees by brachiating—swinging by the arms; who had prehensile feet as well as grasping hands. They were probably not specialized in the tremendous elongation of the arms that we observe in the gorilla, the chimpanzee and the orang-utan of today—animals which have displayed the conservatism which limits evolutionary development and which has induced them to remain tree-dwellers, or half-hearted quadrupedal ground-dwellers like the gorilla, long after their size, strength, intelligence, and dietary requirements demanded a fuller and richer existence as erect, terrestrial bipeds. Note that man, like Zaccheus, owes his importance to the fact that, having climbed a tree, he straightway came down.
>
> One of these Dryopithecus lines had the supreme gift of super-anthropoid intelligence and initiative. Its members took to the ground and eventually stood up on their hind legs, having developed stable supporting feet from the ancient Primate grasping organs. Their arms and hands were set free for prehension. They began to use weapons and tools—a step which initiated human culture and took the strain off their jaws and teeth, previously employed for offensive and defensive as well as masticatory purposes. Gradu-

ally the snout shrank back, and this recession seems to have been accompanied by an overgrowth of the brain. These are associated evolutionary phenomena but the one did not necessarily cause the other.

It is clear that more recent accounts, including the influential *African Genesis* (Ardrey, 1961), are also shaped by nonscientific factors (Cartmill *et al.*, 1986). I have suggested that one solution is to adopt an explicitly historicist rather than presentist approach in reconstructing past behaviors (Pilbeam, 1984). But since the questions asked about the past, even the most obviously scientific ones, reflect current beliefs about what is important in describing behavioral dynamics, it is unrealistic to expect that the past can ever escape the hand of the present. As Cartmill (1983) has cogently written:

> myths are generally good things—and the origin stories that paleoanthropologists tell are necessarily myths. They are myths, whether they are true or not, because they embody a fundamental cultural theme: they define and explain the critical differences between human beings and beasts. Whatever such stories single out as important factors in our origins become important parts of our self image. Conversely, such stories won't be listened to unless they account for the human peculiarities that we think are crucial markers of humanity. They will be listened to most carefully when they echo other themes from the culture of their time.

Andrews, P., and Martin, L. B., 1987, Cladistic relationships of extant and fossil hominoids, *J. Hum. Evol.* **16**: 101-118.

Ardrey, R., 1961, *African Genesis*, Collins, London.

Beynon, A. D., and Wood, B. A., 1987, Patterns and rates of enamel growth in the molar teeth of early hominids, *Nature* **326**: 493-496.

Binford, L. R., 1983, *In Pursuit of the Past*, Thames and Hudson, London.

Boaz, N. T., et al., 1982, Paleoclimatic setting for *Homo sapiens neanderthalensis*, *Naturwisensch.* **69**: 29-33.

Bonnefille, R., 1984, Cenozoic vegetation and environments of early hominids, in: East Africa in *The Evolution of the East Asian Environment*, vol. II (R. O. Whyte, ed.), Center of Asian Studies, University of Hong Kong.

Brain, C. K., 1981, *The Hunters or the Hunted?* Chicago University Press, Chicago.

Bunn, H. T., and Kroll, E.M., 1986, Systematic butchery by Plio/Pleistocene hominids at Olduvai Gorge, Tanzania, *Curr. Anthrop.* **27**: 431-452.

Cann, R. L., et al., 1987, Mitochondrial DNA and human evolution, *Nature* **325**: 31-36.

Cartmill, M., 1983, "Four legs good, two legs bad," *Nat. Hist.* **92**: 64-79.

Cartmill, M., et al., 1986, One hundred years of paleoanthropology, *Amer. Sci.* **74**: 410-420.

Chamberlain, A. T., and Wood, B. A., 1987, Early hominid phylogeny, *J. Hum. Evol.* **16**: 101-118.

Chivers, D. J., et al. (eds.), 1984, *Food Acquisition and Processing in Primates*, Plenum, New York.

Clark, W. E. Le Gros, and Leakey, L. S. B., 1951, The Miocene Hominoidea of East Africa, *Brit. Mus. (Nat. Hist.) Foss. Mam. Afr.* **I**: 117.

Clarke, R. J., 1985, *Australopithecus* and early *Homo* in southern Africa, in: *Ancestors* (E. Delson, ed.), pp. 171-177, Liss, New York.

Conroy, G. C., and Vannier, M. W., 1988, The nature of Taung dental maturation continued, *Nature* **333**: 808.

Dart, R. A., 1953, The predatory transition from ape to man, *Int. Anthrop. Ling. Rev.* **1**: 201-218.

Day, M. H., 1986, *Guide to Fossil Man*, 4th ed., Chicago University Press, Chicago.

Day, M. H., and Stringer, C. B., 1982, A reconsideration of the Omo Kibish remains and the *erectus-sapiens* transition, in: *Congres International de Paleontologie Humaine*, pp. 814-846, Pretirage, Nice.

Deacon, H. J., and Thackeray, J. F., 1983, Late Pleistocene environmental changes and implications for the archaeological record in Southern Africa, in: *Late Cainozoic paleoclimates of the southern* (J. C. Vogel, ed.).

Delson, E., 1987, Evolution and paleobiology of robust *Australopithecus*, *Nature* 327: 654-655.

Excoffier, L., et al., 1987, Genetics and history of sub-saharan Africa, *Yb. Phys. Anthrop.* 30: 151-194.

Fossey, D., 1983, *Gorillas in the Mist*, Houghton Mifflin, Boston.

Giles, E., and Ambrose, S. H. 1986, Are we all out of Africa? *Nature* 322: 21-22.

Goodall, J., 1971, *In the Shadow of Man*, Houghton Mifflin, Boston.

Goodall, J., 1986, *The Chimpanzees of Gombe*, Harvard University Press, Cambridge.

Goodman, M., 1963, Serological analysis of the systematics of recent hominoids, *Hum. Biol.* 35: 377-424.

Goodman, M., and Tashian, R. E. (eds.), 1975, *Molecular Anthropology*, Plenum, New York.

Gould, S. J., and Vrba, E. S., 1982, Exaptation—a missing term in the science of form, *Paleobiol.* 8: 4-15.

Greenwood, J. J. D., 1986, Occam and mankind's genetic bottleneck, *Nature* 324: 21-22.

Grine, F. E., 1981, Trophic differences between "gracile" and "robust" australopithecines: a scanning electron microscope analysis of occlusal events, *S. Afr. J. Sci.* 77: 203-230.

Grine, F. E., 1986, Dental evidence for dietary differences in *Australopithecus* and *Paranthropus*: a quantitative analysis of permanent molar microwear, *J. Hum. Evol.* 15: 783-822.

Grine, F. E., and Kay, R. F., 1988, Early hominid diets from quantitative image analysis of dental microwear, *Nature* 333: 765-768.

Groves, C., 1986, Systematics of the great apes, in: *Comparative Primate Biology*, vol. I (J. Erwin and D. R. Swindler, eds.), pp. 187-217, Liss, New York.

Harrison, T., 1986, A reassessment of the phylogenetic relationships of *Oreopithecus bambolii* Gervais, *J. Hum. Evol.* 15: 541-583.

Holloway, R. L., 1978, Problems of brain endocast interpretation and African hominid evolution, in: *Early Hominoids of Africa* (C. J. Jolly, ed.), pp. 379-401, Duckworth.

Holloway, R. L., 1983, Cerebral brain endocast patterns of *Australopithecus afarensis* hominid, *Nature* 303: 420-422.

Holmquist, R., et al., 1988, Analysis of higher-primate phylogeny from transversion differences in nuclear and mitochondrial parsimony and operator metrics, *Mol. Biol. Evol.* 5: 217-236.

Hooton, Earnest, 1937, *Apes, Men, and Morons*, Putnam, New York.

Howells, W. W., 1972, Analysis of patterns of variation in crania of recent man, in: *The Functional and Evolutionary Biology of Primates* (R. H. Tuttle, ed.), pp. 123-151, Aldine, Atherton.

Isaac, G. Ll., 1971, The diet of early man: aspects of archaeological evidence from Lower and Middle Pleistocene sites in Africa, *World Archaeology* 2: 278-299.

Isaac, G. Ll., 1983, Aspects of human evolution, in: *Evolution from Molecules to Man* (D. S. Bendall, ed.), pp. 509-543, Cambridge.

Johanson, D. C., and Edey, M., 1981, *Lucy: The Beginnings of Mankind*, Simon and Schuster, New York.

Johanson, D. C., and White, T. D., 1979, A systematic assessment of early African hominids, *Science* 202: 321-330

Keith, A., 1911, Klaatsch's theory of the descent of man, *Nature* 85: 508-510.

Kelley, J., 1986*a*, Paleobiology of Miocene hominoids, Ph.D. Thesis, Yale University, pp. 1-365.

Kelley, J., 1986*b*, Species recognition and sexual dimorphism in *Proconsul* and *Rangwapithecus*, *J. Hum. Evol.* 15: 461-495.

Kelley, J., and Pilbeam, D., 1986, The dryopithecines: taxonomy, comparative anatomy, and phylogeny of Miocene large hominids, in: *Comparative Primate Biology*, vol. I, pp. 361-411, Liss, New York.

Kinzey, W. G. (ed.), 1987, *The Evolution of Human Behavior: Primate Models*, SUNY Press, Albany.

Klein, R. G., 1973, *Ice-age Hunters of the Ukraine*, Chicago University Press, Chicago.

Klein, R. G., 1983, The stone age prehistory of Southern Africa, *Ann. Rev. Anthropol.* 12: 25-48.

Landau, M., 1984, Human evolution as narrative, *Amer. Sci.* 72: 262-268.

Latimer, B., et al., 1987, Talocrural joint in African hominoids: implications for *Australopithecus afarensis*, *Amer. J. Phys. Anthrop.* 74: 155-175

Latour, B., and Strum, S. C., 1986, Human social origins: oh please tell us another story, *J. Social Biol. Struct.* 9: 169-187.

Leakey, L. S. B., Tobias, P. V., and Napier, J. R., 1964, A new species of the genus *Homo* from Olduvai Gorge, *Nature* 202: 7-9.

Leakey, M. D., et al., 1976, Fossil hominids from the Laetolil Beds, *Nature* **262**: 460-466.

Leakey, R. E., 1988, Morphology of *Afropithecus turkanensis* from Kenya, *Amer. J. Phys. Anthrop.* **76**: 289-307.

Leutenegger, W., and Shell, B., 1987, Variability and sexual dimorphism in canine size of *Australopithecus* and extant hominoids, *J. Hum. Evol.* **16**: 359-368.

Lieberman, D. E., et al., 1988, A probabilistic approach to the problem of sexual dimorphism in *Homo habilis*: a comparison of KNM-ER 1470 and KNM ER-1813, *J. Hum. Evol.*, in press.

Mann, A. E., 1975, Paleodemographic aspects of the South African australopithecines, *U. Penn. Publ. Anthropo.* **1**: 171.

Marzke, M. W., 1983, Joint function and grips of the *Australopithecus afarensis* hand, with special reference to the region of the capitate, *J. Hum. Evol.* **12**: 197-211.

McHenry, H. M., 1984, Relative cheek-tooth size in *Australopithecus*, *Amer. J. Phys. Anthrop.* **64**: 297-306.

McHenry, H. M., 1986, The first bipeds: a comparison of the *A. afarensis* and *A. africanus* postcranium and implications for the evolution of bipedalism, *J. Hum. Evol.* **15**: 177-191.

McHenry, H. M., 1986, Size variation in the postcranium of *Australopithecus afarensis* and extant species of Hominoidea, *Hum. Evol.* **1**: 149-156.

Nei, M., 1985, Human evolution at the molecular level, in: *Population Genetics and Molecular Evolution* (T. Outa and K. Aoki, eds.), Japan Sci. Soc. Press, pp. 41-64, Tokyo/Springer-Verlag, Berlin.

Nei, M., 1987, *Molecular Evolutionary Genetics*, Columbia University Press, New York.

Nei, M., et al., 1985, Methods for computing the standard errors of branching points in an evolutionary tree and their application to molecular data from humans and apes, *Mol. Biol. Evol.* **2**: 66-85.

Olson, T. R., 1985, Cranial morphology and systematics of the Hadar Formation hominids and "*Australopithecus*" *africanus*, in: *Ancestors* (E. Delson, ed.), pp. 102-119, Liss, New York.

Perper, T., and Schrire, C., 1977, The Nimrod connection: myth and science in the hunting model, in: *The Chemical Senses and Nutrition*, pp. 447-459, Academic Press, New York.

Pilbeam, D., 1978, Recognizing specific diversity in heterogeneous fossil samples, in: *Early Hominids in Africa* (C. J. Jolly, ed.), pp. 505-515, Duckworth.

Pilbeam, D., 1984, Reflections on early human ancestors, *J. Anthrop. Res.* **40**: 14-22.

Pilbeam, D., 1986, Hominoid evolution and hominid origins, *Amer. Anthrop.* **88**: 295-312.

Pilbeam, D., and Zwell, M., 1972, The single species hypothesis, sexual dimorphism, and variability in early hominids, *Yb. Phys. Anthrop.* **16**: 69-79.

Ridley, M., 1986, *Evolution and Classification*, Longman, London.

Rightmire, G. P., 1981, Patterns in the evolution of *Homo erectus*, *Paleobiol.* **7**: 241-246.

Roberts, N., 1984, Pleistocene environments in time and space, in: *Hominid Evolution and Community Ecology* (R. Foley, ed.), pp. 25-53, Academic Press, New York.

Rodman, P. S., 1984, Foraging and social systems of orangutans and chimpanzees, in: *Adaptations for Foraging in Nonhuman Primates* (P. S. Rodman and J. G. Cantt, eds.), pp. 134-159, Columbia University Press, New York.

Rodman, P. S., and McHenry, H. M., 1980, Bioenergetics and the origin of hominid bipedalism, *Amer. J. Phys. Anthrop.* **52**: 103-106.

Rose, M. D., 1984, Food acquisition and the evolution of positional behavior: the case of bipedalism, in: *Food Acquisition and Processing in Primates* (D. J. Chivers, B. A. Wood, and A. Bilsborough, eds.), pp. 509-524, Plenum, New York.

Ruff, C., 1987, Sexual dimorphism in lower limb bone structure: relationship to subsistence strategy and sexual division of labor, *J. Hum. Evol.* **16**: 391-417.

Russell, M. D., and LeMort, F., 1986, Cutmarks on the Engis 2 calvaria, *Amer. J. Phys. Anthrop.* **69**: 317-322.

Sarich, V. M., 1983, Retrospective on hominoid macromolecular systematics, in: *New Interpretations of Ape and Human Ancestry* (R. L. Ciochon and R. S. Corruccini, eds.), pp. 137-150, Plenum, New York.

Sarich, V., 1988, Sound of distance drums, *Nature* **332**: 499.

Sarich, V. M., and Cronin, J., 1975, Molecular systematics of the primates, in: *Molecular Anthropology* (M. Goodman and R. E. Tashian, eds.), pp. 141-169, Plenum, New York.

Sarich, V., and Wilson, A., 1967, Rates of albumin evolution in primates, *Proc. Nat. Acad. Sci.* **58**: 142-148.

Senut, B., and Tardieu, C., 1985, Functional aspects of Plio-Pleistocene hominid limb bones: implications for taxonomy and phylogeny, in: *Ancestors* (E. Delson, ed.), pp. 193-201, Liss, New York.

Singer, R., and Wymer, J. 1982, *The Middle Stone Age at Klasies River Mouth in South Africa*, Chicago University Press, New York.

Skelton, R. R., et al., 1986, Phylogenetic analysis of early hominids, *Curr. Anthrop.* **27**: 21-43.

Smith, B. H., 1986, Dental development in *Australopithecus* and early *Homo*, *Nature* **323**: 327-330.

Smuts, B., et al. (eds.), 1986, *Primates Societies*, Chicago University Press, Chicago.

Stoneking, M., et al., 1986, Rate of sequence divergence estimated from restriction maps of mitochondrial DNAs from Papua New Guinea, *Cold Spring Harbor Symposia on Quantitative Biology* **51**: 433-439.

Stringer, C., 1984, Human evolution and biological adaptation in the Pleistocene, in: *Hominid Evolution and Community Ecology* (R. Foley, ed.), pp. 55-83, Academic Press, New York.

Stringer, C. B., 1986, The credibility of *Homo habilis*, in: *Major Topics in Primate and Human Evolution* (B. Wood, L. Martin, and P. Andrews, eds.), Cambridge University Press.

Stringer, C. B., and Andrews, P., 1988, Genetic and fossil evidence for the origin of modern humans, *Science* **239**: 1263-1268.

Sussman, R. L., Stern, J. T., and Jungers, W. L., 1984, Arboreality and bipedality in the Hadar hominids, *Folia Primatol.* **43**: 113-156.

Tattersall, I., 1986, Species recognition in human paleontology, *J. Hum. Evol.* **15**: 165-175.

Tobias, P. V., 1967, *Olduvai Gorge*, Vol. 2, Cambridge University Press.

Trinkaus, E., 1986, The neanderthals and modern human origins, *Ann. Rev. Anthropol.* **15**: 193-218.

Valladas, H., et al., 1987, Thermoluminescence dates for the neanderthal burial site at Kebara in Israel, *Nature* **330**: 159-160.

Valladas, H., et al., 1988, Thermoluminescence dating of Mousterian 'proto-Cro-Magnon' remains from Israel and the origin of modern man, *Nature* **331**: 614-616.

Wainscoat, J. S., et al., 1986, Evolutionary relationships of human populations from an analysis of nuclear DNA polymorphism, *Nature* **319**: 491-493.

Walker, A., et al., 1986, 2.5- Myr *Australopithecus boisei* from west of Lake Turkana, Kenya, *Nature* **322**: 517-522.

Walker, A., 1981, Dietary hypotheses and human evolution, *Phil. Trans. R. Soc. Lond.* **B292**: 57-64.

Walker, A. C., and Pickford, M., 1983, New postcranial fossils of *Proconsul africanus* and *Proconsul nyanzae*, in: *New Interpretations of Ape and Human Ancestry* (R. L. Ciochon and R. S. Corruccini, eds.), pp. 325-351, Plenum, New York

Ward, S., and Hill, A., 1987, Pliocene hominid partial mandible from Tabarin, Baringo, Kenya, *Amer. J. Phys. Anthrop.* **72**: 21-37.

Weiss, M. L., 1987, Nucleic acid evidence bearing on hominoid relationships, *Yb. Phys. Anthrop.* **30**: 41-73.

White, R., 1982, Rethinking the Middle/Upper Paleolithic transition, *Curr. Anthropol.* **23**: 169-192.

Williams, G. C., 1966, *Adaptation and Natural Selection*, Princeton.

Wolpoff, M. H., 1984, Evolution in *Homo erectus*: the question of stasis, *Paleobiol.* **10**: 389-406.

Wolpoff, M. H., et al., 1984, Modern *Homo* sapiens origins: a general theory of hominid evolution involving the fossil evidence from east Asia, in: *The Origins of Modern Humans* (F. H. Smith and F. Spencer, eds.), pp. 411-483, Liss, New York.

Wolpoff, M. H., et al., 1988, Modern human origins, *Science* **241**: 772-773.

Wood, B. A., and Chamberlain, A. T., 1987, The nature and affinities of the "robust" australopithecines: a review, *J. Hum. Evol.* **16**: 625-641.

Wrangham, R., 1987, African apes: the significance of African apes for reconstructing human social evolution, in: *The Evolution of Human Behavior: Primate Models* (W. G. Kinzey, ed.), pp. 51-70, SUNY, Albany.

In his thoughtful and forward-looking survey of problems and prospects in paleoanthropology, Dr. Pilbeam has identified a number of issues of current interest and activity. Among these, as he recognizes, none is as basic as that of alpha taxonomy, or species recognition. How does one sort fossil specimens into biologically meaningful groups, essentially species, when species are hard enough to define in the living world? Even field biologists hardly ever see species: at best they see highly local populations, and rarely indeed do the two coincide. Yet few would wish to argue that species don't exist, or that they are not the basic unit with which systematists must deal. Speciation is the central irreversible historical phenomenon that we need to detect, or at least infer, in the fossil record, and I deeply sympathize with Dr. Pilbeam's desire to find "an explicit model, appropriately quantified, against which contingent hypotheses can be framed."

But I fear, alas, that any search for a general paleontological model of this kind is likely to be fruitless, at least as long as we are restricted to the criteria available today. This is because the central data of paleontology are morphological, and there is absolutely no necessary relationship between speciation and morphological change (e.g., Vrba, 1980). Many species—our own is one—have achieved high degrees of morphological variability and geographic dispersion without undergoing speciation; while on the other hand, speciation can take place with little or no morphological displacement, particularly in the hard skeletal parts that preserve in the fossil record. In other words, when we attempt to divide up our fossil assemblages, which principally supply us with morphology, we are looking for evidence of an irreversible genetic and historical event, not a morphological one. Of course, paleontological or related information can help

us to make biological decisions in restricted circumstances. For instance, the recent reconfirmation that the so-called first family of Hadar site 333 was indeed buried in an instantaneous event (Radosevich and Retallack, 1988) increases the likelihood that all members of the assemblage belonged to the same social group, hence species, despite the rather large size variation evident in the sample. But factors such as time and geography have no greater connection with species identity than do morphological shifts, and it is thus evident that on currently available criteria, in the vast majority of cases our species allocations are doomed to be highly inferential and subjective.

The upshot of all this is that subjective decisions on the species content of the human fossil record will necessarily continue to mold our perceptions of mode and pattern in human evolution. Back when Earnest Hooton wrote *Apes, Men, and Morons,* many more generic and specific nomina were bandied around in human paleontology than there are today, despite the vastly smaller number of human fossils known. With the postwar eclipse of typology, attention to anatomical minutiae came to seem old-fashioned, while the new appreciation of the importance of biological variation gave lumping a veneer of sophistication. Because the smaller the number of points you have, the easier it is to join them up into a straight line, the resulting steeply descending curve of generic and specific diversity in Hominidae fed ultimately into such absurdities as the single-species hypothesis, which eliminated any consideration of morphology at all in inferring pattern in human evolution, and both reflected and reinforced a particular view of evolution. Now that the pendulum is swinging back toward a more diverse hominid clade, we may expect perceptions of evolutionary pattern to alter, even though many probably agree with Dr. Pilbeam that the human fossil record is at present too sparse at most points to allow a choice between evolutionary modes.

However, the issue of punctuated equilibrium versus gradualism may be more addressable than Dr. Pilbeam would allow on the basis of present evidence, if only in terms of the evolution of our perceptions of the enlarging human fossil record. For if gradualism is the predominant pattern in human evolutionary history, then that history must at least largely be a matter of discovery: each new fossil should, as it is found, fit neatly into an emerging picture, filling in yet another gap (Eldredge and Tattersall, 1975). In fact, the very reverse has occurred: with each new fossil the picture has tended to become more confused, or at least more complex, and phylogenies have regularly needed substantial readjustment to accommodate such new finds. This kind of experience is more in line with what one would expect of a human evolutionary past involving repeated speciations than with the stately progression of one or a few lineages. It strongly hints that human phylogeny is littered with speciations, species, and extinctions, and that the human fossil record reflects a complex set of relationships that demands analysis rather than simply discovery. We should hardly find this surprising in view of the extreme climatic vagaries that have marked a good portion of the documented span of the human lineage; opportunities for population isolation, speciation, and extinction can rarely have been better than during the Pleistocene (Tattersall, 1986).

Which brings us back to species, for we can hardly hope to understand the pattern of human evolution without the ability to recognize its basic units. I have said that, even in theory, objective allocation of fossils to species is more or less impossible using available criteria. However, when one looks at the patterns of variation between closely related species in the living primate fauna, one finds that, in general, species that are classified within the same genus differ but little from one another in the bones and teeth. The vexed question of sexual dimorphism aside, gestalt differences between crania and dentitions are usually restricted to species belonging to different genera. I am totally in agreement with Dr. Pilbeam that one of the most significant achievements of the synthesis was to promote universal recognition of the fact of variability in natural populations; and I recognize equally that such variation will always be a potential confounding factor when closely related species are being compared, if only because there will almost invariably be almost total overlap in the ranges of variation of almost all characters. However, the other side of this is that where distinct and consistent morphs can be identified, differentiation will virtually always have proceeded at least to the level of the species.

It is for this reason I have argued that while disentangling very closely related species will always be tricky, one may nonetheless be fairly confident that the number of hominid species represented in the fossil record is underestimated (Tattersall, 1986), and that where distinct and consistent morphs exist in that record, it is almost certainly justified to recognize them as distinct species. This argument is gaining acceptance quite rapidly. As Dr. Pilbeam has pointed out, it is now legitimate to inquire how many species are represented in the *Homo habilis* assemblage (rather than whether the taxon is distinct at all); or to ask whether the monolithic concept of *Homo erectus* may be breaking down (rather than to debate the amount of change that took place in this "lineage" over its long time-span); or, again, to question how many hominid species may be represented in the fossil record of the middle and late Pleistocene (rather than to have to defend the self-evident proposition that *Homo erectus* and *Homo sapiens* are indeed distinct or distinguishable species). In certain quarters it is even possible nowadays to utter the words *Homo neanderthalensis* without undue embarrassment. It is being realized, in other words, that names are not simply clutter, but that more of them will be needed to reflect the biological diversity of the hominid clade. With Dr. Pilbeam, I welcome this development.

American Museum of Natural History

Eldredge, N. and Tattersall, I., 1975, Evolutionary models, phylogenetic reconstruction, and another look at hominid phylogeny, in: *Approaches to Primate Paleobiology* (F. S. Szalay, ed.), pp. 218-243, Karger, Basel.

Radosevich, S. C. and Retallack, G. J., 1988, Paleoecology of hominids from the site AL-333, Hadar, Ethiopia, *Amer. Jour. Phys. Anthrop.* **75**: 258.

Tattersall, I., 1986, Species recognition in human paleontology, *Jour. Hum. Evol.* **15**: 165-175.

Vrba, E. S., 1980, Evolution, species and fossils: how does life evolve? *S. Afr. Jour. Sci.* **76**: 61-84.

Eric Delson

Even before Darwin, the "species problem" had been one of the foremost topics for debate in evolutionary biology, including paleoanthropology. Much of the recent literature on species concepts has been ably summarized by Bock (1986 and this volume). I agree with him that the biological species concept is robust and overarching, encompassing such supposedly distinct alternatives as the "evolutionary" species of Simpson (1961) or the "recognition" concept of Paterson (e.g., 1985). However, I strongly disagree with Bock's acceptance of biospecies as theoretically nondimensional, with no time depth, discernible only by comparison to sympatric, contemporaneous populations. Biospecies are multidimensional, theoretically as well as taxonomically, with time as one important aspect of their existence. If species multiply (in Bock's words) through lineage splitting via allopatric isolation, the beginning of a new species *can* be fixed temporally as that time interval (not moment or point) between the first rupture of hereditary continuity and the (often inferred) onset of renewed sympatry. Paleontologists seek to recognize paleospecies that correspond to living biospecies. Even most neontologists do not deal with biospecies as such, but with morphospecies analogized to biospecies through the study of more characters than paleontologists have available. Thus, the problem of central importance today is to develop empirical approaches to delineating species in the fossil record (or in museum collections generally) that correspond to those few that can be defined through direct application of the biological species concept. A paleoanthropological example of the confusion resulting from competing species concepts is offered by the genus *Homo*.

In their symposium papers, Pilbeam and Tattersall both discussed the recent increase in the number of widely accepted species of *Homo*. By 1970 or so, the three species *H. sapiens*, *H. erectus*, and *H. habilis* were rather firmly entrenched, and for over two decades newly discovered or reinterpreted morphs were allocated to one of them rather than named as distinct species. In the past five years, however, each of these species has been suggested to include two or more similar and broadly contemporaneous species erroneously "lumped" together. The studies of Wood (1985) and colleagues (e.g., Lieberman *et al.*, 1988) and of Stringer (1986, 1987) have led many workers to question the inclusion of all "early *Homo*" in *H. habilis*. Some apparently early fossils may in fact represent *Homo erectus* (see Clarke, 1985), but the range of morphological variation observed in specimens from Olduvai and East Turkana usually allocated to *H. habilis* now is considered at least "disturbing" by a majority of researchers. The situation is even more complex for the two younger species.

Homo erectus was first identified in Asia, but various Middle Pleistocene fossils from Africa have been allocated to this species in the past 30 years. Recently, several authors have questioned the inclusion of such specimens in *H. erectus* because they were said to have lacked one or more of the autapomorphies diagnosing the Asian populations (e.g., Andrews, 1984; Stringer, 1984; Wood, 1984; Tattersall, 1986). Others have questioned the formal separation of *H. erectus* from *H. sapiens* on grounds analogous to those invoked by Bock, namely that a continuous lineage should not be arbitrarily divided (e.g., Jelinek, 1981; Hublin, 1986). A third group of researchers (Howells, 1980; Rightmire, 1984, 1987, 1988) has continued to support a broad definition of *H. erectus* as a species distinct from *H. sapiens*. In their review of this situation, Turner and Chamberlain (1989) argue that the purported autapomorphies of Asian *H. erectus* may not be exclusively present in Chinese and Javanese fossils or may be indeterminate in Africa due to specimen damage. They support, albeit tentatively, retention of a single polytypic (and probably polymorphic) species *Homo erectus*, and I would concur.

Finally, the greatest range of argument rages about the delineation of *Homo sapiens*. Over the past decade, the general consensus has been that early or "archaic" *H. sapiens* evolved either in Europe or Africa from a late regional variant of *H. erectus*. In turn, this group spread broadly over the Old World, replacing the remaining *H. erectus* populations and differentiating into regional variants such as the Neanderthals, eastern Asians and the "Rhodesian" group in sub-Saharan Africa. The origin of modern humans is alternatively suggested to have been from a Neanderthal or Rhodesian/archaic ancestry or simultaneously from several regional variants linked to each other by partial gene flow and to living human variants in similar geographic areas. This pattern has been further complicated by Tattersall (1986, this volume), Pilbeam (this volume), and others who suggest that more than one biospecies may be subsumed in this broadly construed version of *Homo sapiens*. They advocate distinguishing the Neanderthals as a separate species and suggest relegating the "archaic *sapiens*" populations to another one at least. Rightmire (1988) has most recently urged separation of the "archaics" as a distinct species (avoiding comment on the Neanderthals), while Stringer and Andrews (1988*a,b*) separate the Neanderthals but do not discuss the "archaics" taxonomically. Each of these alternatives conflicts not only with those who would retain the concept of a single broadly defined species developed since 1980, but even more with those who suggest Neanderthal ancestry for some or all living humans (see, e.g., Wolpoff *et al.*, 1988). Which aspects of these conflicting views should be accepted?

142

Clearly, there must be some morphological or taxonomic baseline employed in any empirical discussion of species recognition. For paleoanthropology, especially in the later phases of human evolution, the obvious standard is variation in living people and the taxonomic level of separation accepted for modern populations. Generally, living human groups are considered to belong to a single polymorphic and "polytypic" (i.e., regionally varying) subspecies. Admittedly, part of this determination is sociopolitical, as distinguishing among living humans at the subspecies level might lead to invidious comparisons and racist inferences by bigots searching for "scientific support" of their prejudices. Yet, there is some systematic basis for such a monolithic view of living humans, given the apparent overall morphological and genetic similarity (and continuity) among moderns and the variation known within subspecies of such wide-ranging primates as *Papio hamadryas*.

If this determination of *H. s. sapiens* for living people is accepted, it then seems to me that Neanderthals can only be classed as a second subspecies of *H. sapiens*. Other populations possibly representing temporal subspecies of this species include: the Arago-Petralona-Heidelberg group (not including Swanscombe and comparable fossils, which would be classed instead as early members of a Neanderthal lineage); the Rhodesian group (Kabwe, Saldhana, Ndutu, possibly Bodo), which might be morphologically similar to the preceding but differentiated geographically; and the more derived African group of Ngaloba, Omo Kibish 2, and Florisbad. Following further study, additional subspecies might be delineated for Asian populations such as those represented by Narmada and the Dali and Jinniushan specimens. Would Tattersall and Pilbeam separate each of these units as a full species, returning to the 1950s' profusion of nomina as mere "handles"; or do I go too far in "lumping" and fall into

Campbell's (1972) trap of naming all variants as subspecies? I suggest it is reasonable to equate temporal and geographic variation and thus apply subspecific names to the relatively distinct groups discerned in any well-documented fossil record where both "axes" of variation are observable.

It would be useful to have a better standard than subjective opinion, and I think that may be possible in the case of the Neanderthals. I suggest that variation among the known specimens be assessed for a variety of characters and compared to that observed in populations of living humans across Eurasia. This is a greater area of distribution than known for Neanderthals, but that would offset the time depth of the fossils. If the variation observed for Neanderthals is comparable to or greater than that seen in living humans, I would accept more readily that the two represent different species; but if the Neanderthals evidence less variation, they might better be included in *Homo sapiens*.

A further factor is archaeological. Where cultural residues are known, the earliest members of *H. s. sapiens* (e.g., Qafzeh, Skhul, perhaps Djebel Irhoud) are associated with Mousterian industries not significantly different from those found with Neanderthals in southern Europe or the Near East. This does not prove that the makers were conspecific, as Acheulean artifacts are associated in Europe with early *H. sapiens* and in Africa with *H. erectus*, but any paleoanthropological "solution" to this question must involve both biological and cultural remains and adaptations.

As Pilbeam said in his symposium paper, paleoanthropology does not usually bring new theory to evolutionary biology, but it is an active area of application of new ideas. Human fossils are often employed as examples of whatever evolutionary pattern or process an author is discussing, as witness Bock (1986 and this volume). The human fossil record, especially for the last few hundred thousand years, is rather well known and thus open to a variety of interpretations. The evolution of *Homo sapiens* as interpreted here exemplifies rapid diversification and morphological change within the confines of a species delimited by a probable allopatric isolation interval at its origin. It thus serves as a valuable focal point for discussion of the empirical limits of a species-level taxon on the one hand, while demonstrating the temporal aspect of species multidimensionality on the other.

Lehman College and the
CUNY Graduate School

Andrews, P., 1984, An alternative interpretation of characters used to define *Homo erectus, Cour. Forsch-Inst. Senckenberg* **69**: 167-175.

Bock, W. J., 1986, Species concepts, speciation and macroevolution, in: *Modern Aspects of Species* (K. Iwatsuki, P. H. Raven, and W. J. Bock, eds.), pp. 31-57, Univ. of Tokyo Press, Tokyo.

Campbell, B. G., 1972, Conceptual progress in physical anthropology: fossil man, *Ann. Revs. Anthropol.* **1**: 27-54.

Clarke, R. J., 1985, A new reconstruction of the Florisbad cranium, with notes on the site, in: *Ancestors: The Hard Evidence* (E. Delson, ed.), pp. 301-305, Liss, New York.

Howells, W. W., 1980, *Homo erectus*: who, when and where, *Yearbook Phys. Anthropol.* **23**: 1-23.

Hublin, J. J., 1986, Some comments on the diagnostic features of *Homo erectus*, in: *Fossil Man: New Facts, New Ideas* (V. V. Novotny and A. Mizerova, eds.), pp. 175-187, Anthropos, Brno.

Jelinek, J., 1981, Was *Homo erectus* already *Homo sapiens*? in: *Les Processus de l'Hominisation*, pp. 85-89, CNRS, Paris.

Lieberman, D. E., Pilbeam, D. R., and Wood, B. A., 1988, A probabilistic approach to the problem of sexual dimorphism in *Homo habilis*: a comparison of KNM-ER 1470 and KNM-ER 1813, *J. Hum Evol.* **17**: 503-511.

Paterson, H. E. H., 1985, The recognition concept of species, in: *Species and Speciation* (E. S. Vrba, ed.), pp. 21-29, Transvaal Museum Monograph No. 4, Pretoria.

Rightmire, G. P., 1984, Comparisons of *Homo erectus* from Africa and southeast Asia, *Cour. Forsch.-Inst. Senckenberg* **69**: 83-98.

Rightmire, G. P., 1987, Species recognition and *Homo erectus, J. Hum. Evol.* **15**: 823-826.

Rightmire, G. P. 1988, *Homo erectus* and later Middle Pleistocene humans, *Ann. Rev. Anthropol.* **17**: 239-259.

Simpson, G. G., 1961, *Principles of Animal Taxonomy*, Columbia University Press, New York.

Stringer, C. B., 1984, The definition of *Homo erectus* and the existence of the species in Africa and Europe, *Cour. Forsch.-Inst. Senckenberg* **69**: 131-143.

Stringer, C. B., 1986, The credibility of *Homo habilis*, in: *Major Topics in Primate and Human Evolution* (B. A. Wood, L. Martin, and P. Andrews, eds.), pp. 266-294, Cambridge University Press, Cambridge.

Stringer, C. B., 1987, A numerical cladistic analysis for the genus *Homo, J. Hum. Evol.* **16**: 135-146.

Stringer, C. B., and Andrews, P., 1988a, Genetic and fossil evidence for the origin of modern humans, *Science* **239**: 1263-1268.

Stringer, C. B., and Andrews, P., 1988b, Response [to Wolpoff et al.], *Science* **241**: 773.

Tattersall, I., 1986, Species recognition in paleontology, *J. Hum. Evol.* **15**: 165-175.

Turner, A., and Chamberlain, A., 1989, Speciation, morphological change and the status of African *Homo erectus, J. Hum. Evol.* **18**: 115-30.

Wolpoff, M. H., Spuhler, J. N., Smith, F. H., Radovcic, J., Pope, G. G., Frayer, D. W., Eckhardt, R., and Clark, G., 1988, Modern human origins (letter), *Science* **241**: 772-773.

Wood, B. A., 1984, The origin of *Homo erectus, Cour. Forsch.-Inst. Senckenberg* **69**: 99-111.

Wood, B. A., 1985, Early *Homo* in Kenya, and its systematic relationships, in: *Ancestors: The Hard Evidence* (E. Delson, ed.), pp. 206-214, Liss, New York.

Preparation of this paper was supported by a grant from the PSC/CUNY Research Award program, No. 667370.

Frederick S. Szalay

Dr. Pilbeam has given a comprehensive summary of what taxonomic procedures have or should have been applied to fossil hominids, and cogently summarized aspects of an enormous literature dealing with hominid behavioral reconstruction. It was of particular importance that Pilbeam pointed out that assumptions about variability in the extant world should form the foundation of our taxonomic procedures. It must be noted, although I cannot here expand on this, that evolutionary interpretation of the evidence and the taxonomizing of the record are two separate, albeit complementary, procedures. The latter must follow the former, as all method should fall out of theory.

I will briefly discuss serious problems with the interpretation of the fossil record of the hominids that are not due either to the record itself or to the existing taxonomic framework. This is understandable as such efforts to comprehend the causal forces and historical events underlying evolutionary history, *lineage paleobiology,* present the most complex of problems within evolutionary biology. In essence, I ask the rhetorical question in this paper, without the appropriate discussion that should follow: Can we expect meaningful answers to the evolutionary question—Why does something exists as it does?—without attempting to answer the specifics of how something has come to be in a certain way?

Perhaps as a result of the difficulties faced, seemingly widely applicable theoretical panaceas have often been embraced. As a direct influence of the punctuated equilibrium view of evolutionary change and of the corollary taxic outlook on evolutionary processes, there are a number of curiously flawed yet widely espoused explanations about humans and hominids and other organisms. Sociobiological theories, based largely on gene selection and kin selection theory as implied causal forces, have produced adaptive (i.e., outcome) explanations that sidestep both historical events as causes and functionally causal proximate mechanisms. The results are an incomplete, or often grossly flawed, understanding of why something has evolved the way it did, and how and why it is adaptive. I will very briefly comment on some of these problems as they relate to several of the points raised.

Punctuation and Taxonomy: Traps for Lineage Paleobiology Reconstruction

Phenon differences are the bases of all taxonomies (but not of microevolutionary theories and the theoretical biological species concept), and paleontologists in particular must depend on morphological distinctions. Dealing with samples of the past in terms of traditional taxonomy, however, is a potential trap that can completely dictate the interpretive framework for behavioral reconstruction.

If a species concept is untestable in the present time level, as Hennig's theoretical concept of species (based on the Simpsonian evolutionary species) is with its dependence on splittings of the lineage, then this interplay between the theoretical and operational will immediately channel our approach to the phylogeny and behavioral ecology of past entities. An axiomatic assumption of splitting for all known statistical samples severely inhibits the understanding of history, particularly hominid history. All samples of the past under cladistics, by fiat, become "monophyletic species," never segments of lineages (see the vast majority of most recent pictorial phylogenies of hominids). A "splitting" event is a consequence of isolation, it is not of biological significance until sympatry presents the biologically and reproductively diagnostic distinction of the two biological species.

If a taxonomic species concept becomes the operative theoretical species concept for evolutionary theorizing, and in turn for deductive schemes, then it is easy to see how punctuation can be attached to speciation. Yet clearly if we had independent means of ascertaining splittings, the two could be independently testable. As it stands, they cannot be and the circularity relating both to punctuation and the evolutionary species concept of Simpson and Hennig (or the monophyletic species concept) is a fact of life. Small phenon differences (usually of a part of an organism) can only support punctuation if these are viewed as different species, and vice versa. Often taxonomic species are but segments of a lineage (i.e., the historical *path* of an evolving species), as is probably the case for many hominid samples.

The concept of the nondimensional biological species of Mayr presents us with both an ontology and epistemology that fulfill the theoretical need for testability. The multidimensional, taxonomic, species concept on the other hand serves the need for taxonomy. Without a record of paleontological sympatry and synchroneity, therefore, the enumeration of species-level taxa alone in the hominid record will not advance the cause of evolutionary understanding. On the contrary, it will imply something that we cannot prove—namely, the lack of continuity between populations over vast areas.

Approaching hominid (or any other) paleobiology without the primacy of time, geography, and the functional nature of the biological differences of the samples is immediately locked into a *taxic* and cladistic, and not evolutionary, approach with a host of corollary assumptions. Pundits of cladistic theory assure us that the "process independent" cladograms of distributional analysis are the proper bases for "patterns" (of phylogeny) on which we can proceed with that baggage of functional and behavioral and ecological biology to arrive at historical biology. Neff (1986, p. 116) has well summed up the evolutionary perspective on phylogenetics: "The cladistic analysis itself is relatively trivial: it is only summarizing the information already entirely contained within the characters." It is the understanding of the taxonomic properties of characters that allows proper tests of character transformation hypotheses, and this requires process-laden research. The biggest danger is the generation of *exact* answers to *wrong* or *irrelevant* questions, rather than the preferable and approximate answers to the evolutionarily and therefore theoretically more meaningful questions.

The Confusion over Lineage Paleobiology Reconstruction

I believe that there are several robust foundations for the reconstruction of the evolutionary behavioral ecology of past samples based on a synthesis of information and approaches. But either a purely genealogical, or functional, or sociobiological (a form of adaptational perspective) approach (and attempts "logically" continue to "purify"—and therefore isolate from one another—these artificially separate efforts) is likely to produce a grossly distorted picture of analysis. Asking complex questions that embody the multidimensionality of functional and evolutionary causality is not circular but merely the right evolutionary procedure. Furthermore, the often axiomatic separation of proximate and "ultimate" causality results in incomplete and handicapped research programs from their inceptions.

The null hypothesis of the adaptationist program, recently supported by Williams (1985) in contradistinction to his previous stand, is that change is channeled by selection (until proven otherwise), and that this change only makes sense causally in light of its historical analysis. Yet in spite of the importance of these historical determinants ("ultimate causes"), the forces and immediate events affecting an organism's survival and reproduction are dependent on the interplay between its unfolding genotype (proximate mechanisms) and its total environment. Still, a phylogenetic framework for asking the questions about the most recent adaptive shift remains of utmost importance in adaptational analysis, as outlined elsewhere (Szalay, 1981), without any need to follow the dictates of a cladistic distribution analysis.

Accounts of origins of characters and organisms must differentiate between selection *for* and selection *of* attributes, as stressed by Sober (1984). It follows that evolutionary histories, not merely explanations that can properly focus on outcomes rather than causes, must carefully differentiate between approaches and data in a historical sequence that represents causation versus consequence. Comparative functional analysis of proximate mechanisms that are *causes* in a historical and developmental context can yield the temporally most recent forces or events that generate consequences. Outcome-based causal explanations of sociobiological analyses (focusing exclusively on differential reproduction, ignoring the obvious causal aspect of survival-promoting attributes) are most often correlative rather than causal in their approach; they often merely extend deductive consequences of such a partial theory of natural selection to specific organisms.

The most basic criticism of purely sociobiological accounts of adaptations (and therefore implied history) is that this approach often considers the phenotype as merely a gonadal extension, being completely focused on outcomes of reproduction without the vast panorama of adaptive variation in organisms that are dictated by both history and survival. In the hands of those who are unfamiliar with the biology of the organisms they analyze sociobiologically, information is treated as if in the "struggle for survival" everything was equal except differential reproduction. Differential reproduction (up to that point in time!) is not a causal factor in the evolution of what is to become a most recent adaptive shift, except as a historical force through the genome. Differential reproduction is but first and foremost a consequence of a *particular* differential survival.

Not "Scenarios" but Historical-Narrative Explanations

It follows from these few undeveloped points that reconstruction of lineage-specific adaptations (outcomes of causal forces and events) cannot be accomplished by either new terms for the outcomes or by the deductive application of only the consequences of gene or kin selection theory. It is exactly the differences in different lineages that we are trying to account for, rather than focusing on some generalities in the evolution of many organisms. Historical-narrative explanations (Bock, 1981) are the proper form of evolutionary accounts of all phenetic change (adaptations included) because events and therefore the specific forces of evolution are always unique, albeit based on underlying nomological-deductive explanations. The mere application of the deductions of a body of theory cannot accomplish this.

The largely taxic approaches to hominid paleobiology have tended to follow a punctuationist and cladogram-based analysis. A "genealogy first" approach reflects the general disregard of cladistics toward the great temporal value of the fossil record (beyond taxic diversity) and functional and historical biology of characters beyond their distribution analysis. Some anthropologists, probably as a consequence of this new (and in fact) reversed scale of what is "more" scientific in historical biology, now even speak pejoratively of paleobiological accounts as "hero myths," as if the historical-narrative explanations were not properly scientific in their probability-based accountability. In addition, purely sociobiological explanations have come to dominate the field of adaptational analysis. Virtually every recognizable difference of humans from nonhumans is now regarded as adaptation based on aspects of sociobiological theory, but often without application of Darwinian sexual selection based on the functional (physiological) understanding of signal systems, or a causally linked temporal hierarchy of the attributes together with the cause-and-effect interplay of the evolution of the traits involved.

The specific consequence of both of these approaches for the understanding of human evolution is the widespread lack of appreciation of the causal interdependence of functional complexes tied to bipedality, established in the proto-hominids. Until the early departure toward bipedality is understood in the light of a strong web of selective factors such as feeding and antipredator activity, and in terms of our own and other hominoids' behavioral biology, we will not have gone far on the road toward this evolutionary understanding of human attributes.

Hunter College

Bock, W. J., 1981, Functional-adaptive analysis in evolutionary classification, *Am. Zool.* **21**: 5-20.

Neff, N. A., 1986, A rational basis for a priori character weighting, *Syst. Zool.* **35**: 110-123.

Sober, E., 1984, *The Nature of Selection*, MIT Press, Cambridge.

Szalay, F. S., 1981, Phylogeny and the problem of adaptive significance: the case of the earliest primates, *Folia primatol.* **36**: 157-182.

Williams, G. C., 1985, A defense of reductionism in evolutionary biology, in: *Oxford Surveys in Evolutionary Biology* (R. Dawkins and M. Ridley, eds.), pp. 1-27, Oxford University Press, Oxford.

The Influence of the Evolutionary Paradigm

Richard M. Burian
Virginia Polytechnic Institute and State University

The central concern of this essay is the relationship between the synthetic theory of evolution and neighboring sciences. In writing about "the evolutionary paradigm," I hope to play the role of a philosophical gadfly. In particular, I shall argue that, in one of the most important ways in which philosophers and scientists use the term "paradigm" these days, *there is no evolutionary paradigm*—and hence no influence of "the" evolutionary paradigm.

Obviously I do not mean to suggest that Darwinism has been without influence. Rather, I wish to probe the way we think about the practice and the unity of evolutionary theory and evolutionary biology in general. I will suggest that the muddy concept of a paradigm, as commonly used these days, is one that we can do quite well without, thank you very much. I suggest that bypassing that concept will help us to focus more clearheadedly on the influence of the current variant of Darwin's theory: the so-called synthetic theory of evolution.

Given the special interest of this symposium in assessing the directions in which evolutionary biology is headed, I will emphasize a characteristic of evolutionary theory that I think is of great importance in thinking about its future: namely, its peculiarly *historical* character. I claim that a full appreciation of the nature of historical theories, historical reasoning, and their role in evolutionary biology ought to shape much of our thinking about the relation of evolutionary biology to other branches of biology and to the sciences more generally. What I have to say about that topic is not particularly original. A good bit of it has been said quite eloquently by Gould and others. But it is very much worth trying to make it stick for, as I hope to show, there is a moral of deep interest to be drawn from Darwinism, a moral that yields some strong suggestions about the directions open to evolutionary theory as we come once again, as we do in every generation, to a major crossroads.

About Paradigms

Although I will pay some attention to the term "paradigm," my principal concern is not semantic, but with the social and intellectual structure of evolutionary biology. The point of interest can be put in terms of an evolutionary analogy. A species is composed of many variant individuals, often conveniently grouped into varieties. Similarly, there are many varieties of evolutionary biology and many variant positions within each variety. Just as the evolution of species depends on the underlying variation of the individuals of which it is composed, so the development of evolutionary biology depends on the underlying variation among evolutionary biologists. To this extent, it is as worthwhile to ask after the unity in the diversity of evolutionary biology as it is to ask after the unity in the diversity of biological species. The point of worrying about paradigms is to show that some common views regarding the unity of evolutionary biology are not true. Please bear with me, therefore, while I start by clearing some terminological underbrush.

The use of the term "paradigm" in history and philosophy of science traces back primarily to Thomas Kuhn's *Structure of Scientific Revolutions* (1962/1970). There is a large literature discussing Kuhn's notion of a paradigm. It has been pointed out repeatedly that the term is multiply ambiguous.[1] Kuhn himself now admits this and has introduced some new terminology in an attempt to recapture what he takes to be the two fundamental points he was making about the character of major scientific theories and research programs (1970, pp. 271ff., and the fuller treatment in Kuhn, 1974). The two points are, in fact, fairly straightforward and seem quite commonsensical if we don't read too much into them. They are:

1. Major research programs are built on exemplary texts that record exemplary experiments and interpretative accomplishments. Thus Newton's *Principia* and Darwin's *Origin* are what Kuhn now calls *exemplars.* These two books showed, by example, how to do science in a certain style, specifically how to interpret and apply major new theories. One of the terms derived from Greek for an exemplar of this sort is "paradigm." Part of what Kuhn meant to capture by his use of that term is this: *science is built on exemplars.* Kuhn correctly notes that there are exemplars of very many different types, some at a very high level and others at a low level. Newton's and Darwin's books are high-level exemplars (i.e., paradigms). Low-level ones are ubiquitous in the teaching of science—for instance, the exemplary problems with which we force our students to cope in a freshman lab or the problems and problem solutions in a standard textbook. Such exemplars are the means by which we teach our students to become scientists; they are the cornerstones in the system of apprenticeship that we employ to handle that delicate job.

2. The practices of the scientists working in a given discipline are typically built on a series of complicated implicit agreements and understandings. These are very diverse in nature: they cover the basic assumptions of the discipline; the proper interpretation and application of various mathematical formulae; the reasons for choosing one technique or experimental organism over another; judgments regarding the relative reliability of various techniques, laboratories, and even people; judgments regarding the social as well as the intellectual structuring of the discipline, and so on. Sociological frameworks of this sort, which help to structure the work, content, and education in a given field, Kuhn now calls *disciplinary matrices* (1970, p. 271; 1974, pp. 468ff.). His original terminology treated the whole range of implicit agreements involved in such socially forged networks as *paradigms* because, he thought, the agreements came about without explicit articulation from the use of exemplars—i.e., the standard texts, techniques, problems, and problem solutions from which one learned as a student of the discipline.

We are now in a position to ask to what extent there is an evolutionary paradigm. Using Kuhn's own separation of paradigms into exemplars and disciplinary matrices, this question is transformed into two questions. First, is the practice of evolutionary biology correctly described as based on some central exemplars? The answer to this question is obviously affirmative. One need only mention Dobzhansky, Mayr, Simpson, and Stebbins—or, in a different vein, sickle cell anemia, variation among hemoglobins, and *Biston betularia*—to see how easy it would be to establish this claim. The second question is whether some one disciplinary matrix dominates the practices of evolutionary biologists. This is a large question that cannot be properly resolved on this occasion. I shall, however, offer some good reasons for being skeptical about the presence of anything like a single disciplinary matrix during most of the history of modern evolutionary biology. Not least of these is the fact that evolutionary biology is not a single discipline, but a complex interdisciplinary field that lies in a region that overlaps onto the territory of very diverse disciplines.

Some Historical Notes

In the present section I offer a rough-and-ready treatment of some historical points that show how implausible it is to treat evolutionary biology before the development of the synthetic theory as falling within a single disciplinary matrix. In the next section I support the parallel conclusion with respect to the synthetic theory itself.

The large-scale historical point can be put rather simply. Darwin's *On the Origin of Species* (1859) is, without question, an exemplar—it served as a paradigm in the first of the two senses distinguished above. It is a text to which evolutionary biologists have paid an enormous amount of attention ever since it was published and, to this day, even those evolutionary biologists who have not seriously read the *Origin* are deeply influenced by it. It is a work that has penetrated evolutionary theory and the practice of evolutionary biology very deeply. Yet in spite of this, it is arguable whether the *Origin* or any other influence has established a dominant disciplinary matrix within evolutionary biology.[2]

Among the many ways of getting at this issue by means of historical investigations I can pursue only one here, and that very sketchily. This is to examine the relationships among various versions of Darwinism. (It would also be useful to examine the many alternative theories that have played a major role in evolutionary biology at various times and places, but I haven't time to address this topic today.) In this connection, it is worth recalling that for a substantial portion of the history of evolutionary biology, *no* version of Darwin's theory of evolution *by means of natural selection* was the dominant accepted theory. Indeed, in all of the relevant national traditions, Darwinian theory received quite different interpretations so that, looked at from an international perspective, the Darwinian party did not share common assumptions of the sort Kuhn includes in disciplinary matrices. The central point is that it is implausible to claim that there was anything resembling a single disciplinary matrix in evolutionary biology at least until the general acceptance of the synthetic theory of evolution around the latter 1940s—and, as I will argue below, it is not really very plausible then.

In support of these claims, it is useful to begin with Mayr's point that Darwin put forward a congeries of theories (1985). For present purposes I will mention only three: that evolution is gradual, that it consists of a process of descent with modification, and that the most significant evolutionary force among the many Darwin recognized is natural selection. I shall focus on the latter two to some extent in this section. Let us now recall the reception of Darwin's theories in very general terms. The initial success of the *Origin* did not (as is sometimes naively assumed) yield widespread acceptance of the theory of evolution *by means of natural selection*; at most it established that descent with modification could account for the major phenomena of biogeography, paleontology, and systematics, and for the adaptations of plants and animals. To be sure, the theory of natural selection played a major role in this initial success, for it offered a plausible mechanism by means of which evolutionary change could be seen as creating adaptations.[3] Nonetheless, for a very long time the particular mechanisms of evolution were treated extremely pluralistically by most theorists—including Darwin himself, especially in the later editions of the *Origin* and in the *Descent of Man*—and there was an immense amount of debate over the claim that the historical path of evolutionary change was dominantly the effect of natural selection as opposed to saltatory mutation, inherited effects of use and disuse of organs, direct effect of climate, internal orthogenetic drives, and so on.

A central tenet of contemporary Darwinism is that natural selection is the predominant cause of evolutionary pattern. This claim was nowhere fully accepted in Darwin's day; Darwin himself lamented the failure of his work to convince his peers on this score. Indeed, as is shown by an examination of primary sources (Kellogg, 1907; Seward, 1909) and as is widely recognized in recent historical writings (Mayr, 1982; Bowler, 1983), belief in the importance of natural selection as a factor in evolution reached a nadir around 1909, the centenary of Darwin's birth and the fiftieth anniversary of the publication of the *Origin*. Although it was nearly universally granted that Darwin's mechanism played *some* role in evolution, by this time there were relatively few defenders of the idea that natural selection is a major contributor—let alone *the* major contributor—to the fundamental patterns of evolutionary history.

Less well known except among specialist historians is the fact that each of the major national traditions interpreted Darwin quite differently (Glick, 1974; Kohn, 1985). I will speak, absurdly briefly, of England, France, Germany, and Russia in order to drive this point home. Although I am talking in very crude general terms, the sketch offered here is, I believe, an adequate first approximation. In England, descent with modification was rapidly accepted and natural selection taken seriously; the Darwinian theory came to be allied with gradualism and biometry. By the turn of the century, most Darwinians treated small and copious variations as the raw material for natural selection, emphasized the fine-grained character of adaptation, and stressed the causal importance of the intense Malthusian scrutiny of every variant as the key to evolutionary dynamics. In France, Darwin was treated as a utilitarian cheapener of Lamarck, offering nothing particularly new or interesting outside of the already available evolutionary theories. Even descent with modification had great difficulty in making its way and, insofar as it did, transformational and variational versions of the theory were not properly distinguished (see note 3). A few of Darwin's defenders emphasized his pluralism with regard to the mechanisms underlying evolution, but they conceded that he overstressed natural selection. In Germany, too, the distinction between Lamarckism and Darwinism was not very clear, but between the influence first of Haeckel and then of Weismann, Darwin's theory became associated with preformationism on two grounds: that the organism contained the history of its lineage (cf. the biogenetic law) and that the developmental unfolding of the organism was a consequence of the inherited materials produced in that history and a necessary condition for the independence of variation from environmental influence.[4]

In Russia, finally, Darwinism was reinterpreted to remove its Malthusian moment. In a new book, Todes (1989) reviews this history, arguing that at least two major considerations influenced this stance. One of these is biological—the vast emptiness of the steppes, which were the central arena for the studies of Russian ecologists and naturalists. To the students of the ecology and evolution of the biota of this vast region, struggle against the climate seemed far more intense and important than intraspecific competition. The other influence was, in a sense, political (though common to the political left and the political right), and had to do with the widely acknowledged need to increase population in Russia in order to exploit available resources efficiently. Malthus, it seemed, was just wrong about Russia: increasing the population under the appropriate social arrangements was the means to guarantee *enough* food for everyone. As things stood, the primary factor holding down the population was the lack of sufficiently intense agriculture to produce food. But without sufficient population, it was impossible to institute appropriate agricultural and productive techniques, systems, and reforms.

Both of these influences made the Malthusian starting point utterly implausible to Russian theorists and led them to reinterpret Darwin's theory along lines ultimately popularized in the West by Kropotkin—i.e., to admit competition with the environment and between species, but to insist on the fundamental importance of *cooperation within species*. Such an approach was thoroughly integrated into the strong evolutionary tradition of Russian biology.

Although I have been speaking about the differences among national traditions, much the same sort of disagreement about the proper content of Darwinism occurred *within* many of these traditions. The differences between transformational and variational theories of evolutionary mechanisms (see note 3) were by no means clear; toward the turn of the century almost everyone except Weismann, whose speculations were widely rejected, was confused in this respect. Again, there were serious disagreements regarding just what should be accepted from Darwin and what should count as the core of Darwinian theory. Worse yet, insofar as Darwin's various subtheories were recognized, the interrelations between them became uncertain. Was gradualism required to make sense of natural selection, or to support descent with modification? Such questions had become extraordinarily troublesome. Many figures wished to claim the authority of Darwin in support of their own views, while also rejecting—in specific contexts, for specific purposes—various important Darwinian doctrines. The resultant tangles became extremely complicated.

The lay of the land as I am depicting it can be nicely summarized by suggesting that the history of the first 75 or 100 years of Darwinism could be written under the rubric of *Struggling for the Mantle of Darwin*. Throughout this history, the *Origin* and some of Darwin's other writings served as exemplars, but there were constant attempts to reinterpret Darwin's ambiguous and pluralistic theory along widely divergent lines. Thus, the *Origin* was read very differently by different parties, and it was used to support a great many mutually incompatible positions; frequently, these divergent readings were intended to help forge the sort of consensus that Kuhn has characterized as the crucial, though tacit, center of a disciplinary matrix and to convert the resultant consensus into the doctrinal core of evolutionary biology. The fact that many divergent biological disciplines, often drawing on different problems and techniques, were affected by these divergences, made the task of reaching full consensus very difficult.

Why should *this* exemplary text have served as such a symbol of authority? Because many evolutionists—with the exception of the French and certain of the more extreme Lamarckian and orthogenetic opponents of Darwin—wished to draw on Darwin's reputation as founder of mainstream evolutionary theory and as the most influential naturalist/evolutionist of the age. But the struggle to cloak such divergent doctrines in the mantle of Darwin, which continues even to this day, is a nice symptom of the fact that there was not and is not a single disciplinary matrix in evolutionary biology. I conclude that the influence of Darwinism on neighboring sciences should be understood differently than on the basis of the influence of "the" evolutionary paradigm.

The Evolutionary Synthesis

The synthetic theory of evolution is a moving target. Nonetheless, in first approximation it can be characterized fairly briefly, for it was put forward by a series of founding documents in the period from 1937 to roughly 1950. (I take the first of these to be Dobzhansky [1937] and the last Stebbins [1950]. Among the more important books along the way one must include Mayr [1942] and Simpson [1944], though many other writings should be cited as well.)

The central point of the synthesis was to demonstrate the adequacy of Mendelian genetics (especially population genetics) plus an updated version of Darwin's theory of evolution by means of natural selection, joined in the manner illustrated in the founding documents, to serve as the theoretical basis for explaining all evolutionary phenomena. The following doctrines are characteristic of the synthetic theory: the immense variability of natural populations; the genetic (indeed, Mendelian) basis for evolution; the importance of geographic speciation; the adaptive nature of observed differences among organisms; the primacy of natural selection in causing the evolutionary patterns found in the paleontological record; the gradualness of evolution; the compatibility of all macroevolutionary phenomena with the mechanisms of (gradual) microevolution (thus ruling out saltational models); and the importance of what Mayr called "population thinking."[5] Bruce Wallace's paper in this volume exemplifies quite well the sort of stance I would include within the synthesis.

In certain respects the synthetic theory, so-called, is better viewed as a treaty than as a theory.[6] By this I mean that one could not use the population genetic foundations of the theory to predict or retrodict large-scale evolutionary patterns or fundamental features of the taxonomic system. Nor can population genetics alone determine the prevalence, evolutionary importance, or historical trajectory of major traits like sexuality—indeed it cannot even provide a full answer to Darwin's problem, the origin of species. Yet in spite of this, the synthetic theory did a great deal to reduce the conflict between evolutionists belonging to different disciplines. For example, it served to contravene the paleontologists' belief that Mendelian variation cannot offer a sufficient explanation for macroevolutionary phenomena; to undermine the geneticists' early insistence that genetic (and hence evolutionary) change is discontinuous and saltational; and to counteract the systematists' conviction that laboratory experiments on mutations and Mendelian variation were irrelevant to the sorts of variation and evolutionary change found in natural populations. Precisely because the synthetic theory aimed to establish the *compatibility* of the standard population genetic accounts of microevolution with all known evolutionary (especially macroevolutionary) phenomena, it disarmed conflicts between disciplines bearing on evolutionary history. It allowed the claims about the *patterns* and *results* of evolution to be drawn from other disciplines while insisting that the *mechanisms* revealed by population genetics were the only ones needed to bring those patterns about.

Not surprisingly, the evolutionary synthesis has changed with time. For one thing, the tools available to theorists and field workers have grown considerably more sophisticated, especially with the introduction of computers and molecular techniques. One controversial claim of interest to us about the developments from, say, 1950 to 1970, a claim I believe is correct, is that the synthesis hardened, at least to some extent, into unexamined dogma, sometimes dismissing alternatives on the basis of prejudgment rather than hard evidence (Gould, 1983). Early on, the very weakness of the compatibility claim was viewed as one of the *strengths* of the synthesis. In principle, virtually all the known phenomena and patterns that ought to be explained by an evolutionary theory *could* be explained by some variant of the synthetic theory—and so it was not necessary to contemplate or turn to any rival theories. As the synthesis hardened, "could be explained" turned into "are explained," yielding outright dismissal of competing theories.

There is not time here to go into examples in detail, but I shall cite three of the many that could be adequately documented to illustrate the point. These are the treatment by many theorists of the late Sewall Wright's shifting balance theory (which, after the mid-1950s, was frequently dismissed as placing far too great an emphasis on fixation of random variants in small populations), the change in Simpson's views about quantum evolution and its relationship to natural selection, and the increasing panselectionism of many of the leading figures in the field. (Another symptom of this change, pointed out to me some years ago by Marjorie Grene, is the disappearance from later editions of the founding texts—and from the literature of the theorists of the synthesis generally—of people like Goldschmidt, Robson and Richards, Schindewolf, and Willis. These figures had served as rhetorical targets in the founding debates, and their disappearance signals the fact that their nonselectionist alternatives came to be considered irrelevant and no longer threatening.)

If this characterization of the synthesis as a treaty is approximately correct, it enforces the conclusion I wish to draw: that there is no single disciplinary matrix to which the adherents of the synthesis subscribe. Nor should this be surprising. The scientific advocates of the synthesis are drawn from systematics, population genetics, paleontology, botany, zoology, biogeography, and an immense variety of additional disciplines. To that extent, even though their commitments overlap and even though they share some exemplary texts, their disciplinary allegiances (and their primary training) belong to very different fields. It should not take much reflection on the consequences of this fact to recognize that their socialization as scientists prevents them from sharing a common disciplinary matrix— the supposed disciplinary matrix of evolutionary biology or evolutionary theory. In the last section of the paper I will explore a few consequences of this fact for the future of that theory. But first I shall address one more topic.

The Synthetic Theory as a Theory of History

The synthetic theory, like Darwinism generally, claims that the details and many of the basic patterns of organismic evolution are, at heart, historically contingent. Gould has argued persuasively that Darwin's central accomplishment in this regard was to construct a theory that treated adaptation as response to the historical sequence of selective demands of the environment (including other organisms), a theory that accounted for taxonomic and morphological order in terms of "historical pathway, pure and simple" (1986, p. 60). These Darwinian explanations contrast with alternatives couched in terms of "intrinsic purpose and meaning," or of laws of form, and so on. For Darwinians, Gould claims, homology requires, and is explained by, common descent, whereas similarity of functional form without common descent (analogy), however striking, is accounted for by the adaptive power of selection. Many of you will recognize that this is a very substantial and controversial claim, for it commits one to the view that the only correct account of the identity of homologous structures— for example, of a particular metatarsal in different vertebrates—is identity by descent.

We recognize the occurrence of biological evolution and delineate phylogenies in part by means of "accidents of history." The term is apt. Cladistic classifications, insofar as I understand them, place organisms into taxa defined in terms of shared derived characters ("synapomorphies" in cladistic terminology). While our assessments of particular traits as synapomorphies may be mistaken, the principle behind such classifications is fundamentally sound. And the corresponding practice seems to me to generate an interesting argument against the derivation of basic evolutionary patterns from the fundamental laws or axioms of evolutionary theory.

Compare, for example, biological with stellar evolution. Stellar evolution is transformational—i.e., in the absence of highly unusual interactions with other cosmic bodies, the stages of the life history of each star can be derived from its intrinsic properties (mass and composition) and appropriate initial or boundary conditions (Lewontin, 1983, p. 63). In the terminology of some philosophers of biology (e.g., Brandon, 1982, and Brandon, submitted), the effects of such other factors as the *history* of the materials out of which a star was formed (which almost certainly came from other stars) are "screened off" by the physical properties of the star. That is, "accidental" properties like those relevant to evolutionary studies of biological entities are not needed and are of no help in determining either the parentage or the behavior of stars, their likely fate, or the patterns of evolution of populations of stars. In part this is because stars are sufficiently isolated that the dominant determinants of their behavior, once certain initial conditions have been realized, are fundamental physical laws rather than interactions with their environment or with one another. In part it is because (in the absence of strong interactions with other stars) the evolution of the ensemble of stars is, in effect, a straightforward summation of the evolution of each individual star.

There are good reasons for supposing that the same is not true for organisms. If the laws of thermodynamics, for example, were powerful enough to determine the patterns of evolutionary history in detail, the evolutionist's use of "accidental" clues would amount to a deep mistake; instead of supplying crucial information bearing on the behavior and fate of organisms (or other biological entities), it would mask the fundamentally law-driven course of evolution. If laws of form determined ontogenies rigidly, organisms, like stars, would simply have one or another of the available ontogenies, and the transition from one ontogeny to another within a lineage would not be marked by any clues about the history of the lineage. But organisms and lineages *do* record the accidents of history. The gill slits of mammalian embryos suffice to make the point, though the phenomenon they illustrate is ubiquitous. In the end, both cladistics and evolutionary biology as a whole depend deeply on the contingent fact of evolutionary tinkering (Jacob, 1982).

Since evolutionary theory is concerned, among other things, with analyzing genealogical connections and patterns of genealogical affinity among organisms, it must build upon the essential historicity of biological evolution. The same historicity applies when the aim is to describe patterns of evolution among DNAs, proteins, organisms, taxa, or clades, or to develop evolutionary laws relating, for example, morphological change to cladogenesis or phylogeny.

This historicity is unavoidable; it cannot be escaped by developing a generalized mechanics for evolution. Two examples illustrate the point. First, the effects of particular molecular mechanisms—and even the content of the genetic code itself—are highly context dependent. Thus whether a given string of DNA will yield or affect the expression of a particular product depends on the cellular and genetic context within which it is placed. There is no prospect of a generalized mechanics of gene expression powerful enough to take all of the contextually relevant factors into account (except, perhaps, statistically[7]). That is why the analysis of gene expression is a brute force, messy problem rather than a neat theoretical enterprise. Second, speciation depends in part on such matters as mate recognition, which, in turn, depends on the use of "accidental" characters *by the organisms themselves*. I have in mind H.E.H. Paterson's account of Specific Mate Recognition Systems, and the role it has played in the thinking of people like Elisabeth Vrba and Niles Eldredge.[8] To the extent that separate lineages acquire independent evolutionary fates because the organisms of those lineages employ contingent and accidental differences as cues in mate recognition, the entry of historical accidents into a sound account of evolutionary history is forced on us by the organisms themselves.

This historical component of the Darwinian explanation of underlying form has often been overlooked. Like other historical theories, evolutionary theory must presuppose ahistorical laws as background. These in turn (assuming they are correct) provide some of the constraints[9] within which history runs its course. Nonetheless, the theory must also offer a means for weighing the causal relevance and relative importance of multiple processes, patterns, and singularities whose historical roles are not wholly determined by the background laws. For this reason, as well as others (e.g., the complications added by the hierarchical structuring of organisms and of evolutionary processes[10]), evolutionary theory is, and will continue to be, characterized by a proliferation of alternative models and smaller scale theories applicable to particular cases. To this extent the fundamental laws and principles of the theory cannot be expected to yield rigorous deductions of specific outcomes even when appropriate boundary conditions are supplied—although those outcomes *could* be derived from first principles plus boundary conditions *if only one causal process (or a small number of causal processes in a fixed relationship) were involved*.

Thus basic evolutionary principles, even when supplemented with appropriate boundary or initial conditions, do not provide the wherewithal for a full derivation of major evolutionary patterns or the resolution of typical evolutionary disputes.[11] This is one reason for the seemingly inconclusive character of many debates over the dominant historical patterns in evolution (e.g., gradualism vs. punctuation) and the mechanisms underlying those patterns (e.g., the causes of trends, the relative importance of selection and drift, the importance of ecological catastrophes, and the debates over the units of selection and the relevance of hierarchical structure). In all these cases, we are dealing with questions of relative frequency. In all these cases, examples can be found that support the existence of whichever pattern or the efficacy of whichever mechanism. And, in all these cases, the patterns and mechanisms are compatible with the leading principles of the synthetic theory *provided that those principles are stated abstractly enough*.[12]

Pluralism

The distance from the abstract principles of variation, heritability, and differential fitness and the concepts on which they are founded to an account of the types and frequencies of the patterns of evolution and their causes is very great indeed. Their very abstractness means that the principles are not sufficient, by themselves, to resolve disputes like those just mentioned; the real work must go on closer to the data and with specific models. And many of the models and scenarios in current use involve *specifications* of the abstract principles that depart in varying degrees from the spirit and content of the beliefs of the founders of the evolutionary synthesis. To this extent, even though no suitable radical alternative to the synthetic theory is in sight, *the fate of the synthesis as a coherent system of particular beliefs about evolutionary causes and patterns is still up in the air.*

This characterization may appear unduly pessimistic to some. I wish to counteract this appearance. On the one hand, the situation does not call for pessimism—new techniques now enable us to learn an immense amount that, until recently, was far beyond our means. On the other hand, the pessimism about the limited power of fundamental theories is, I believe, justified. Evolutionary biology is, unavoidably, an historical discipline with a rich but still highly limited base of data available to it. Given this, it is unreasonable to expect to derive its principal results from a theory whose core consists solely of abstract or ahistorical (time symmetrical) laws. To put the point in a rather extreme way: I suspect that even such biologically basic matters as the specific content of the genetic code and the unique role of DNA in cellular organisms are contingent outcomes of historical processes. Given current knowledge, it seems unlikely that these fundamental properties of terrestrial organisms are necessary consequences of evolutionary laws applied to some class of carbon-rich planets that maintain, for a certain extended interval, a certain amount of surface water and a fairly temperate regime. Should this be correct, there can be little question but that the course of evolution, even on a fairly large scale, is fraught with the consequences of historical accidents and contingencies.

The point is not that ahistorical universals are irrelevant or unimportant— quite the contrary, for they, plus the relevant boundary conditions (such as those pertaining to the primordial earth), set the baseline for what would occur in the absence of selection or of any processes peculiar to living systems. Physical and chemical laws are causally prior to the origin of life. Other universals may pertain specifically to entities exhibiting certain of the structural complexities characteristic of living things. But no matter: *all* relevant universals provide the setting within which the contingent history of living beings is played out. Just as the study of the geology of our planet cannot be properly pursued without reliance on both the fundamental laws of physics and chemistry as applied to planets and the specific accidental conditions pertaining to this planet, so the study of evolution generally and of the evolution of living forms on this planet cannot be properly pursued without reliance on the underlying laws of physics and chemistry plus any genuine laws pertaining to the features of complex systems of the sorts that happen to have evolved here. But this leaves an important question open: *How much of the shape of the evolutionary history that we study* has been determined by the accidents of circumstance (from molecular abundances at particular times and places to continental drift, volcanoes, and cometary impacts) that have impinged on the biota of the planet? Such problems are found at all levels, from the molecular to the macroevolutionary.

To solve such problems, one needs to determine the "inertial baseline" from which biotic evolution and/or selection depart—e.g., to determine what would happen to relevant sorts of complex genetic and biochemical systems, once they were up and running, in the absence of selection. A promising line of inquiry bearing on this topic has recently been opened by Stuart Kauffman (cf. esp. Kauffman, in press). He shows how one can evaluate deep statistical features of very general classes of genetic systems so as to reveal important ensemble properties that would be manifested by genomes, proteins, cells, and organisms *in the absence of selection*. If this can be done, whether with Kauffman's protocols or with others currently being developed, it may be possible to make realistic estimates of the contribution of selection to the present genomic structures of organisms and of the extent to which similar structures should have been expected in the absence of selection.

More generally, various lines of work promise to yield improved estimates of the specific contributions of selection, drift, the structure of the environment, and rare catastrophes as well as a better understanding of the patterns and structures that would arise no matter what as the automatic consequences of DNA and chromosomal mechanics and other structure-producing features of organisms. As a result, we can expect new data and new theoretical toeholds that can be put to use in evaluating the preponderance and importance of alternative modes and patterns of evolution and the various causes of those patterns. It is too early to tell whether this will enable us to resolve some of the longstanding issues that have plagued evolutionary theorists, but there are plenty of avenues to explore.

The apparent importance of the accidents of history, revealed by the fossil record and the distribution of properties among organisms, suggests that those accidents have played an enormous role in shaping the biota we study and the evolutionary patterns we seek to understand. It is of great interest to learn to what extent this is true. Indeed, one of the most challenging intellectual problems posed by evolutionary biology is developing the proper tools to analyze the interplay between accident and law in shaping the familiar world around us.

Morals for Theorists at the Crossroads

It would be an act of hubris for any of us to try to predict the future of evolutionary biology in detail, but especially so for an interested bystander like me. Furthermore, a serious estimate of where evolutionary theory is headed should examine a number of themes not here addressed. One of these concerns the role of hierarchies of various sorts in shaping evolutionary history. A second concerns the role of molecular work in transforming the practice of evolutionary biology. A third concerns the proper analysis of the logical structure of evolutionary theory and the ways in which it acquires its empirical content.[13] The views expressed below would be considerably enriched by developing these themes at length, but space prohibits opening up any additional topics. In any case, the two issues that dominate this paper—the thoroughly interdisciplinary character of evolutionary biology and the historicity of the phenomena it studies—yield some ideas about the way things are likely to go. I will close by putting a few of these forward in the hope of provoking lively and thoughtful responses.

The historicity of evolutionary phenomena suggests certain limits on what can be expected from evolutionary theory. For this purpose, I include with evolutionary theory recent attempts to extend that theory or to connect it with other grand theories, like the attempts of Brooks and Wiley or Wicken, for example, to connect the theory of evolution to nonequilibrium thermodynamics (NET) (Brooks and Wiley, 1986; Wicken, 1987; cf. also Dyke, 1987; Weber *et al.*, 1988). NET is, of course, relevant to evolution, and it may tell us a fair amount about the character of the stable and self-perpetuating systems that are possible in a wide range of circumstances. But such considerations can capture at the very most certain baselines and thermodynamic constraints within which evolution occurs.

Richard Lewontin has suggested that the history of life can well be viewed as a history of the ways organisms have found to get around constraints (cf. Maynard Smith *et al.*, 1985, p. 282). Unless theories that characterize some constraints on organismic evolution (as NET does by studying "universal" constraints on the evolution of various kinds of dissipative structures) can also capture the role of particular historical circumstances in the breaking of constraints—and also, I would add, in determining lineage splitting, particular features of organisms or species, and the evolutionary effects of biological interactions and behaviors—those theories will not be able to capture the interaction between law and history that characterizes evolution.[14]

It is this interaction between law and history that requires any satisfactory general theory of evolution to have the peculiar character of a *schematic theory*.[15] By this I mean that while such a theory provides a framework for describing and explaining evolutionary sequences and patterns, it is necessary to fill in that framework by means of particular empirical analyses of the historical circumstances of the organisms in question, including the peculiarities of their environment and the characteristics of traits and behaviors that will be advantageous in that environment. Thus, there is no character that is, of its own right, of high adaptive value; all characters have adaptive values relative to (partly accidental) historical circumstances.

It is here that the logical structure of the synthetic theory is so crucial. Robert Brandon's analysis of that structure, which is consilient with the position I am now advocating, makes the point nicely. Brandon (1980, p. 432) states the principle of natural selection as follows: "(Probably) If a is better adapted than b in E, then a will have more offspring than b in E." The interesting thing about this interpretation of the principle of natural selection is that, thus formulated, it provides no guidance regarding which traits or behaviors in which environments yield better adaptation than alternative traits. It is at just this point that empirical content is supplied to the principle by work undertaken in various independent disciplines, and it is at just this point that the relevance of the sorts of historical knowledge on which I have been focussing becomes inescapable.

If, indeed, historical and empirical work imported from a great variety of disciplines is required at this point, the character of the synthetic theory as a treaty is closely connected to its logically schematic structure. And this structure, in turn, is tightly connected to the following four home truths. First, there are very many ways that organisms can earn livings. Second, an organism's success in earning a living depends not only on luck, but also on its environment and on who its competitors are. Third, no adequate answer as to how it is possible to earn a living can be derived primarily from general thermodynamic or evolutionary considerations, important as these are. And fourth, there are ways of achieving reproductive success without being particularly good at making a living. If we take these home truths seriously, it should be clear that no single disciplinary matrix can provide satisfactory guidance regarding the issues raised within basic evolutionary theory. The lack of a single dominant disciplinary matrix in evolutionary biology is a consequence of the nature of evolutionary phenomena, and particularly of the role of historical accidents in affecting the evolutionary success, failure, and transformation of lineages. For this reason, I submit, we would be foolish to expect the unification of evolutionary theory within a single paradigm—and, what's more, we should count the failure to achieve such unification as a Good Thing.

Notes

Acknowledgments: I am grateful to Marjorie Grene for her criticisms of a draft of parts of this paper and to the National Endowment for the Humanities for support of research in the history of genetics, including evolutionary genetics. The paper has been revised in light of some especially helpful criticisms kindly provided by Ernst Mayr.

1. Margaret Masterman (1970), for example, diagnoses 21 senses of "paradigm."

2. Ernst Mayr (pers. commun.) suggests that the *Origin* established a definite theoretical framework or set of principles. He suggests that, after Darwin, descent with modification acquired a central place in biological reasoning that it had not had before, and that therefore it is a mistake to claim that Darwin failed to establish a dominant disciplinary matrix in evolutionary biology. This criticism is mistaken, for it fails to recognize that a disciplinary matrix (at least as Kuhn intends the term) is built on common problems, techniques, training, and standards of evaluation established by education *within a reasonably well-defined discipline*. Anatomists, biogeographers, zoologists, botanists, breeders, natural historians, etc., even if they are evolutionists sharing the *Origin* as an exemplar, do not share a disciplinary matrix. The best reading of the evidence, I believe, does not reveal a common disciplinary matrix for Darwinian evolutionists 1859-1909, even when one restricts one's attention to England.

3. Mayr (pers. commun.) considers this a myth, pointing out correctly that common descent was broadly accepted in spite of the fact that natural selection was rejected by most naturalists, including even T. H. Huxley. I think, nonetheless, that natural selection "broke

the ice" for descent with modification. It made it seem plausible that a thoroughly naturalistic account could be given of adaptations, even to those who rejected Darwin's account of the role of natural selection in evolution. As Lewontin (1983) points out (an article which Mayr reminded me of!), natural selection broke with the spirit of all prior evolutionary theories (such as Lamarck's). Those theories were "transformational"—they required that the evolution within a lineage be a sum of the changes that occurred to individual organisms. Typically, such theories have difficulty with adaptation, requiring ad hoc or secondary causes to explain adaptations. Darwin's "variational" theory, in contrast, took variation as somehow given, so that the source of evolutionary change was some sort of external action upon available variation rather than a building up of new permanent variation within the organism for exploitation. (Darwin himself, to be sure, was obstinately pluralist; use and disuse of organs as a source of evolutionary change is a transformational mechanism, quite different, in this respect, than natural selection.)

4. Mayr (pers. commun.) correctly cautions that Weismann and other panselectionists were very isolated by the turn of the century in Germany. Various forms of orthogenesis and mutationism were preferred by the majority of German biologists with evolutionary interests at that time.

5. This list deemphasizes the contribution of genetics to the evolutionary synthesis. It is based on Mayr's gloss (1980) on various contributions to the synthetic theory. Mayr (pers. commun.) considers the two most important contributions of genetics to the synthesis to be evidence for the facts that "inheritance is particulate, not blending; and that inheritance is hard, not soft (Lamarckian)." He adds that these contributions "have comparatively little to do with population genetics."

6. The term "treaty" is taken from Depew and Weber (1988). Both that essay and Burian (1988) amplify on some of the points made here. See below for some connections with other analyses of the synthetic theory as a metatheory or a schematic theory.

7. I have in mind results of the sort that Stuart Kauffman has obtained in simulating some of the general properties of gene regulation networks. Relatively accessible presentations of some of his results are available (1985, 1986). Kauffman (in press) brings these lines of work up to date. This extraordinarily promising book covers an enormous range of topics: origin of life, coevolution of organisms and environments, evolution of complex systems and their adaptations, evolution of ligand binding and catalytic function in proteins, evolution of a connected metabolism, evolution of patterns of gene regulation, evolution of development and its regulation, and so on.

8. Cf., e.g., Paterson (1982). This line of work is discussed by Eldredge (1985); further references to related work by Eldredge, Vrba, and others may be found there.

9. The theme of ahistorical universals is nicely developed by Kauffman. In light of his work, it is useful to distinguish between universals resting on fundamental physico-chemical laws and those resting on statistically near-universal features of the relevant classes of complex systems (such as those mentioned above). The theme of constraints is usefully discussed in Maynard Smith et al. (1985). In their terminology, constraints deriving from physico-chemical laws would be classed as "universal," those from the general features of complex systems as (relatively) "local."

10. Hierarchical structure and its importance is discussed in passing in Burian (1988). A good start on the literature may be gotten from Eldredge (1985) and the following allied sources: Vrba and Eldredge (1984), Eldredge and Salthe (1984), Salthe (1985), and Grene (1987). These issues also connect in interesting ways with the huge literature on the units-of-selection problem.

11. Cf. Brandon (1978, 1980). Brandon argues that it is the *specification* of these principles so that they pertain to particular cases (e.g., particular organisms and environments) that provides evolutionary theory with empirical content. The principles provide the schemata which, when specified, make empirical claims. It is for this reason that I count evolutionary theory as a schematic theory. Related positions, using various labels, have been taken by Caplan, Tuomi, Wasserman, and others; some references are supplied in Burian (1988).

12. The *locus classicus* for such statements is Lewontin (1970). Lewontin's abstract version of the theory of natural selection can be boiled down to the following formula: heritable variation of fitness yields evolution by means of natural selection. This formula is compatible with group selection, non-Mendelian systems of inheritance, and even inheritance of acquired characters. To that extent, the formula seeks to represent the core of Darwinism, not the synthetic theory.

13. I find Brandon's argument, characterized in n. 11, persuasive; the principle of natural selection, characterized below, obtains its empirical content from the specifications of degrees of adaptedness for particular kinds of biological entities and kinds of environments.

14. Kauffman's work, insofar as I understand it, has some chance of meeting these desiderata.

15. See the references and discussion in n. 11.

References

Bowler, P., 1983, *The Eclipse of Darwinism*, Johns Hopkins University Press, Baltimore.

Brandon, R., 1978, Adaptation and evolutionary theory, *Studies in the History and Philosophy of Science* **9**:181-206.

Brandon, R., 1980, A structural description of evolutionary theory, in: *PSA 1980*, vol. 1 (R. Giere and P. Asquith, eds.), pp. 427-439, Philosophy of Science Association, East Lansing, MI.

Brandon, R., 1982, The levels of selection, in: *PSA 1982*, vol. 1 (P. Asquith and T. Nickles, eds.), pp. 315-324, Philosophy of Science Association, East Lansing, MI.

Brandon, R., submitted, The levels of selection: a hierarchy of interactors, draft chapter of a book MS, *Adaptation and Environment*.

Brooks, D.R. and Wiley, E.O., 1986, *Evolution as Entropy: Toward a Unified Theory of Biology*, Chicago University Press, Chicago.

Burian, R., 1988, Challenges to the evolutionary synthesis, *Evolutionary Biology* **23**:247-269.

Darwin, C., 1859, *On the Origin of Species by Means of Natural Selection, or the Preservation of Favoured Races in the Struggle for Life*, John Murray, London.

Depew, D. and Weber, B., 1988, Consequences of nonequilibrium thermodynamics for the Darwinian tradition, in: *Entropy, Information, and Evolution: New Perspectives on Physical and Biological Evolution* (B. Weber, D. Depew, and J. Smith, eds.), MIT Press, Cambridge, MA.

Dobzhansky, Th., 1937, *Genetics and the Origin of Species*, Columbia University Press, New York.

Dyke, C., 1987, *The Evolutionary Dynamics of Complex Systems*, Oxford University Press, New York.

Eldredge, N., 1985, *Unfinished Synthesis: Biological Hierarchies and Evolutionary Theory*, Oxford University Press, New York.

Eldredge, N. and Salthe, S.N., 1984, Hierarchy and evolution, *Oxford Surveys in Evolutionary Biology* **1**:182-206.

Glick, T. (ed.), 1974, *The Comparative Reception of Darwinism*, University of Texas Press, Austin.

Gould, S.J., 1983, The hardening of the Modern Synthesis, in: *Dimensions of Darwinism: Themes and Counterthemes in Twentieth-Century Evolutionary Theory* (M. Grene, ed.), pp. 71-93, Cambridge University Press, Cambridge.

Gould, S.J., 1986, Evolution and the triumph of homology, or why history matters, *American Scientist* **75**:50-59.

Grene, M., 1987, Hierarchies in biology, *American Scientist* **75**:504-510.

Jacob, F., 1982, Evolutionary tinkering, in: F. Jacob, *The Possible and the Actual*, University of Washington Press, Seattle, WA.

Kauffman, S., 1985, Self-organization, selective adaptation, and its limits: a new pattern of inference in evolution and development, in: *Evolution at a Crossroads: The New Biology and the New Philosophy of Science* (D. Depew and B. Weber, eds.), pp. 169-207, MIT Press, Cambridge, MA.

Kauffman, S., 1986, A framework to think about evolving genetic regulatory systems, in: *Integrating Scientific Disciplines* (W. Bechtel, ed.), pp. 165-184, Nijhoff, Dordrecht, The Netherlands.

Kauffman, S., in press, *Origins of Order: Self-Organization and Selection in Evolution*, Oxford University Press, Oxford.

Kellogg, V.L., 1907, *Darwinism Today*, Henry Holt, New York.

Kohn, D. (ed.), 1985, *The Darwinian Heritage*, Princeton University Press, Princeton.

Kuhn, T., 1962/1970, *The Structure of Scientific Revolutions*, University of Chicago Press, Chicago (2nd ed., 1970).

Kuhn, T., 1970, Reflections on my critics, in: *Criticism and the Growth of Knowledge* (I. Lakatos and A. Musgrave, eds.), pp. 231-278, Cambridge University Press, Cambridge.

Kuhn, T., 1974, Second thoughts on paradigms, in: *The Structure of Scientific Theories* (F. Suppe, ed.), pp. 459-482, University of Illinois Press, Urbana.

Lewontin, R.C., 1970, The units of selection, *Annual Review of Ecology and Systematics* **1**:1-18.

Lewontin, R.C., 1983, The organism as the subject and object of evolution, *Scientia* **118**:63-82.

Masterman, M., 1970, The nature of a paradigm, in: *Criticism and the Growth of Knowledge* (I. Lakatos and A. Musgrave, eds.), pp. 59-89, Cambridge University Press, Cambridge.

Maynard Smith, J., Burian, R., Kauffman, S., Alberch, P., Campbell, J., Goodwin, B., Lande, R., Raup, D., and Wolpert, L., 1985, Developmental constraints and evolution, *Quarterly Review of Biology* **60**:265-287.

Mayr, E., 1942, *Systematics and the Origin of Species*, Columbia University Press, New York.

Mayr, E., 1980, The role of systematics in the evolutionary synthesis, in: *The Evolutionary Synthesis: Perspectives on the Unification of Biology* (E. Mayr and W. Provine, eds.), pp. 123-136, Harvard University Press, Cambridge, MA.

Mayr, E., 1982, *The Growth of Biological Thought*, Harvard University Press, Cambridge, MA.

Mayr, E., 1985, Darwin's five theories of evolution, in: *The Darwinian Heritage* (D. Kohn, ed.), pp. 755-772, Princeton University Press, Princeton.

Paterson, H.E.H., 1982, Perspectives on speciation by reinforcement, *South African Journal of Science* **78**:53-57.

Salthe, S.N., 1985, *Evolving Hierarchical Systems*, Columbia University Press, New York.

Seward, A.C. (ed.), 1909, *Darwin and Modern Science*, Cambridge University Press, Cambridge.

Simpson, G.G., 1944, *Tempo and Mode in Evolution*, Columbia University Press, New York.

Stebbins, G.L., 1950, *Variation and Evolution in Plants*, Columbia University Press, New York.

Todes, D., 1989, *Darwin Without Malthus: The "Struggle for Existence" and Russian Evolutionary Thought in the Nineteenth Century*, Oxford University Press, New York.

Vrba, E.S. and Eldredge, N., 1984, Individuals, hierarchies and processes: towards a more complete evolutionary theory, *Paleobiology* **10**:146-171.

Weber, B., Depew, D., and Smith, J.D., 1988, *Entropy, Information, and Evolution: New Perspectives on Physical and Biological Evolution*, MIT Press, Cambridge, MA.

Wicken, J., 1987, *Evolution, Thermodynamics, and Information*, Oxford University Press, New York.

Alberto Cordero

Let me begin by confessing that I do not know whether there is a Kuhnian evolutionary paradigm. As far as sociological influence is concerned, the fertility of certain exemplary texts is beyond dispute, perhaps even principled in the following sense:

(Probably) If scholar A follows the Master more closely than scholar B in environment E, then A will have more offspring than B in E.

Other than this, however, the notion of "paradigm" seems to me too vague and the sociological reductionism from which it springs too arbitrary, even after its reformulation in the second edition of *The Structure of Scientific Revolutions*. I do agree with Richard Burian, therefore, that bypassing the Kuhnian concept will help us to focus more clearheadedly on the influence of evolutionary biology.

Burian's presentation is rich in intriguing suggestions. I want to discuss a little the following three because of their relation to contemporary issues in both science and philosophy of science. The first is the suggestion that some theories are better viewed as treaties developed to satisfy the needs of interdisciplinary peace. The second concerns the interaction between law and history in certain explanations. The third concerns the schematic character of theories like the synthetic theory.

Treaties

Burian points out that because the synthetic theory aimed to establish the compatibility of the poorly predictive standard population genetic accounts of microevolution with all known evolutionary phenomena, it disarmed conflicts at the price of becoming increasingly more schematic from the logical point of view. What I want to claim is not necessarily incompatible with Burian's account

of conceptual change in evolutionary biology; it depends on how seriously he wants us to take his political metaphor. At any rate, the point I would like to press is the old one that the philosophically interesting issue about interdisciplinary influence in science is not primarily peace or disarmament but the existence or nonexistence of *reasons* for trying to save certain theories—for example, the standard account of microevolution—by means of conceptual generalization (i.e., by making the theory increasingly "schematic").

Let us review, very briefly, how interdisciplinary influence actually does proceed. Neither conflict nor peace seems to be a necessary element.

Consider the impact of Darwinian biology on the study of stellar evolution. The success of Darwin's account of biological speciation led in the second half of the nineteenth century to a gradual assimilation of a new form of scientific thinking, what we now call evolutionary reasoning, resulting from the discovery that the universe does not merely exist as a spatial order but also possesses a history not necessarily reducible to that order. Classifications of stars on the basis of spectral features began in the late 1860s. The results correlated well with the colors of the stars, as Vogel and others discovered, reasoning that, if a domain is ordered, and if that ordering can be viewed as the increase or decrease of the factors on the basis of which the ordering is made, then it is reasonable to suspect that the ordering may be the result of an evolutionary process (Shapere, 1977).

However, that peace is not a necessary aim of interdisciplinary contact is shown by the paralyzing effect that, later on, thermal physics had on evolutionary biology in the closing years of the nineteenth century (Geikie, 1895). The recognition in geological studies of the second law of thermodynamics soon brought into question the huge time scales implied by the early uniformitarians. The Earth's warm days, it appeared, could only be short-lived. Indeed, within a few years after the publication of the *Origin*, one of the most prestigious Christian physicists, Lord Kelvin, rationally cut down the age of the Earth to about 10 million years, in contradistinction to the 300 explicitly proposed by Darwin in the first edition as the minimum time required "since the latter part of the secondary period." Kelvin's objection was not satisfactorily answered until the discovery of radioactivity as a source of heat in the early years of the present century, which is one of the reasons why evolutionary biology took so long to gain full acceptance within science.

If the above sketch is roughly correct, then in both the early studies of stellar evolution and the conflict between the *Origin* and physics, interdisciplinary influence appears to have primarily taken the form of *rational* support or opposition from successful scientific ideas. The important point is that the contemporary interdisciplinary influences considered by Burian (i.e., influences centered around evolutionary studies of molecular mechanisms, mate recognition, or near equilibrium thermodynamics) appear to be no different in this respect: no concessions to anything other than *consistency* with contemporary background knowledge seem to be required in order to understand any of these cases of interdisciplinary influence.

This is not to say, however, that the characterization of background knowledge is an unproblematic matter. Yet, there are at least two home truths worth remembering:

1) Background knowledge is the sum total of information presently perceived as both successful and free from specific doubts. As such, it includes presently a good deal of putative knowledge about the world, comprising items as varied as most of the quantum dynamics of protons, DNA chemistry, the fossil record,

near-equilibrium thermodynamics, and macroevolutionary phenomena. It does not include items that fail as yet to be clearly successful or entirely free from specific doubts, such as the theory of quarks, string theory, Copenhagen quantum dynamics, or information about the existence of alternative solar systems within our galaxy.

2) The lesson of taking background knowledge seriously is a *learned* one (Shapere, 1984). It is precisely because both science and the history of science have contingently taught us to take certain beliefs more seriously than others that interdisciplinary influence within the natural sciences is better viewed as proceeding, not through "concessions," but through compelling scientific reasons ultimately rooted in common background knowledge, without at the same time denying the existence of some level of opportunism among individual scientists. Needless to say, contemporary background knowledge is mostly scientific knowledge, hence neither neutral with respect to theory nor unproblematic with respect to truth (unlike the "given" of old empiricism).

Law and History

Now for my second comment. Treaties or no treaties, Burian seems to me right about the growing importance of contingent historical explanations. Indeed, disciplines dealing with complex objects seem to be compelled by their own goals to resort to contingent historical explanations, including *present theories about the universe and the nature of our physical laws.*

Consider, for example, the following question: How did billions of galaxies emerge from the primeval plasma thrown out by the Big Bang? Recent galactic maps, some of which stretch several hundred million light-years, show galaxies sitting on the surface of bubbles that surround huge voids. According to string theory, the universe may have been built on a scaffolding of minute threads that, although tinier than an atom, carry the energy of the birth of the universe inside them and are powerful enough to pull the matter around them.

Why are these strings distributed the way they are? The notion of radical contingent cosmology becomes almost irresistible in the updated revival of the Kaluza-Klein treatment of the development of the physical world (Harrison, 1981). Many scientists searching for Grand Unification Theories (GUT) think that the fundamental field symmetries are ultimately the geometrical symmetries associated with a world of eleven dimensions. We do not notice the seven extra dimensions, these theorists hasten to add, because our cosmic neighborhood is simply one in which they ended up rolled to a very small scale as a result of a particular symmetry breaking. In a nutshell, the story is that shortly after the Big Bang the now hidden seven-dimensional structure moved somewhat away from exact sphericity. The question, of course, is why should our universe adopt this seven-four split. In this respect, one of the most exciting hypotheses is that the seven-sphere configuration is only one of many possible quantum arrangements. Our universe (or, perhaps, just our cosmic region) simply picked up its peculiar configuration through quantum chance; but things might have been quite otherwise. Indeed, it seems possible that alternative cosmological regions might even exist beyond our present observable horizon. If so, since the structure of the force fields (the strong force, the weak force, electromagnetism, and gravitation) depends on the geometrical symmetries of the squeezed dimensions, the "fundamental" forces would differ from one region to the other in astonishing ways (differences in the orbits, wave patterns, etc.).

Schematism and the Unity of Science

My third point is about the schematic character of all the above "theories of history." Especially with respect to predictability, the theoretical schematicity characteristic of some of our most fundamental theories would appear to be best seen as a context-dependent development. In the case of the simplest theories of stellar evolution, all the relevant phenomena are accounted for fully and well in terms of the acknowledged microdynamics (i.e., that of atoms and nuclei). In the case of organic evolution, on the other hand, the dynamics acknowledged in population genetics just happens to leave most of the intended evolutionary phenomena underdetermined, among other reasons because the interactions involved do not allow for isolation in any meaningful sense. Happily for our intellectual souls, a relevant causal account of some aspects of organic evolution is still possible, yet not in "purely microbiological" terms but in larger "interdisciplinary" terms. The question does not seem entirely one about causal isolation, however. The object of cosmology is as "isolated" as anything can be, yet —to the extent that the fundamental laws of cosmology are quantum mechanical—its development is explained in part as the result of both radical chance and a new form of holistic (quantum mechanical) environmental contingency.

Nor is schematicity necessarily accompanied by loss of empirical content. The unification theories of physics do schematize, for example, the traditional conservation laws, yet at the same time *supplement* the scientific account of the universe with remarkably precise predictions (recall esoteric entities like the Z particle, or—in the case of GUT—all those previously unexpected details about the life of protons), and even added complexity, as with respect to the dimensionality of physical space-time.

And so, perhaps disciplines do tend to become schematic as a result of continued critical *descriptive* generalization, although I would add without necessarily becoming thereby metaphysical. In any case, what are we to make of this finding? Schematism may spring sometimes from sociological or psychological needs for peaceful coexistence; granted. Lacking adequate warrant for radical sociologism or psychologism, however, the philosophically interesting question remains at heart epistemological.

Is there, then, an epistemological pressure to schematize in cases like evolutionary biology or cosmology? The workings of contemporary scientific background knowledge appear, again, to be of interest in this regard. Science has taught us a lot about numerous aspects of life over the last few centuries, with at least the following consequences: 1) It is not up to particular disciplines to agree or disagree with a dramatically growing body of certain scientific beliefs, characterized here as background knowledge. 2) Natural entities do not really belong to any discipline; moreover, as a result of the massive descriptive improvements secured by the traditional natural sciences, scientists have become better equipped to study increasingly complex entities. One interesting result is that, in natural science, the locus of explanation no longer appears to be the traditional piecemeal discipline but—in a subtle new way—*science as a whole*.

All this suggests, I think, the development of a remarkable and growing *contingent* scientific unity after all, even if this may have cost some individual disciplines like evolutionary biology to become so theoretically schematic as to lose practically all its former internal strength. The new unity is not of the sort adequately capturable in sociological terms, of course, but rather unity rooted in the growing domain of a peculiar kind of quasi-cumulative belief, "background knowledge," a rational descendant of both the "given" of old empiricism and the substantive rational platform of old rationalism, which history and contemporary science seem to teach us to take very seriously indeed.

Queens College, CUNY

Geikie, Sir Archibald, 1895, Twenty-five years of geological progress in Britain, *Nature* **51**: 369.

Harrison, E. R., 1981, *Cosmology*, Cambridge University Press.

Shapere, Dudley, 1977, Scientific theories and their domains, in: *The Structure of Scientific Theories* (F. Suppe, ed.), 2nd ed., Univ. of Illinois Press.

Shapere, Dudley, 1984, Objectivity, rationality, and scientific change, *Proceedings PSA 1984* **2**: 637, Phil. Sc. Association, East Lansing, MI.

Peter Manicas

Like Burian, I do not want to claim that Darwin was without influence, especially as regards what we call the social sciences. Still, one must not make too much of this. As Burian points out, importantly, Darwin was read very differently by different national traditions *and* by different figures within these traditions. This is not surprising. As Burian notes, "many alternative positions could be read into the *Origin.*" Moreover, and part of this, its initial success was *not* that it established evolution "by means of natural selection," but that it succeeded in establishing "that descent with modification . . . could account for the major phenomena of biogeography, paleontology, and systematics, and for the adaptations of plants and animals." Indeed, although it is often said (and then ignored), it was Herbert Spencer who used "survival of the fittest" and who did this before *Origin* was published. Spencer's Lamarckian version of "evolutionary theory" has surely had far more impact on the social sciences than *Origin* has had. This is a long story which, however, I will not try to tell here.

Second, with Burian, I would agree that "there is no evolutionary paradigm," that while *Origin of Species* was an exemplar, neither it nor any other text "has established a dominant disciplinary matrix within evolutionary biology." His argument for this is important to his main conclusion that "any satisfactory general theory of evolution" is required to have "the peculiar character of a schematic theory," "a framework for describing and explaining evolutionary sequences and patterns," filled in "by means of particular empirical analyses of the historical circumstances of the organism in question." I want finally to agree fully with this. Indeed, I want to offer, counterfactually, that had such an understanding been available at the end of the nineteenth century, when the social sciences were becoming institutionalized

as "disciplines" in their characteristic current form, then we might well have had a far more plausible and productive social science.[1] Putting the matter simply, perhaps too simply, instead of defining themselves in terms of a conception of an ahistorical physics, they should have defined themselves exactly as Burian sees evolutionary biology, as historical sciences.

It is important to notice, first off, that Burian's view of the character of evolutionary biology is anything but the taken-for-granted view. Indeed, if it were, it would be easy to see how the many disciplines and subdisciplines so ably represented at this conference fit together and, accordingly, it would be easy to see why so much of what seemed like contradictory postures between, for example, the morphologists and the biochemists, were really complementary. Moreover, I have few doubts that quite successful working biologists will for a long time be entranced by a view of their work that could not possibly be true. In order to reinforce Burian's articulation and to accentuate its difference from the taken-for-granted, let me add a few of my own words to what he has said.

We can think here of two notions of a proper science. The first and dominant view was codified in Ernest Nagel's influential *The Structure of Science.*[2] Roughly, it goes as follows: Since any event is caused, it is possible in principle to identify the complete causal nexus. Since causal laws take the form of universals, the full set of these plus knowledge of all the boundary conditions would enable one to give a full explanation of the event. It would ideally take the form of a deduction; accordingly, prediction and explanation (retrodiction) are symmetrical. On this view historical laws are merely process laws, laws governing bounded change in a system, such as explaining the evolution of a star from time T_1 to time T_2. Any failure to predict, like any failure to give a complete explanation, is a function of our ignorance—of the exact laws and boundary conditions operating at some time and place.

This defines a sense of "determinism," so that one can also say that at the level of tiny particles, either there are no causal laws—indeterminism (in which case we must be satisfied with statistical regularities)—or we need to keep on looking.

Most social scientists believe in determinism; so they keep on looking. If the "prediction" fails, they identify heretofore unrecognized "variables," they enlarge the pertinent "system," they do more complicated regressions.

The other view takes history seriously. It agrees that every event is caused, even that it may be in principle possible to identify the complete causal nexus; but it denies that there are always laws under which events can be subsumed. This view does not identify process laws as historical laws; and while it affirms that there are process laws—the ahistorical laws of physics and chemistry that apply everywhere and everywhen—it holds that there are no historical laws, laws that tell us that some time-bound process or set of processes will have some predictable trajectory. It rejects Spencer for Darwin.

Burian argues that evolutionary biology is a historical science in the sense that "Darwin's central accomplishment . . . was to construct a theory that treated adaptation as response to the historical sequence of selective demands of the environment (including other organisms), a theory that accounted for the taxonomic and morphological order in terms of 'historical pathway, pure and simple.'" As he writes, these explanations "contrast with alternatives couched in terms of 'intrinsic purpose and meaning,' of laws of form, etc." but, importantly, they *also* contrast with explanations couched in terms of ahistorical laws.

It is exactly in this sense that biological evolution contrasts with the standard view's best case, stellar evolution. Stellar evolution, finally, is just like stellar mechanics in that "the astronomically relevant properties of stars can be *derived* from initial conditions and fundamental physical laws. . . . Each stage in the history of a star can be *derived* from its intrinsic properties (mass and composition) and appropriate initial or boundary conditions" [my emphases].[3]

This does not mean that biological phenomena are either wholly or partly uncaused (or wholly or partly unexplainable); nor is it the case that "chance" (as perhaps Peirce held) is some sort of irreducible cause, despite the fact that, as Burian writes, "the course of evolution, even on a fairly large scale, is fraught with the consequences of historical accidents and contingencies." They are "historical accidents" in the sense that there is no reason to believe that the world is one closed system—the world of Laplace—and they are "contingencies" in the sense that although they might *not* have occurred, their occurrence is causally explainable.

The main point is fairly obvious: Explanation and prediction are not symmetrical exactly because the world is not one closed system. On the view I am urging, we have the determinism of a world that contains many, many open systems, causally interacting in surprising ways—sometimes unpredictably, indeed, sometimes *in principle* unpredictably—exactly because in this world, causal outcomes may be genuine novelties constituting entirely new conditions for what comes later.

Of course, among the pertinent causal "systems" are the mechanisms represented as "ahistorical universals," universal gravitation, for example. Nothing occurs in violation of a law of nature. In this sense they set the constraints within which history runs its course. Chemical processes in organisms do not violate chemical laws, but chemical laws are not sufficient to explain organisms or taxa.

This returns us to the synthetic theory of evolution, the wedding of population genetics to an updated version of evolution by means of natural selection. While they are surely powerful as explanatory principles (mechanisms), the basic principles of the new synthesis, even when supplemented with appropriate ceteris paribus clauses, "do not provide the wherewithal for full derivation of major evolutionary patterns or the resolution of typical evolutionary debates." Still less can they offer any sort of explanation of the particular species that have appeared on this earth. To even begin to do this, one needs, in addition to these important principles, an enormous amount of quite detailed concrete empirical knowledge (of which most will never become available). One needs natural history.

Suppose then that the social sciences had taken evolutionary biology so understood as its ideal. What would this mean? First, we would need to acknowledge that social science is a historical science in exactly the sense that evolutionary biology is: There is no necessity that anything that has existed had to exist, but given that it did, it becomes part of the causes of what then happened. It is thus that history is "the shank of social science." We would need to acknowledge that process laws are not historical laws—despite the persistent confusions of systems-theorists and especially economists; we would need to acknowledge that what happens in society is the causal outcome of many mechanisms—physical, chemical, biological, psychological, and sociological—operating on what is itself a historical outcome. We would need to acknowledge that since causes are not additive, multiple regression and other such techniques serve to confuse the analysis of variation with causal analysis.

To be sure, each of these disciplines could add to our knowledge of the causes of what happens, but it is outrageous to assume that one can give a "psychological" or "sociological" or "sociobiological" explanation of any concrete action, event (the Bolshevik Revolution, the Great Crash), or any practice or pattern (the rearing and schooling of children in America, gender or race relations in Great Britain as compared to the United States, the political economy of underdeveloped Africa). We would have to acknowledge that the standard view of science, still so prominent in all the textbooks in the social sciences, is surely misapplied to the social sciences. Indeed, it begins to look like a plausible view of science only if one doggedly thinks of celestial mechanics as the only real science!

1. I have tried to sketch this critical history in my *A History and Philosophy of the Social Sciences* (New York and Oxford: Basil Blackwell, 1987).

2. Ernest Nagel, *The Structure of Science* (New York: Harcourt, Brace, 1961).

3. For closed systems, process laws *are* historical laws. Process laws are merely causal laws: under closure NaCl will dissolve in H_2O. Causal laws are operative in closed and open systems, although in an open system, the outcome need not be what it would have been had the system been closed.

Stanley N. Salthe

I will explore some possible meanings of the phrase "evolutionary paradigm" and comment on our continued fixation on a single one of them.

Evolutionary paradigms (in the sense of disciplinary matrices) could be constructed at at least three different levels of generality. At its most general, evolution is merely the *irreversible accumulation of historical information* in any sort of object, be it a system or not. Its synonyms here include "history" and "individuation." At this level it can be discriminated against development, which can, somewhat tightly, be defined as *predictable irreversible change.* Any dynamic material system—the "dissipative structures" of Prigogine (e.g., 1980), including organisms, ecosystems, and the surface of the earth, as well as Bénard cells, dust devils, hurricanes, ocean currents, and the Red Spot on Jupiter—engages in both kinds of change simultaneously. The sort of change we encounter depends on our orientation and needs. So, for example, when confronted with tornadoes, we take a developmental attitude in our efforts to predict them. Here evolution is a serious problem—to be converted to some developmental discourse if at all possible—as it is also in our relation with the unpredictability of an aging automobile! On the other hand, in doing biographical work individuation is our primary interest, developmental aspects of a life seeming by comparison boring.

The influence of this most general sort of evolution is often woven together with that of development when observing change. Very frequently the two kinds of change are conflated, as in Burian's astronomy example. I think it will be important to keep this distinction clear because the notion that evolution is the central theoretical framework for biology will come to be challenged again from the standpoint of development. Development refers to material systema-

ticity and consists of locally lawful processes; evolutionary principles are as empty as Burian claims. In any case, we remind ourselves that historicity is obviously much broader than Synthetic Evolutionary Theory.

A more specified subclass of "evolution" is "organic evolution." This notion, importantly suggested by the one figure in *The Origin of Species,* and seriously discussed in the nineteenth century by, for example, Moritz Wagner (1841), has today come to focus on populations of reproducing *types* characterized by limited fidelity. The objects being marked by historical traces are here viewed as *tokens* of these types, increasing in numbers and spilling over their geographical ranges in a kind of entropic drive (powered by growth and reproduction) to maximize the number of areographic states (Rapoport, 1982) that any type might occupy—Darwin's "descent with modification." Extinction is the common fate of all types, but this can be delayed, even in the presence of a general catastrophe, by occupying as many coordinates on the earth's surface as possible. The influence of this notion of evolution as an important component of the Western scientific creation myth is increasing. I think we should note as a formal proposition that it might be possible to construct a synthetic evolutionary "treaty" around this general conceptual form without natural selection as the only, or central, mechanism. Many cladists in fact hold such an opinion, as do Brooks and Wiley (1986).

In any case, a still more highly specified notion of evolution has been constructed by Darwinians to explain *why* certain types have persisted and others not. Here the simultaneous spread of types over the earth's surface is taken formally to produce a competition, decided by sorting according to some fittingness with respect to environmental features, taken broadly. If these features don't change, there will be no significant evolution—that is, we have

174

here a Newtonian construct (Depew, 1986), treating the tokens of the types as if they were without power to change according to their own internal drives. Internal drives to change are treated stochastically, as if there were no systematicity or creativity about them. (In fact, whenever positive science treats creativity, it is always as a chance phenomenon—caprice has been it's model of the creative act.) The general influence of this version of organic evolution among neighboring sciences is growing apace—witness, for examples, D. T. Campbell's (1974) "evolutionary epistemology," B. F. Skinner's (1981) "selection by consequences," E. O. Wilson's (1975) "sociobiology," Herbert Simon's (1969) "satisficing" (the idea for which he received the Nobel Prize), Burnet's (1959) "clonal selection theory" of immunity, and similar models of neuronal development.

We might worry a bit about such a general acceptance of this particular model *as the central part of* evolutionary thinking because of the consequences for the moral imagination of believing that beautiful phenomena like wings and eyes, and rich ones like the human mind, have resulted solely from the operation of a mechanism that is just that—mechanical—and therefore thin (we have built this theory partly on the model of those other things we build!). Mechanisms, even stochastically scrambled ones, generate only short-term decisions. It has been remarked many times that natural selection cannot foresee the future. Here we are set up for extolling expediency (after all, it is what is claimed to have produced us, is it not?). Finally, this mechanism is heavily based (in this overcrowded world) on the notion of competition, which becomes an ever deeper principle of our thought as selection models continue to conquer newer subject areas in what begins to appear as a self-mirroring imperialistic drive.

And anyway, can it really be that a combination of mechanical determinism and stochasticity can produce an intelligible or compelling model of the emergence and elaboration of living systems? I think there are grounds for questioning this. The failure so far to explain, for example, the origin of radically new ways of life (what the layman thinks of as *really* evolution), including the origin of life, might be cited. Avoidance of such problems under the almost forgotten rubric "preadaptation" is, I think, symptomatic, as is also the continued refusal to deal seriously with parallel evolution, convergence, and iterative evolution. In all these cases the stock answer is that an ad hoc filling in of details of large numbers of contingencies as boundary conditions, along the lines of the covering law model as suggested by Burian, would do it without new principles—*if* we could do it.

What this fails to see is that, if the few principles we do use have the kinds of social implications that natural selection has (take a good look again at Jacques Monod's masterful—and morally almost demonic—*Chance and Necessity* to get a sense of these), that cannot be a satisfactory solution given that we are, as evolutionary biologists, indirectly working on *nothing less than an important part of our culture's very own creation myth*. Is the combination of the pointlessness of chance with the tyranny of necessity, competitive exclusion, expedience, and obedience to external forces what we really want to think of as the sources of our origins? The moral implications are immense,[1] and none other than Thomas Henry Huxley was already warning about a hundred years ago (1893) that we ought to "combat them." Combating them while believing them takes an existential sophistication available to very few, and does not to my mind call up images of "joy for all" (see John Moore's contribution, this symposium) in the idea of evolution.

Finally, these points say nothing about a possible hardening of the imagination around a few "powerful" (that is, materially empty) ideas. The ascendancy of any single conceptual mode would be as intellectually stultifying as the particular nature of this mode threatens to be morally. And it would surely be a sign of senescence in our scientific culture. This might be delayed to some extent if evolutionary biologists, the source of the selection idea for others, would take up the pluralism suggested by Richard Burian in his paper. Such moves would place realistic and humane constraints on the undoubted power of the selection idea.

Brooklyn College

1. Despite the efforts of Dobzhansky and George Simpson to explicitly make this point in many of their writings, I have never been able, even after considerable struggle, to understand natural selection theory as being inconsistent with fascism. Why should it be? If one believes that science is a discourse separate from all others in society, any consistency here is purely accidental, and can be hedged round if necessary with detoxifying text. The trouble is, fewer and fewer observers, apparently including in their time both Dobzhansky and Simpson, hold that science is a separate, value-free enterprise.

Brooks, D. R., and Wiley, E. O., 1986, *Evolution as Entropy: Toward a Unified Theory of Biology*, University of Chicago Press, Chicago.

Burnet, F. M., 1959, *The Clonal Selection Theory of Acquired Immunity*, Cambridge University Press, Cambridge.

Campbell, D. T., 1974, Unjustified variation and selective retention in scientific discovery, in: *Studies in the Philosophy of Biology* (F. J. Ayala and T. Dobzhansky, eds.), pp. 139-162, University of California Press, Berkeley.

Depew, D. J., 1986, Nonequilibrium thermodynamics and evolution: a philosophical perspective, *Philosophica* **37**: 27-58.

Huxely, T. H., 1893/1898, Evolution and ethics, in: *Evolution and Ethics and Other Essays* (T. H. Huxley, ed.), pp. 46-116, Appleton, New York.

Monod, J., 1971, *Chance and Necessity: An Essay on the Natural Philosophy of Modern Biology*, Knopf, New York.

Prigogine, I., 1980, *From Being to Becoming: Time and Complexity in the Physical Sciences*, Freeman, San Francisco.

Rapoport, E. H., 1982, *Areography: The Geographical Strategies of Species*, Pergamon Press, Oxford.

Simon, H. A., 1969, *The Sciences of the Artificial*, MIT Press, Cambridge.

Skinner, B. F., 1981, Selection by consequences, *Science* **213**: 501-504.

Wagner, M., 1841, *Reisen in der Regentschaft Algier*, Leipzig.

Wilson, E. O., 1975, *Sociobiology: The New Synthesis*, Harvard University Press, Cambridge.

Summary

Max K. Hecht

The title of the symposium, *Evolutionary Biology at the Crossroads*, is derived from questions posed by the popular press and various interpreters of the evolutionary process. The usage of "crossroads" implies that the science of evolutionary biology has arrived at a point in its development such that major changes in its basic premises may be in order. Criticisms have been directed by some against the neo-Darwinist approach because it has been considered inadequate to explain all of the data available. In addition, there remains the problem as to what impact evolutionary biology has had or should have on allied areas of research and thought, and on the perception of the place of our species in nature.

Time constraints limited the number of areas that could be addressed and the breadth of the major presentations in the symposium's six sessions. Important areas that contribute to the debate within evolution, such as developmental biology, ecology and behavior, were treated only peripherally.

The introductory address by John Moore provided an historical background to modern evolutionary biology. Notably, he called attention to the gradual development of evolutionary ideas since their beginning in the eighteenth century and to the exponential growth in the data base of evolutionary biology in the twentieth century.

The second address by Bruce Wallace described the basic tenets of the evolutionary process at the level of the population. He discussed the role of genes in populations, natural selection, and neutrality, and whether the Modern Synthesis is sufficient for explaining the mechanisms controlling evolution. The panelists—Walter Bock, Richard Borowsky, Lee Ehrman, and Marvin Wasserman—were in essential agreement with Wallace and elaborated on details of the population-level processes. It might be said that their collective conclusion was an extrapolationist view that states that the processes and models at the population level could be extended to explain the patterns of evolution at higher systematic or hierarchical levels. Walter Bock outlined his concept of the species and its applicability to paleontology and higher hierarchical levels.

At the beginning of the third session, Anthony Hallam outlined five basic contributions of paleontolgy to the study of pattern and process, and the problems uncovered by this area of study concerning the Modern Synthesis. He also discussed that the mode of evolution, expressed primarily through the comparison of gradualism and punctuated equilibrium, has initiated much new research and sufficient debate to renew interest in paleontological contributions to evolutionary theory. Although critical of punctuated equilibrium and similar dissident views, Hallam expressed the view that these hierarchical hypotheses were important in the formation of questions and seminal ideas derived from the fossil record. Hallam and the other panelists—Arthur Boucot, Antoni Hoffman and Jeffrey Levinton—remain persuaded that patterns in the fossil record can be understood and explained within the framework of an expanded view of the Modern Synthesis. Both the successes and failures of recent paleontological studies in elucidating patterns and modes of evolution were then described by Hoffman and Levinton. They commented on macroevolutionary patterns and derived generalizations such as patterns of extinction cycles. Both commentators were in agreement that the synthesis was compatible with the fossil record. Some dissident views supporting a more hierarchical position were expressed at the symposium, but no commentary was submitted for this volume. On the other hand, Boucot questioned Hallam's idea that paleontology cannot elucidate mechanisms of evolution. He believes that the history of communities as viewed in the fossil record can eventually contribute to an understanding of mechanisms.

In the fourth session, Stephen O'Brien discussed the methodologies and theoretical applications of molecular biology to the determination of phylogenetic relationships. Using the relationships among the Carnivora as an example, he demonstrated the unique contribution of molecular biology. O'Brien emphasized the concordance of results using different molecular techniques as indications of the robustness of the conclusions. Malcolm McKenna was in agreement with most of the general relationships proposed within the Carnivora, and discussed their general concordance with some of the prior studies in both paleontology and morphology. He was concerned with the methods of analysis and interpretation of data, and was uncertain that the conclusions should be accepted as final.

A history of humans, the subject of the fifth session, was outlined by David Pilbeam, focusing on the fossil record. His approach was to integrate the basic paleontological data, functional analysis of human and primate morphology, and molecular data, as well as an interpretation of behavioral data, into a general synthetic approach to the evolution of the human species. This discussion was followed by a critique by three panelists. Eric Delson discussed the species concept as applied in anthropology. An alternative view was presented by Ian Tattersall, which would result in a different array of species. Delson and Tattersall disagree with each other in the use of the species at the hominid level. Delson is closer to Bock's prior statement, but then only in partial agreement. Fred Szalay described a method of analysis of evidence that he believes will result in better interpretations of human history.

In the last session Richard Burian assessed the impact of the evolutionary paradigm on neighboring disciplines. He criticized the use of the term "evolutionary paradigm" because of the historical origin of the term "paradigm." (It should be noted that the term is misused in his sense in this volume.) In further criticizing the use of the words "theory" and "paradigm," Burian states that the synthetic theory has functioned more as a treaty than a theory. As yet he does not believe that there is an alternative to the Modern Synthesis. Peter Manicas and Alberto Cordero then presented their views of the influence of evolutionary theory on the social and physical sciences respectively. Perhaps the most radical dissent among the participants is that of the biologist and philosopher Stanley Salthe, who criticized evolutionary biologists for their reliance on natural selection as a primary mechanism.

In conclusion, the question remains: Is evolutionary biology at a crossroads? From the above discussion it would appear that the majority of the participants would answer mostly in the negative, although some would answer more positively. The same question has been recently asked and answered in different ways. Grene (1990) has answered this question ambiguously as more No than Yes. There is probably no certain answer to the question because much is dependent on how broad and pluralistic one views the Modern Synthesis.

Grene, Marjorie, 1990, Is evolution at a crossroads? *Evol. Biol.* **24:** in press.